CATEGORY CODES (contd.)

0618   6 Parts: Brass-Miscellaneous
0700   7 Equal Brass Instruments
0710   7 Mixed Brass (Brass-Perc)
0711   7 Parts: Horn-Woodwind
0712   7 Parts: Brass-Woodwind
0713   7 Parts: Winds-Keyboard
0717   7 Parts: Wind(s) String(s)
0718   7 Parts: Brass-Miscellaneous
0800   8 Equal Brass Instruments
0810   8 Mixed Brass (Brass-Perc)
0811   8 Parts: Horn-Woodwind
0812   8 Parts: Brass-Woodwind
0813   8 Parts: Winds-Keyboard
0817   8 Parts: Wind(s)-String(s)
0818   8 Parts: Brass-Miscellaneous
0900   9 Equal Brass Instruments
0910   9 Mixed Brass (Brass-Perc)
0911   9 Parts: Horn-Woodwind
0912   9 Parts: Brass-Woodwind
0913   9 Parts: Winds-Keyboard
0917   9 Parts: Wind(s)-String(s)
0918   9 Parts: Brass-Miscellaneous
1000   10 Or More Equal Brass Instruments
1010   10 Or More Mixed Brass (Brass-Perc)
1011   10 Or More Parts: Horn-Woodwind
1012   10 Or More Parts: Brass-Woodwind
1013   10 Or More Parts: Winds-Keyboard
1017   10 Or More Parts: Wind(s)-String(s)
1018   10 Or More Parts: Brass-Miscellaneous
1100   Brass Choir
1101   Brass Ensemble-Band
1102   Brass & WW Ensemble-Band
1103   Brass & Miscellaneous Ensemble-Band
1104   Brass Ensemble-Orchestra
1105   Brass & WW Ensemble-Orchestra
1106   Brass & Miscellaneous Ensemble-Orchestra
1107   Brass-Electronics
1109   Brass-Harp
1110   Trumpet-Organ
1111   Horn-Organ
1112   Trombone-Organ
1113   Brass Ensemble-Organ
1114   Brass & Miscellaneous Instruments-Organ
1116   One Brass Instrument-Voice(s)
1117   Brass Ensemble-Voice(s)
1118   Brass & WW Ensemble-Voice(s)
1119   Brass & Miscellaneous Ensemble-Voice(s)
1125   Posaunenchor

Brass Ensemble Music Guide

Compiled by
Paul G. Anderson

The Instrumentalist Company
1418 Lake Street, Evanston, Illinois

PREFACE

The present work is the second in a series of bibliographies of music in print for brass instruments. The first volume lists study and solo materials for all the brass instruments. This volume encompasses information on brass chamber music, brass ensembles with various accompanying groups, and ensembles combining brass with other instruments. All titles listed were extracted from current publishers' catalogs and recorded in appropriate categories.

Because of the magnitude of this project, errors are undoubtedly present and omissions unfortunately occur. It is hoped that future revisions will improve both accuracy and coverage. Nevertheless, I do believe that the completion of this two-volume compilation supplies those interested in brass music with the most extensive index available today.

In my own study of the information included here, I have become increasingly convinced of the good quality and wide range of music presently available for brass performance. It is my hope that a perusal of these two books will result in the purchase and performance of a more varied and interesting brass repertoire.

Paul G. Anderson
Iowa City, Iowa
December, 1977

TABLE OF CONTENTS

PART 1: CATEGORY INDEX

ADDITIONAL BRASS ENSEMBLE CATEGORIES

GENERAL INFORMATION

ORGANIZATION

The two main sections of this book are (1) a listing of ensemble music employing one or more brass instruments, and (2) a Composer Index which lists each work alphabetically by composer. Where the composer's name is unknown (anonymous works, folk songs, etc.) the entry is listed alphabetically by title.

MUSIC BY CATEGORY

The main body of the book records entries in appropriate categories and in the following format:

GABRIELI, G.–JONES. CANZONA NO 1. 2TPT, HN, TRB, TU   B23

| Composer-Arranger | Title | Instrumentation | Publisher |

If an entry is too long to be entered on one line, instrumentation is dropped to a second line and indented.

Composer-Arranger. Diverse spellings of composers' names present problems in alphabetization. When possible, the spelling of names conforms to that found in *Baker's Biographical Dictionary of Musicians, Fifth Edition with 1965 Supplement.* Names following a hyphen indicate the arranger's, editor's, or compiler's name. The ampersand (&) is used to indicate two composers' or arrangers' names. When only the arranger's name is available, information is presented as:

BROWN, J.R.-ARR

Title. Some titles are shortened to fit the desired format. This is accomplished by the use of abbreviations or ellipses and by translation of spelled numbers into arabic numerals. When feasible, titles are recorded in the language used in the publishers' catalogs. Conditions arise, however, which require the translation of some titles into the English language. It is regretted that use of diacritical markings was precluded by the computer facilities used to prepare this book.

Instrumentation. A large percentage of music composed for the brass ensemble includes the possibility of performance with some variation in instrumentation. The following characters are used to indicate instrumentation.

,   the comma separates parts (voice lines)
()   the parentheses encompass alternate parts
-     the hyphen connects two instruments doubling one part
/   the virgule (slash) connects two instruments performed
       by one player
*   the asterisk indicates accompaniment idiom

Example:

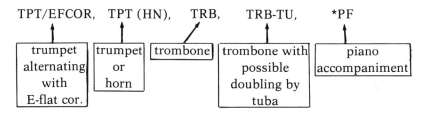

TPT/EFCOR,   TPT (HN),   TRB,   TRB-TU,   *PF

| trumpet alternating with E-flat cor. | trumpet or horn | trombone | trombone with possible doubling by tuba | piano accompaniment |

Publisher. A complete listing of publisher codes together with publishers' names and addresses begins on page 251.

COMPOSER INDEX

The second section of this book gives an alphabetical listing of composers together with titles of all music listed herein. Entry format is as follows:

| Composer's name |

GABRIELI, G.

    CANZONA NO 1   0510

| Title | | Category code |

The category code refers to the front section of the book where the given entry may be located. Many titles are abbreviated in the section. Titles having more than one composer are listed under the first appearing name only. Most composers' names include initials. Since it was impossible to always determine initials, a search for a specific title should be carried on in two locations: (1) last name only, or (2) last name plus initials. For example, it might be necessary to search the BACH and the BACH, J.S. entries to locate a desired title.

Classification of Ensemble Music

Each category of music is assigned a four-digit code. The first two digits indicate the number of parts; the final two specify a particular type of performing group. The code 0310 will indicate a total of three parts (03) with all parts written for French horn (01).

Each entry is listed according to the smallest possible combination of parts required for performance. *Ad libitum* parts are not considered in determination of category, but reference to these parts is included in the main entry. A composition for trumpet and horn with an *ad libitum* violin part is recorded under the category for two brass instruments (0210) with an entry comment concerning the violin part. If appropriate, a cross reference is included in additional categories.

Special Terminology

Regardless of complexity, all *percussion* parts listed for a given composition are counted as one instrument. The actual number of players required depends to some extent upon the ability of the performers. As this introduces an unknown quantity (therefore denying the possibility of cataloging within this guide), all percussion parts were counted as though intended for one performer. Furthermore, all percussion instruments are considered a part of the brass family when included in an otherwise all-brass composition.

For the purposes of this book, a *narrator* is considered a musical instrument and is counted as one part.

A problem arises with the term *basso continuo* (or similar terms such as *continuo* or *thorough bass*). Such a part might be realized by any one of several instruments such as harpsichord, piano, or organ; or, as is often the case, by the harpsichord in combination with a cello or bassoon. For simplicity and uniformity in filing, this book will consider the *continuo* part as being performed by one person on a keyboard instrument.

Entries recorded under the category "Music with Ten or More Parts" include all larger combinations of music considered to be of chamber music character, but not concert music for orchestra or band.

TABLE OF ABBREVIATIONS

A	alto	MZ	mezzo soprano
ACC	accompaniment	NAR	narrator
AHN	alto horn	NO	number(s)
ARR	arranger	OB	oboe
B	bass	OPT	optional
BAR	baritone	OPH	ophicleide
BC	basso continuo	ORCH	orchestra
BGL	bugle	ORG	organ
BK	book(s)	PA	pianoforte
BR	brass	PERC	percussion
BSN	bassoon	PF	pianoforte
BSTHN	basset horn	PIC	piccolo
C	contra	R	rental only
CAST	castinets	RCDR	recorder
CEL	celesta	REV	revised
CEMB	cembalo	RHY	rhythm section
CL	clarinet	RS	rhythm section
CMPL	compiler	RT	recorded tape
COR	cornet	S	soprano
CTT	cornett	SAX	saxophone
CYM	cymbals	S CYM	suspended cymbal
DB	double bass (str. bass)	SDR	snare drum
DR	drum	SER	serpent
ED	editor or edition	STR	string(s)
EFCL	E-flat clarinet	T	tenor
EFCOR	E-flat cornet	TAM	tam tam
EHN	English horn	TAMB	tamborine
EU	euphonium	TC	treble clef
FL	flute	TIMP	timpani
FLG	flügelhorn	TPT	trumpet
FR	from	TRANS	transcription
GLOK	glockenspiel	TRB	trombone
GNG	gong	TRI	triangle
GTR	amplified guitar	TU	tuba
HN	horn	UN	instrument(s) unknown
H	Hoboken	V	voice(s)
HP	harp	VA	viola
HPCD	harpsichord	VC	violoncello
INST	instrument(s)	VIB	vibraphone
J	jazz	VN	violin
JDB	jazz double bass	VOL	volume(s)
K	Köchel	XYL	xylophone
MAR	marimba	WW	woodwind(s)
MND	mandoline	WW5	woodwind quintet
MS	manuscript	7/3	[opus] 7, ♯3
MVMT	movement(s)		

CATEGORY INDEX

TWO-PART MUSIC

2 TRUMPETS

DESBORDES, L. 6 DUO CONCERTANTES   B85
DEXTER. AU CLAIR DE LA LUNE   C71
DEXTER. COUNTRY DIALOGUES   C71
DOFLEIN. DER FUCHSTANZ   A51
DOFLEIN. LEICHTE DUETTE (2 BKS)   A51
EBEN, P. DUETTI   F31
EDMONDS, H. COOL SOUNDS DUETS   B31
EHMANN, W.(CMPL). GEISTLICHES ZWEIERSPIEL   A51
ERDMANN, R.W. ENGLISCHE DUETTE FUR 2 TPT   A51
FANTINI, G.-GLASEL. 8 DUETS FOR TPTS   C25
FANTINI, G.-GLASEL. 8 DUETS   B15
FOX ALBUM OF CORNET DUETS (2 VOL).   C25
FOX, F. BEC-9   G66
GASSMANN, A.L. AM WALDRAND, LANDLICHE SOLO-DUETTE (3 VOL)   C80
GASTOLDI-KIWI. PIECES FOR EQUAL INSTRUMENTS   A51
GATES, E. ODD METER DUETS   C46
GATES, E. ODD METER DUETS   G61
GATTI, D. 33 CELEBRATED DUETS   C11
GEARHART. DUET SESSIONS   F43
GEARHART, LIVINGSTON & CASSEL. TRUMPET SESSIONS   F43
GIBBONS, O.-BALDWIN. FANTASIA   G83
GIESBERT. AUS DEM BAROCK   F31
GIESBERT. BAROCKE SPIELSTUCKE (2 BKS)   F31
GLASEL, J. SIXTEENTH-CENTURY CARMINA   C25
GOLSON. TWO-PART INVENTIONS   N22
GUIDE, F.D. DUO, OP.20   D36
HARVEY, P. GRADED STUDY DUETS   A78
HAYES. DOZEN & ONE, A   C77
HENNING, C.T. 50 DUETS   F60
HENNING, C.T.-SANSONE. 59 DUETS   F60
HERING, S. MINIATURE CLASSICS   C11
HERING, S. MORE MINIATURE CLASSICS   C11
HERING, S. TRUMPETS FOR TWO   C11
HOUDY, P. PROMENADE   D36
HOUSTON, R.-COLIN. AVANTE GARDE DUETS   B31
HUFFNAGLE, H.J. RHYTHM DUETS   C46
HUFFNAGLE, H.J. STREAMLINED DUETS (2 VOL)   C46
HYMAN. COUNTERPOINT FOR 6 VALVES   M85
HYMAN. DUETS IN ODD METERS & FAR-OUT RHYTHMS   M85
JANETZKY, K. A DUE   B69
JELICH, V. RICERCARE   A51
KARLIN, F. DUETS IN JAZZ   B31
KETTERING. 15 CAROLS   B40
KINYON, J. BREEZE-EASY PROGRAM PIECES   H06
KNELLWOLF, J.B. DUETTE FUR 2 TPTS (4 VOL)   C80
KOENIG, H. 6 OPERATIC DUETS   B53
KRAFT. DUALITIES   C40
KUFFNER, J.-HAGEL. 30 DUETS   C91
KUFFNER, J.-NAGEL. 36 DUETS   C91
KUFFNER, J. 20 SELECTED EASY DUETS   F60
LA VIOLETTE, W. LA VIOLETTE DUET ALBUM   A62
LACHOWSKA. DUETY NA TRABKI   D63
LACHOWSKA. DUETY NA TRABKI   E72
LANCEN. TWINS, THE   C71
LANG. DUO   B84
LASSUS, R.D. 2 MOTETS   B85
LASSUS, R.D. TWO-PART MOTETS   P19
LUBIN, E. MELODY DUETS NO.1   C46
LUBIN, E. MELODY DUETS NO.2   C46
MAGANINI, Q.E.-SMITH. AIR & RONDO ON A THEME BY HAYDN   B85
MAGANINI, Q.E. FANFARE   B85
MANFREDINI, F.-JOOSEN. CONCERTO   D64

```
MARC-CARLES, E.  DANSES DANS LE STYLE ANCIEN                    D63
MARIE.  30 EASY DUETS                                          B53
MARSHALL-KLEIN.  TWO BY TWO                                    F43
MARTIN.  JAZZ DUETS, BK. 1                                     M77
MATHEZ.  TANDEM                                                A71
MAZAS.  DUETS                                                  C25
MC MULLEN, P.  3 MOVEMENTS                                     F43
METIS, F.  JAZZ DUETS                                          B31
MILES, B.  12 THEMES WITH JAZZ IMPROVISATION                   A03
MOENKEMEYER.  MASTERS OF THE 16TH & 17TH CENTURIES             K19
MOZART, L.-DIETRICH.  MUSIC BOOK                               A51
MOZART, L.  4 SHORT PIECES                                     F81
MOZART, W.A.-SMITH.  12 EASY DUETS                             F23
MURPHY, J.-WELDON.  DUETS "INVENTIONS"                         B31
MUTTER.  5 SPIELSTUCKE                                         C54
NEIBIG, A.  26 DUETS                                           C91
NELSON.  TOP TONE DUETS                                        B31
NELSON, E.  ADVANCED DUETS (2 VOL)                            B31
NIEHAUS.  TRUMPETS TODAY JAZZ DUETS                            N10
NORBY.  3 SUITES                                               H30
NORGARD.  TROMPETMUSIK                                         H30
NUTEN, P.  DUO CAPRICIOSO                                      D80
OSTRANDER, A.  FIRST PALS                                      B85
OWEN, D. (ARR).  21 DUETS                                      D14
PAISNER, B.  PRACTICAL PART PLAYING                            C46
PAISNER, B.  SWING DUETS                                       C46
PAUDERT, E.  6 DUETS                                           B53
PAUDERT, E.-VOISIN.  6 DUETS                                   C91
PELZ, W.  PEP SESSION                                          E80
PHILIPPE.  DIVERTISSEMENT                                      D67
PIETZSCH, H.-BROILES.  24 DUETS                                C91
PIETZSCH, H.  24 LEICHTE INSTRUCTIVE DUETTE                    A20
PIETZSCH, H.  24 LIGHT INSTRUCTIVE DUETS                       B53
POOLE, C.  JAZZ FOR JUNIORS                                    A03
POOLE, C.  JAZZ FOR SENIORS                                    A03
POOT, M.  3 PETITS DUOS                                        D63
PORRET, J.  DUO'S DE CONCOURS 1E, 2E,5E,6E                     D92
PORRET, J.  12 DUOS PROGRESSIFS, OP.254                        D92
PORTA, B.-WIENANDT.  DUO FOR EQUAL INSTRUMENTS                 E77
QUIRSFELDER.  KANONS                                           A51
RACUSEN, D.  CANONIC ETUDES                                    F43
RAPHLING, S.  DANCE SUITE                                      B85
REBNER, E.W.  INVENTIONEN FUR 2 TPT                            D88
REDER.  5 AMERICAN MARCHES                                     E41
REDER.  5 FRENCH MARCHES                                       E41
REDER.  5 PARADE GROUND MARCHES                                E41
REDER.  4 TATTOOS & NIGHT PIECES                               E41
REHFELDT, H.L.  WISCONSIN RIVER WALTZ                          F27
RIMSKY-KORSAKOV, N.A.-KING.  2 DUETS FOR HNS OR TPTS           D16
ROSSINI, G.  POWER ETERNAL (STABAT MATER)                      D18
RUSSELL, R.  ABSTRACT #2                                       C40
SACHSE, E.  6 DUETS                                            C91
SARO, J.H.  STUDIES IN CANON FROM                              B53
SCHAEFFER, D.(ARR).  CHRISTMAS DUETS.  (OPT PF)                E80
SCHAEFFER, D.(ARR).  DUETS ARE FUN                             E80
SCHAEFFER, D.(ARR).  READING RHYTHMS                           E80
SCHAEFFER, D.(ARR).  2 RHYTHMIC DUETS                          E80
SCHAFER, K.H.  9 SPIELSTUCKE FUR 2 TPT                         A51
SCHNEIDER, W.  ERSTES TROMPETENSPIEL                           F31
SCHNEIDER, W.  KLASSISCHE SPIELSTUCKE                          A51
SCHNEIDER, W.  SONATA FOR 2 TPTS                               D98
SCHNEIDER, W.  12 STUCKE BAROCKER MEISTER                      A51
```

SCHRAMM, H. PARTITA	D74
SCHUBERT, F.P.-GOLDMAN. 5 LITTLE DUETS	D74
SCHUBERT, F.P.-GOLDMAN. 5 LITTLE DUETS	E77
SEEBOTH, M. 3 DUETTE	C60
SMALL, C. CLARK TERRY PLAYS CHARLIE SMALL'S DUETS	B31
SMITH, C.B. TWO OF A KIND	D18
SONTAG. JOLLY TWO	C09
STIEBER, H. TURMMUSIK NR.1	C75
STOKER, R. LITTLE SUITE	C71
STORM, C. SAILS ON A SILVERY SEA	F07
STOUTAMIRE & HENDERSON. DUETS FOR ALL	E80
STRAVINSKY, I. FANFARE FOR A NEW THEATRE	A78
SYLVIUS. 20 ORIGINAL DUETS, BK. 2	C25
TARR & GLOVER (ED). MORAVIAN BRASS DUET	M80
TELEMANN, G.P.-BUSH. 6 CONONIC SONATAS	M79
THOMAS, R. 4 DUETS FOR YOUNG MUSICIANS	C33
TROMBLY, P. CANZONA	A13
TWINN, S. OLD ENGLISH SONGS	C71
ULRICH, H.J. 5 DUETTE	H30
VALENTINO-NAGEL. 18 LEICHTE STUECKE	F31
VAN DER MAESBRUGGE, M. EN PETITS CARACTERES. (OPT PF)	D67
VANDERCOOK, H.A. ARM IN ARM	F07
VANDERCOOK, H.A. BOBOLINKS	F07
VANDERCOOK, H.A. FLAMINGOES	F07
VANDERCOOK, H.A. PROGRESSIVE DUETS	F07
VANDERCOOK, H.A. TRUMPET TWOSOME	F07
VEACH, D. TWIN TORONADOS	C11
VIERDANCK, J.-ENGEL. CAPRICCI FUR 2,3,&4 TPT OR FLUGELHN	A51
VIERDANCK, J.-SCHEIFES. 2 CAPRICCIOS	F81
VIVALDI, A.-JOOSEN. CONCERT	D64
VOXMAN, H.(CMPL). SELECTED DUETS (2 VOL)	F07
WALTER, J. CANONS IN THE CHURCH MODES	A51
WATERS. CLASSIC DANCES	C71
WEHNER. 20 MODERN DUETS	N19
WEICHLEIN, R.-KUMMERLING. TROMPETENDUETTE	C75
WEINER. 14 INVENTIONS	A71
WELDON, C. BOWER MURPHY DUETS INVENTIONS	B31
WHITE. FANTASIA	P19
WILLIAMS, E. ARTISTIC DUETS	B31
WILLIAMS, E. BEST DUETS OF ERNEST WILLIAMS	B31
WILLIAMS, E. 114 EASY DUETS	B31
WILLIAMS, E. PROGRESSIVE ELEMENTARY SOLOS & DUETS	B32
WURM, W. 41 DUETS	C91

2 HORNS

BACH, J.S.-HOSS. 2 GAVOTTES	F60
BARBOTEU, G. 4 DUOS	B24
BATES, W.-CURWIN. FLOURISHES FOR BRASS	B20
BELLOLI, A.-LELOIR. PICCOLI DUETTI	D11
BERGMANN-RIVERS. 7 CANONIC STUDIES	F31
BLANC, J. GRAND DUETS	G28
BODNAR, I. 21 EASY SHORT PIECES	B84
BORRIS, S. LEICHTE DUETTE	F53
BORRIS, S. PARTITA FUR 2 HORNER	F53
BORRIS, S. 2 SONATINEN FUR 2 GLEICHE HORNER	F53
BRAHMS, J. SLUMBER SONG	D18
CACCIAMANI-LELOIR. 8 DUOS	D11

MOENKEMEYER. MASTERS OF THE 16TH & 17TH CENTURIES	K19
MOZART, L.-SCHEIFES. 4 KLEIN STUKKEN	F81
MOZART, L.-DIETRICH. MUSIC BOOK	A51
MOZART, W.A.-SIMON. 12 DUOS FOR 2 WIND INSTS	D63
MOZART, W.A. 12 DUOS FUR 2 BLASINSTRUMENTE	A90
MOZART, W.A.-MARX. 12 DUOS, K.487	D55
MOZART, W.A.-LELOIR. 12 DUOS	A71
MOZART, W.A.-SMITH. 12 EASY DUETS, K. 487	F23
MOZART, W.A.-CERMINARO. 12 PIECES, K. 487	C91
MOZART, W.A. SONATA IN E-FLAT	B44
MOZART, W.A.-HOSS. SONATA IN E-FLAT	B44
MOZART, W.A.-JANETZKY. 12 STUCKE, K.487	C75
MOZART, W.A.-STOSSER. 12 STUCKE, K.487	C75
MOZART, W.A. 12 WALDHORN DUETS, K.487	A89
MOZART, W.A. 12 WALDHORN DUETS, K.487	E44
MOZART, W.A.-PAUL. 12 WALDHORNDUETTE, K 487	B73
MOZART, W.A.-PAUL. 12 WALDHORNDUETTE, K.487	E50
NICOLAI, O.-AFFELDER. DUET #4	C91
NICOLAI, O. DUET NO. 1	E14
NICOLAI, O. DUET NO. 2	E14
NICOLAI, O. DUET NO. 3	E14
NICOLAI, O. DUET NO.4, 5 & 6	E14
NICOLAI, O. 5 DUETS FOR 2 HNS	E14
NICOLAI, O. DUETS NOS. 4, 5, 6	E14
NICOLAI, O. 3 DUETTE FUR 2 WALDHORNER	C75
NICOLAI, O. 3 DUETTE	C75
NIGGLI, F. 8 JAGDLIEDER FUR 2 HNS IN F	C80
NORMAND. METHODE DE TROMPE	D36
OSTRANDER, A. FIRST PALS	B85
PAUDERT, E. 6 DUETS	B53
POTTAG, M.P.(ED). 60 FRENCH HORN DUETS	A62
QUIRSFELDER. KANONS I	A51
RACUSEN, D. CANONIC ETUDES	F43
RIMSKY¬KORSAKOV, N.A.-GNESIN. 2 DUETS	E14
RIMSKY¬KORSAKOV, N.A.-KING. 2 DUETS	D16
RUSSELL, R. ABSTRACT #2	C40
SABATINI, G. NOCTURNE	B44
SARO, J.H. STUDIES IN CANON FORM	B53
SCHAEFFER, D.(ARR). DUETS ARE FUN	E80
SCHAEFFER, D.(ARR). READING RHYTHMS	E80
SCHENK, J.-REYNOLDS. 6 SONATAS FOR 2 HNS	D71
SCHNEIDER, W. KLASSISCHE SPIELSTUCKE	A51
SCHNEIDER, W. 12 STUCKE BAROCKER MEISTER	A51
SCHUBERT, F.P.-LELOIR. 5 DUOS	F52
SCHUBERT, F.P.-GOLDMAN. 5 LITTLE DUETS, VERSION A	D74
SCHULLER, G. DUETS FOR UNACCOMPANIED HORNS	E51
SERVAIS, T. CONCORDE	D67
SHAW, L.E. BIPPERIES	C78
SPIES. TIMES TWO	A78
STICH, J.V. DUETS FOR HORNS	A33
STICH, J.V.-LELOIR. 8 HORN DUOS	D11
STICH, J.V.-LELOIR. 12 HORN DUOS	D11
STIEBER, H. TURMMUSIK NR.1	C75
STOUTAMIRE & HENDERSON. DUETS FOR ALL	E80
THEMMEN. 10 CANTOS	B44
TWINN, S. 12 OLD ENGLISH SONGS	C33
ULRICH, H.J. 5 DUETTE	H30
VOXMAN, H.(CMPL). SELECTED DUETS (2 VOL)	F07
WEHNER. 20 MODERN DUETS	N19
WILDER, A. 22 DUETS	H09
WILLIAMS, J.C. DUO-STUDIES	F60
WILLIAMS, J.C. 24 DUO-STUDIES	G46

2 TROMBONES

AMSDEN, A. CELEBRATED DUETS	A55
APPLEBAUM, S.S.-SCHAEFFER. F-ATTACHMENT BASS TROMBONE DUETS	B31
ARBAN, J.J.B.L. ARBAN DUETS FOR TRB & BAR.	A70
BACH, J.S.-POCHUT. 12 DUOS DE J.S.BACH (2 VOL)	D36
BACH, J.S.-ROCHUT. 3 DUOS FOR 2 TRB & 2 FUGUES FOR 3 & 4 TRB	F16
BACH, J.S. FOUR TWO-PART INVENTIONS. 2BTRB	D14
BACH, J.S.-MILLER. 12 TWO-PART INVENTIONS	B98
BAIRD. 23 DUETS	E00
BARETTE. 6 DIVERTIMENTI	C60
BARTOK, B.-KURZ. 18 DUOS (TENOR & BASS)	A78
BENDIK-STORCK. EASY CELLO DUETS (2 BKS)	F31
BERLIOZ, H. EXCERPTS FR. "THE TROJANS" & "DAMNATION OF FAUST"	B85
BLAZHEVICH, V.M. CONCERT DUETS	C91
BLAZHEVICH, V.M. CONCERT DUETS	D71
BLEGER, M.-OSTRANDER. DUETS	C91
BLEGER, M.-COUILLAUD. 12 DUOS CONCERTANTS	D36
BLUME, C.-GIBSON. 12 DUETS (2 VOL)	C91
BLUME, O.-DOBROSERDOV. DUETS, BK.1	D81
BLUME, O. 12 MELODIOUS DUETS	C11
BOISMORTIER. ROKOKO DUETTE (2 VKS)	D90
BORDOGNI, G.M.-COUILLAUD. ETUDES EN DUO	D36
BORDOGNI, G.M.-COUILLAUD. 6 VOCALISES A 2 VOIX	D36
BORRIS, S. KLEINE SUITE FUR 2 POSAUNEN, OP.116	F53
BUCQUET-OSTRANDER. SUITE IN G MINOR	B85
BUSH, I. DUET SESSION	B31
CASSEL, D. & GEARHART. BASS CLEF SESSIONS	F43
CONCONE, G.-OSTRANDER. 5 DUETS	D14
CORELLI, A. SONATA IN G MINOR	B85
CORELLI, A.-OSTRANDER. SONATA IN G MINOR	B85
CORNETTE, V. 6 CONCERT DUETS	B53
CORNETTE, V. 20 ELEMENTARETUDEN	A51
CORNETTE, V. 20 LESSONS IN USEFUL KEYS	B53
CORRETTE, M.-BROWN. 2 DIVERTIMENTI, OP.7	C91
COUILLAUD, H.L. 4 STUDIES IN THE FORM OF DUOS	D36
COUPERIN, F. CONCERT EN SOL MAJEUR	F87
DEDRICK, A. 19 PROGRESSIVE DUETS	D14
DEVIENNE-HESS. DUO CONCERTANTS	D21
DI LASSO, O. 12 DUETS	E00
DIEPPO, A.G.-OSTRANDER. VIRTUOSO STUDIES	B85
EHELLEMMES, R. 25 POLYPHONIQUES D'APRES GRANDS MAITRES	D41
FESCH, W.D. 3 SONATEN	D90
FRENCH DUETS (12 ORIGINAL DUETS).	B98
GEARHART, CASSEL, & HORNIBROOK. BASS CLEF SESSIONS	F43
GENZMER, M. 12 DUOS	E65
GODARD, B.L.P. BERCEUSE (JOCELYN)	B13
GRIGORIEV, B. & VOSTRYAKOV(CMPL). 24 DUETS	D81
GUILLEMENT. 6 SONATAS	C60
HANDEL, G.F.-PULIS. PRELUDE	B98
HARRIS, A. ORIGINAL DUETS	B31
HARTZELL, D. BLUES FOR TWOS	F74
HENNING, C.T. 24 EASY DUETS	B53
HENNING, C.T.-OSTRANDER. 24 EASY DUETS	C91
HENNING, C.T. LEICHTE UBUNGEN	C75
HINDEMITH, P. STUECKE	F31
HOUSTON. JAZZ FOR TWO	B31

KAHILA, K. ANDANTE-ALLEGRO	B85
KARLIN, F. DUETS IN JAZZ	B31
KINYON, J. BREEZE-EASY PROGRAM PIECES	H06
KINYON, J. BROADWAY SHOWCASE	H06
KREISLEF, A.V. ANDANTE & PRESTO	F60
LA VIOLETTE, W. DUET ALBUM	G85
LASSO-SMELTEKOP. 12 DUETS	E00
LASSUS-POWELL. 2 FANTASIAS	F60
LISZT, F. LIEBESTRAUM	B13
LOCKE, M.-SMELTEKOP. ONE DOZEN DUETS	E00
MARTIN. JAZZ DUETS	M77
MATEJ, J. 10 TWO-PART & 10 3-PART INVENTIONS	G81
MILLER & NELSON. ADVANCED DUETS	B31
MILLER, D.G. FRENCH DUETS	B98
MOZART, W.A.-SMITH. ANDANTE	E80
MOZART, W.A.-POWELL. 11 DUETS, K. 487	F43
MOZART, W.A.-SMITH. 12 EASY DUETS, K. 487	F23
MOZART, W.A.-BAZELAIRE. SONATE	D36
MUELLER. 35 DUETS	F62
NELSON, B. ADVANCED DUETS	B31
PEDERSON, T. 5 DUETS FOR BASS TRBS	F27
PEDERSON, T. 5 DUETS FOR TENOR & BASS TRBS	F27
PEDERSON, T. 5 DUETS FOR TENOR TROMBONES	F27
PEDERSON, T. 10 PIECES FOR TENOR & BASS TRBS	M93
PEDERSON, T. 10 PIECES FOR 2 BASS TRBS	M93
PEDERSON, T. 10 PIECES FOR 2 TENOR TRBS	M93
PORRET, J. DUO'S DE CONCOURS #3 & #4	D92
PORRET, J. 12 DUOS FACILES	D92
RACUSEN, D. CANONIC ETUDES	F43
RAPHLING, S. SONATINA	B85
REGNER, H. SPIELHEFT I	C54
RUSSO, W.J. DUETS, OP.35	B31
SCHAEFFER, D. (ARR). CHRISTMAS DUETS	E80
SCHAEFFER, D. (ARR). DUETS ARE FUN	E80
SCHAEFFER, D. (ARR). 21 RHYTHMIC DUETS	E80
SMALL, C. URBIE GREEN PLAYS CHARLIE SMALL'S DUETS	B31
SPEER, D. 2 SONATAS	E14
STOUTAMIRE & HENDERSON. DUETS FOR ALL	E80
TANNER, P. DUETS, BK 1	C77
TANNER, P. TROMBONE DUETS, VOL.1	G21
TCHAIKOVSKY, P.I.-DEDRICK. SAILING SONG	D14
TELEMANN, G.P. SONATA #4	D55
TELEMANN, G.P.-BAHR. SONATA	D14
UBER, D.A. 23TH CENTURY DUETS (2 VOL)	A03
UBER, D.A. 10 CONCERT DUETS	B85
VOXMAN, H.(CMPL). SELECTED DUETS (2 VOL)	F07
WIENANDT. DUETS	F60
WILLIAMS, E. EASY DUETS, 114 DUETS,EASY TO INTERMEDIATE	B31
ZOBEL. PALS IN BRASS	D18

2 TUBAS

ALBERT. FIVE	M80
BACH, J.S.-MAC MORRAN. BACH FOR 2 TUBAS	N81
BACH, J.S.-AUGUSTINE. DUETS & TRIOS	F60
BLAZHEVICH, V.M.-WEKSELBLATT. 2 CONCERT DUETS	F23
BLEGER, M.-COUILLAUD. 12 CONCERTANTE DUOS	D36
CARNAUD, J. 30 DUOS PROGRESSIFS	C38

```
CATELINET, P.B.  SUITE IN MINIATURE                         C71
CHEDEVILLE.  3 ROCOCO DANCES                                P19
DE JONG, C.  MUSIC FOR 2 TUBAS                              B92
GARRETT.  DUET                                              M80
GARRETT.  FANTASIA                                          M80
GIBBONS, O.  FANTASIA.  2TU                                 P19
GOLDMAN, R.F.  DUO FOR TUBAS, OR BSNS                       B85
JONES, R.  21 DISTINCTIVE DUETS                             N98
KRUSH, J.  LARGO & ALLEGRO                                  M80
KRUSH, J.  LARGO AND ALLEGRO                                P42
LUEDEKE.  8 BAGATELLES                                      F80
NELHYBEL, V.  11 DUETS FOR TUBA                             C40
NEUENFELDT, M.V.  CHORALE AND MARCH                         P42
PRESSER, W.H.  7 DUETS                                      F80
ROIKJER.  10 INVENTIONS                                     H30
RUSSO, W.J.  DUETS--21 ETUDES                               B31
RYKER.  SONATA                                              D94
SEAR, W.E.  ADVANCED DUETS (2 BKS)                          B44
SINGLETON (ED).  3 RENAISSANCE DUETS                        F59
STAMITZ, K.-LONG.  DUET                                     M80
STOUTAMIRE & HENDERSON.  DUETS FOR ALL                      E80
STROUD.  TUBANTIPHON                                        G66
SWEELINCK, J.P.  POLYPHONIC RHYME #4.  2TU                  P19
WHITE.  FANTASIA                                            P19
WILSON, D.M.  DUET                                          N42
```

2 MIXED BRASS (BRASS-PERC)

```
ALEXANDER.  TRIO OF DUOS.  TPT, TRB                         F59
AMSDEN, A.  AMSDEN'S PRACTICE DUETS                         A55
    2TPT(2HN, 2TRB, 2EU, 2TU)
BACH, J.S.  CANON ALLA DUODECIMA.  TPT, TU                  N42
BACH, J.S.  CANON ALLA DUODECIMA.  TPT, TU                  P19
BACH, J.S.-DEDRICK.  INVENTION #10.  TPT, TRB              D14
BACH, J.S.  INVENTION #13.  TPT, TRB                        D14
BACH, J.S.  INVENTIONS #3, 4, 10, 14.  TPT, TRB            D14
BACH, J.S.  8 INVENTIONS.  TPT, TRB                         E00
BACH, J.S.-SMELTEKOP.  7 MORE INVENTIONS.  TPT, TRB         E00
BACH, J.S.-DEDRICK.  TWO-PART INVENTION # 3.  TPT, TRB     D14
BACH, J.S.-DEDRICK.  TWO-PART INVENTION # 4.  TPT, TRB     D14
BACH, J.S.-DEDRICK.  TWO-PART INVENTION #14.  TPT, TRB     D14
BACH, J.S.-DEDRICK.  TWO-PART INVENTION NO. 14.  TPT, TRB(EU)  D14
BAINES, F.A.  3 SHORT PIECES.  TPT, TRB                     G26
BORDEN, D.  15 DIALOGUES.  TPT, TRB                         B98
BOZZA, E.  4 ESQUISSES.  TPT, TRB                           D36
BURGER.  5 BICINIA.  TPT, TRB                               D52
BUTTERFIELD, D.  7 DUETS.  TRB, TU                          H71
CANIVEZ, L.  DUO CONCERTANT, OP.7.  TPT, TRB                F81
CANIVEZ, L.  DUO CONCERTANT, OP.8.  TPT, HN(EU)             F81
CATELINET, P.B.  SUITE IN MINIATURE.  TRB, TU               C71
COPERARIO.  FANTASIA.  TPT, TRB                             P19
CORELLI, A.  SONATA IN G MINOR.  TPT(HN), TRB              B85
CORELLI, A.-OSTRANDER.  SONATA IN G MINOR.  HN, TRB         B85
DEFOSSEZ.  4 PETITS PIECES.  TPT, TRB                       J39
DEFOSSEZ, R.  4 PETITES PIECES.  TPT, TRB                   D80
DIEMENTE, E.  DESIGNS.  TPT, TRB                            G66
DIEMENTE, E.  ORBITS I.  HN, BTRB                           N91
DIJK, J.V.  SERENADE.  TPT, HN                              B74
```

DIJK, J.V. SERENADE. TPT, HN	B99
FILIPPI. DIVERTIMENTO. EU(HN), TU	M98
FRACKENPOHL, A.R. BRASS DUO. HN(EU), TU	M98
GLINKA, M.I.-KING. 4 SHORT FUGUES. TPT, TRB(HN, EU)	D16
GOEDICKE, A.F. CONCERT SUITE. TRB, TU	N42
GOLDMAN, E.F. DUO. TRB, TU	D74
HAGER. FRIEDENSBOTE, DER. TPT, TRB	E03
HARTLEY, W.S. BIVALVE SUITE. EU, TU	G83
HARTLEY, W.S. CONCERTO. SOLO TU, PERC(6)	G68
HARTZELL, D. MUTT & JEFF. TPT, TRB	F74
HEINKE, J. MUSIC FOR TRB & PERC. TRB, PERC	B35
HOVHANESS, A.S. MYSTERIOUS HORSE BEFORE THE GATE, OP. 235	E65
TRB, BELLS, 2VIB, PERC, TAM TAM	
IANNACCONE, A. SONATINA. TPT, TU	F77
JELICH, V.-EHMANN. RICERCARE FUR TPT & TRB. TPT, TRB	A51
KAHILA, K. ANDANTE-ALLEGRO. HN, TRB	B85
KAZDIN, A. 12 DUETS FOR TPT & HN. TPT, HN	D16
KING, R.D. FRENCH SUITE. TPT, EU	D16
KRIVITSKI. DIPTYCH. TPT, TRB	N42
KRIVITSKI. DIPTYCH. TPT, TRB	P19
KUPFERMAN, M. AVAILABLE FORMS. TPT(CL), TRB(BSN)	C40
LASSO-SMELTEKOP. 12 DUETS. HN, TRB	E00
LESTER. 3 DUETS. TPT, TRB	G21
LEVY, F. DUO. FLG, BTPT	G66
LOCKE-SMELTEKOP. 1 DOZEN DUETS. HN, TRB	E00
MIASKOVSKY. FUGUE IN CLASSIC STYLE. TPT, TRB	D14
MICHALSKY, D.R. FANTASIA A DUE. HN, BTRB	G21
MOZART, W.A. 2 WIND DUETS. TRB, TU	N42
MOZART, W.A. 2 WIND DUETS. EU, TU	P19
OSTRANDER, A. 10 DUETS ON HANDEL THEMES. TPT, TRB	B85
OTT, J. TRANSFUSION. TPT, HN	B53
PAYNE, F.L. CONCERT SUITE. TPT, TRB	M80
PRESSER, W.H. 7 DUETS. HN, TU	G66
RAPH, A. 3 DISPLAY DUETS. TPT, TRB	B85
RAPHLING, S. PRELUDE & TOCCATA. TPT, TRB	B85
ROBERTS. SUITE FOR 2 WINDS. TPT, TRB	B44
SCHWADRON. DUO IN ODD METERS. TPT, TRB	E83
SCHWARTZ, E.S. ESSAYS. TPT, TRB	P38
SEEGER, P. KLEINE MUSIK. EU, FLG	D98
SERVAIS. RENCONTRE. TPT, HN	D67
SINGLETON (ED). RENAISSANCE DUETS. EU, TU	F59
STAMITZ, K. DUET. EU, TU	M80
STOKER, R. 4 DIALOGUES. HN, TU	C71
TACK. ALEXANDRA. TPT, EU	F81
TACK. AU REPOS. TPT, EU	F81
UBER, D.A. DOUBLE PORTRAITS. TRB, TU	A94
UBER, D.A. PROGRAM DUETS. TPT, TRB	B85
UBER, D.A. RECITAL HALL DUETS. HN, TRB	D14
VIVALDI, A. SONATA DA CAMERA. TPT, TRB	B85
VIVALDI, A.-MAGANINI. SONATA DA CAMERA. TPT, TRB	B85
VOBARON, F. 40 ETUDES (2 BKS). TRB, TU	B46
WILSON, D.M. DUET. TRB, TU	N42

2 PARTS: HORN-WOODWIND

BACH, JAN. FOUR 2-BIT CONTRAPTIONS. HN, FL	N29
BARSAM, Y. 3 ENCORES FOR HN & BSN. HN, BSN	C94
BLANC, J. 3 SONATAS FOR HORN & BSN. HN, BSN(VC)	D11

```
BOUCARD, M.  SUITE CHAMPETRE.  HN, FL                        A71
DOBRZYNSKI, I.  DUO.  HN, CL                                 D11
DOBRZYNSKI, I.F.  DUET FOR CL & HN.  HN, CL                  D63
DUVERNOY, F.N.-LELOIR.  SONATA #1.  HN, BSN(VC)              D11
DUVERNOY, F.N.-WEELINK.  SONATA #2.  HN, BSN(VC)             D11
DUVERNOY, F.N.-LELOIR.  SONATA #3.  HN, BSN(VC)              D11
MAKOVECKY, J.-WEELINK.  DUO CONCERTANTE #1.  HN, CL          D11
MAKOVECKY, J.-WEELINK.  DUO CONCERTANTE #2.  HN, CL          D11
MAKOVECKY, J.-WEELINK.  DUO CONCERTANTE #3.  HN, CL          D11
OTT, J.  5 DUETS FOR HORN AND OBOE.  HN, OB                  A65
STICH, J.V.-LELOIR.  SONATA.  HN, BSN                        D11
WILDGANS, F.  3 INVENTIONEN, OP. 19A.  HN, CL                B73
```

2 PARTS: BRASS-WOODWIND

```
HARTLEY, W.S.  DUET FOR FLUTE AND TUBA.  TU, FL             F80
LASSUS, R.D.  2 PIECES.  TU, FL                             P19
VAUGHAN-WILLIAMS, R.  4 BICINIE.  TU, CL                    P19
```

2 PARTS: WIND(S)-STRING(S)

```
AMRAM, D.W.  3 SONGS FOR MARLBORO.  HN, VC                  E65
LUENING, O.  SHORT PHANTASY.  HN, VN                        E68
MACOVECZ, J.-LELOIR.  3 SONATAS FOR HN & VIA.  HN, VA       D11
SCHWARTZ, E.  SIGNALS.  TRB, DB                             N29
WEISS, A.A.  PASSACAGLIO.  HN, VA                           E68
```

2 PARTS: BRASS-MISCELLANEOUS

```
CHILDS, B.  INTERBALANCES IV.  TPT, NAR                     F88
CHILDS, B.  MARY'S IDEA.  TU, HPCD                          G66
CUMMINGS.  KRAKEN, THE.  TU, PERC                           N92
DELP, R. & WEISS.  MODOGENESIS.  TRB, PERC                  G66
HARTLEY, W.S.  DUET.  2 INST ?                              F80
HOFFMANN, E.A.  ALTE BLASERMUSIKEN AUS D. 16.-18.JAHRHUNDERT D78
    2 EQUAL BRASS INST
HOVHANESS, A.S.  MYSTERIOUS HORSE BEFORE THE GATE.  TRB, PERC E65
JARZEBSKI, A.  CONCERTI A 2.  2INST ?                       E72
KRAFT, W.  ENCOUNTERS III.  TPT, PERC                       A43
MORYL, R.  CHAMBERS I.  TRB, FILM OR SLIDES &/OR LIGHTS     A13
MOZART, L.-SCHEIFES.  4 KLEINE STUKKEN VAN L.MOZART.  2INST ? F81
PORRET, J.  12 DUO'S PROGRESSIFS VOOR 2 KOPERBLAZERS        D92
    2 EQUAL BRASS INST
```

THREE-PART MUSIC

3 TRUMPETS

ABACO-MOORE. INVENTION	G21
ALTENBURG, J.E. POLONAISE	E65
ARTOT, D.M. 12 TRIOS	B53
BACH, J.S.-BAUDRIER. 25 CHORALS	A71
BACH, J.S.-MOORE. SUSCEPIT ISRAEL	G21
BACH, K.P.E. FANFARE MARCH	D63
BACH, K.P.E.-YATES. MARCH-FANFARE	D14
BALDWIN. CONCERTO	N42
BALDWIN. 5 CONSORTS	N42
BARAT. TROPETTES D'EUSTACHE, LES	B24
BENGER. PRELUDES & CANONS	B23
BERGMANN. FANFARES HERALDIQUES	D36
BOUTRY, R. FANFARES POUR DES TEMPS LEGENDAIRES	D36
BRITTEN, B. FANFARE FOR ST. EDMUNDSBURY	A78
BRUGK, H.M. 10 KLEINE VORTRAGSSTUECKE	C54
BUSCH, C. SUITE FOR 3 TPTS	G31
BUSCH, C. SUITE FOR 3 TPTS	H06
BUSCH, C. THREE OF US	G85
BUTTS. TRUMPETS ON CALL	A84
BUTTS, C.M. CAPRICCIO FOR 3 TPTS	G90
BUTTS, C.M. SUITE FOR BRASS	E80
BYRNE. INTRODUCTION, BLUES & FINALE	C71
CABUS, P.N. 3 MOUVEMENTS	D67
CACAVAS, J. TRUMPETERS THREE	D63
CARTER. CANON FOR 3	A38
CASSEL, D. & GEARHART. TRUMPET SESSIONS	F43
CATIZONE, J. TRUMPETERS THREE	E80
CHARLTON. WE THREE	C11
CLARK, F.(ARR). SEICENTO	B85
COSTANTINI. RICERCAR	P19
COUPERIN, F.-MAGANINI. TRUMPETS CALL, THE	B85
DARCY, R. TRIPOLI	D18
DONATO, A. SONATINA	F23
DUBOIS, P.M. 5 BAGATELLES	D36
EDELSON, E. CHASE, THE	E80
EHMANN, W. WEIHNACHTSLIEDER	A51
ELWELL, H. STRICTLY FOR TPT	B31
FRANCO, J. GLORIA	A13
GEARHART, L. & CASSEL. TRUMPET SESSIONS	F43
GIBBONS, O.-CLARK. FANTASIA FOR THREE	B85
GIBBONS, O. FANTASIA FOR 3	B85
GIBBONS, O. SILVER SWAN, THE	P19
GIBBS. HARLEQUINADE	C71
HANDEL, G.F. FUGHETTA	E80
HARMON, R. PASACALLE	A43
HARMON, R. PASACALLE	G21
HAUGLAND, A.O. RONDO BREVE	B98
HERBERT. JUST FOR FUN	C11
HODGSON. FANFARES	C71
HOPKINS. TRIUMPHAL MARCH	B13
HOUSTON-COLIN. JAZZ	B31
HUDADOFF, I.(ARR). TRUMPET TRIOS	E80
ISAAC-MOORE. MADRIGAL	G21
JACOBSON, I.D. 3 CANTOS FOR CNTS.	D84
JONES, R. THREE BY THREE	B38

```
KABALEVSKY, D.B.   ANDANTE & SCHERZANDO                          G21
KETTING, O.   KLEINE SUITE                                      B74
KITTEL-MOORE.   EIN FESTE BURG                                   M71
KNIGHT, V.(ARR).   10 TRIOS FOR TRUMPETERS                       A35
KOSENKO.   FANFARE, OP. 15/13                                    P19
KRESSER-WIENANDT.   6 SHORT CONCERT TRIOS                        E80
KRESSER-WIENANDT.   TRUMPET TRIOS FOR CONCERT                    E80
KRUMPFER, H.J.   MUSIK FUR 3 TROMPETEN                           C75
LANCEN.   OLD FRENCH SONGS                                       C71
LANGLEY.   TRIO                                                  C71
LASSUS, R.D.   MOTET "HODIE APPARUIT IN ISRAEL"                  P19
LOTTI.   RICERCAR                                                P19
LUPO.   FANTASIA                                                 P19
MAGANINI, Q.E.   TROUBADORS, THE                                 B85
MANCINI, A.(ED).   CONCERT HIGHLIGHTS                            B31
MANOUVRIER, A.   3 PIECES POUR 3 TPTS                            D36
MARSHALL-KLEIN.   TWO BY TWO                                     F43
MARTIN.   BETTY'S WALTZ                                          B13
MARTIN.   SKYROCKET                                              B13
MATHEZ.   HORS D'OEUVRES                                         A71
MATHEZ.   PETITE CAUSE (GRANDS EFFETS)                           A71
MENDELSSOHN, F.-SMITH.   RONDO CAPRICCIOSO                       D84
MEZO, I.   VARIATIONS FOR 3 TPTS                                 B84
MOENKEMEYER.   MUSIK AUS DER VORKLASSIK                          F31
MORRISSEY, J.J.   TRUMPETS 3                                     C11
MOZART, W.A.-ROSENTHAL.   DIVERTIMENTI.   3 OR 4 TPT, OPT TIMP   D63
MOZART, W.A.-ROSENTHAL.   DIVERTIMENTI                           E67
MUCZYNSKI, R.   TRUMPET TRIO, OP.11/1                            F23
MULLER, J.P.   SUITE D'APRES FANTINI                             D67
MULLER, J.P.   SUITE NO.1                                        D67
MULLER, J.P.   SUITE NO.2                                        D67
NAGAN.   SERENADE FOR LISA                                       C94
NAGEL, F.   EASTER TRUMPETS                                      D73
NAGEL, R.   SOUND OF TRUMPETS, THE                               N88
NELHYBEL, V.   12 CONCERT PIECES                                 B32
NELHYBEL, V.   MUSICA FESTIVA                                    B32
NEMSER.   TRIO NO. 1                                             E80
NORGARD.   TROMPETMUSIK                                          H30
O'NEILL, C.   AUTUMN TONES                                       D74
OSBORN, G.A.   4 FANFARES                                        M98
OSTRANDER, A.   SUITE FOR 3 BRASS                                B85
PETERS-LEIDZEN.   TRUMPET SERENADE                               C25
PHILLIPS, B.   TRIO FOR TRUMPETS                                 D16
PISARI & NANINO.   2 RICERCARI                                   P19
POLSON, R.   EQUALI IN F                                         F79
POLSON, R.   EQUALI                                              G70
POLSON, R.   3 MOODS FOR 3 TRUMPETS                              F79
PORRET, J.   ARCHIMEDE                                           D92
PORRET, J.   BAYARD                                              D92
PRESSER, W.H.   SUITE                                            F80
PRESSER, W.H.   SUITE                                            F88
PURCELL, H.   CHACONNE                                           B85
RACUSEN, D.   CANONIC ETUDES                                     F43
RICHTER.   MAN FROM MARS                                         B13
RICHTER.   VAGABONIA                                             B13
SARTORIUS, H.   BUMBY ROAD, THE                                  B13
SARTORIUS, H.   CAPE COD CHANTY                                  B13
SARTORIUS, H.   EASTWARD HO!                                     B13
SARTORIUS, H.   ROMANY DANCE                                     B13
SCHAEFFER(ARR).   CORNET TRIO ALBUM                              E80
SCHAEFFER(ARR).   ENCORE                                         E80
SCHAEFFER (ARR).   ANCIENT FUGUE                                 E80
```

```
SCHAFER, K.H.   5 SPIELSTUCKE FUR 3 TPTS                              A51
SCHEIFES, H.M.   4 SHORT PIECES FROM OLD MASTERS                      F81
SCHIFFMAN, E.   HOLIDAY FANFARES                                      D16
SCHNEIDER, W.   1ST TROMPETENSPIEL                                    F31
SHELUKOV, V.   TERZETTO.  3TPT                                        P19
SOLOMON.   TANDEM TRIO                                                F60
STEIN, L.   TRIC FOR 3 TPTS                                           E77
STOKER, R.   MUSIC FOR THREE                                          D37
STOKER, R.   ROUNDS & CANONS                                          C71
STOUFFER.   TOCCATA FOR TRUMPETS                          /           E80
STROUD.   THUMBNAIL SKETCHES                                          G66
STROUD, R.   THUMBNAIL SKETCHES FOR TPT TRIO                          B35
TCHEREPNIN, A.N.   TRIO                                               D63
TELEMANN, G.P.-STOUFFER.   TRUMPET TUNE                               D14
TIPPETT, M.   FANFARE NO.3                                            F31
TOMASI, H.   SUITE                                                    B92
TOMASI, H.   SUITE                                                    D36
TOMASI, H.   SUITE                                                    D63
TROWBRIDGE, L.   TRANQUILLO                                           B38
VERNON.   SUITE                                                       F23
VIERDANCK, J.-ENGEL.   CAPRICCI FUR 2-4 TPT OR FLUGELHN               A51
VORCE.   LFS BUFFCNS                                                  C27
WALTER, J.   CANONS IN THE CHURCH MODES                              A51
WEBBE.   GLORIOUS APOLLO                                              G21
WEELKES.   GAY TUNE, A                                                B85
WHISTLER, H.S.   FANFARES OF THE AIR (30 FANFARES)                    F07
WILBYE, J.   MADRIGAL "FLY LOVE ALOFT"                                P19
WILBYE, J.   MADRIGAL "SO LIGHT IS LOVE                               P19
WILBYE, J.   MADRIGAL "WHAT SHALL I DOE?"                             P19
WILHELMER, A.   2 KLEINE SATZE                                        C54
WILHELMER, A.   SONATINE FUR 3 TPTS                                   E50
```

3 HORNS

```
ARTOT, D.M.   12 TRIOS                                                B53
BACH, J.S.-SHAW.   5 BACH TRIOS                                       C78
BACH, J.S.-SHAW.   TRIOS, BK 2                                        C78
BACH, J.S.-SHAW.   TRIOS, BK 3                                        C78
BEETHOVEN, L.V.   TRIO FOR 3 HORNS, OP.87                             B44
BERGENFELD.   CANZONA                                                 E80
BERGENFELD.   2 NEW ENGLAND MINIATURES                                F79
BOISMORTIER-SHAW.   SONATA                                            C78
BORRIS, S.   SUITE FUR 3 HORNER                                       F53
BRUGK, H.M.   10 KLEINE VORTRAGSSTUCKE                                C54
BUCHTEL, F.I.   HORN TRIO BOOK                                        D18
BUTTS.   ARIA & SCHERZO                                               E80
BUTTS.   CALL OF THE HORNS                                            E80
BUTTS.   CHORALE & CALL                                               D14
BUTTS.   TRIODE                                                       D14
BUTTS, C.M.   HCRNS OF BRASS                                          E80
BUTTS, C.M.   ODE FOR HORNS                                           E80
CLARK, F.(ED).   SEICENTO                                             B85
CONLEY, L.   LENTO & LILT                                             D14
COUPERIN, F.   TRUMPETS CALL, THE                                     B85
COWELL, H.   HYMN & FUGUING TUNE NO.12                                A38
CUNNINGHAM.   TERZETT, OP. 54                                         G66
DARDENNE.   CHRISTIA-SUITE                                            B24
DAUPRAT, L.F.   GRAND TRIO #3                                         C11
```

```
DEVERT.  RECUEIL PRATIQUE DU SONNEUR (56 FANFARES)            D36
DUVERNOY, F.N.-WIENANDT.  4 TRIOS FOR HORNS                   F60
DUVERNOY, F.N.-ZIMOLONG.  4 TRIOS                             F50
FREHSE, A.  12 TRIOS, OP.10                                   F60
GALLAY, J.F.  GRAND HORN TRIO OP. 24/3                        D11
GALLAY, J.F.-LELOIR.  GRAND TRIO, OP.23/3                     D11
GALLAY, J.F.-LELOIR.  GRAND TRIO, OP.24/1                     D11
GALLAY, J.F.-LELOIR.  GRAND TRIO, OP.24/2                     D11
GALLAY, J.F.-LELOIR.  TRIO #3, OP. 24/3                       D11
GIBBONS, O.  FANTASIA FOR 3                                   B85
HEUSSENSTAMM.  TRIO, OP. 48                                   G66
HEUSSENSTAMM, G.  HORN TRIO                                   G66
HILL, D.  5 PIECES                                            C78
HORROD, N.S.  SCHERZO FOR 3 HNS                               D11
HUDADOFF, I.(ARR).  HORN TRIOS                                E80
INGALLS, M.  DIVERTIMENTO                                     P49
JACOBSON, I.D.  3 HOLIDAYS FOR HORNS                          D84
JANETZKY, K.(CMPL).  JAGERSTUCKLEIN                           C75
JAUNEZ, A.  6 HORN TRIOS                                      D11
JONES, R.  THREE BY THREE                                     F43
KIBBE, M.  HORN TRIO                                          C78
KLING, H.-TEAGUE.  30 SELECTED PIECES                        A38
MAGANINI, Q.E.  TROUBADORS                                    B85
MAYER, W.R.  TRICINIUM                                        F60
MOZART, W.A.-WALSHE.  DIVERTIMENTO # 2                        C78
MOZART, W.A.-HOWE.  FINALE, VIENNESE SONATINA #6              C78
MOZART, W.A.  5 TRIOS                                         B73
NELHYBEL, V.  MUSICA FESTIVA                                  B32
OSTRANDER, A.  SUITE FOR 3 BRASS                              B85
POTTAG, M.P.(ARR).  TRIO ALBUM                                A62
PRESSER, W.H.  HORN TRIO                                      P49
PURCELL, H.  CHACONNE                                         B85
RACUSEN, D.  CANONIC ETUDES                                   F43
REICHA, A.-LELOIR.  TRIOS FR OP. 82, VOL 1                    D11
REICHA, A.-LELOIR.  TRIOS FR OP. 82, VOL 2                    D11
REICHA, A.-LELOIR.  TRIOS FR OP. 92, VOL 1                    D11
REICHA, A.-LELOIR.  TRIOS FR OP. 92, VOL 2                    D11
REICHA, A.-LELOIR.  10 TRIOS SUITE 1                          D11
REICHA, A.-LELOIR.  10 TRIOS SUITE 2 & 3                      D11
REICHA, A.  6 TRIOS, OP.82                                    F60
REICHA, A.-CHAMBERS.  6 TRIOS, OP.82                          C91
REICHA, A.-FREHSE & GLASENAPP.  6 TRIOS, OP.82                C75
REICHA, A.-LELOIR.  8 TROIS, OP.82                            F52
RIGGINS, H.L.  SUITE FOR 3 HORNS                              C78
ROCHARD.  LE FOLKLORE DE LA CHASSE                            D36
ROSENTHAL, C.A.  4 CLASSICAL TRANSCRIPTIONS                   A43
ROSENTHAL, C.A.(ARR).  4 CLASSICAL TRANSCRIPTIONS             G21
SCHAEFFER(ARR).  ENCORE                                       E80
SCHAEFFER(ARR).  HORN TRIO ALBUM                              E80
SCHAEFFER (ARR).  ANCIENT FUGUE                               E80
SCHEIFES, H.M.  4 KLEINE STUKKEN VAN OUDE MEESTERS            F81
SCHIFFMAN, E.  HOLIDAY FANFARES                               D16
SCHNEIDER, G.A.  18 TRIOS                                     C91
SCHUMANN-HILFIGER.  2 TRIOS                                   D14
SHELUKOV, V.  TERZETTO.  3TPT                                 P19
SOMBRUN.  L'ART DE SONNER DE LA TROMPE, PT 1                  D36
STICH, J.V.-LELOIR.  20 HORN TRIOS                            D11
THIELMAN.  HORNS A PLENTY                                     E80
WEELKES.  GAY TUNE, A                                         B85
ZWIERZINA-BRUCHLE.  TRIOS                                     D11
```

3 TROMBONES

```
ALBINONI, T.-DOCKSTADER.  ANDANTE DOLCE                       G78
ALEXANDER.  2 ESSAYS                                          C40
ARNE, T.A.  VIVACE                                            G78
BACH, J.S.-WELSHMAN.  ALLEGRETTO                              G78
BACH, J.S.-MILLER.  CHORALES (2 VOL).  2TRB, BTRB             B98
BACH, J.S.-ROCHUT.  3 DUOS ... & 2 FUGUES FOR 3 TRB           F16
BACH, J.S.-JAMESON.  FUGA II IN C MINOR                       G78
BACH, J.S.-MYERS.  FUGUE IN G MAJOR                           B98
BACH, J.S.-PULIS.  POLONAISE                                  B98
BACH, J.S.-KELLEHER.  SARABANDE.  2TRB, BTRB                  B98
BACH, J.S.-SAUER.  SINFONIA 4, 6 & 8                          M79
BACH, K.P.E.-YATES.  MARCH-FANFARE                            D14
BARTSCH, C.  CHORAL, DANSE NONCHALANTE,ET FANFARE             D67
BEETHOVEN, L.V.  MOUNT OF OLIVES SUITE                        B85
BEETHOVEN, L.V.-OSTRANDER.  SUITE (THE MOUNT OF OLIVES)       B85
BEETHOVEN, L.V.  SYMPHONIC TRIO                               B44
BEETHOVEN, L.V.-SEAR.  SYMPHONIC TRIO                         B44
BEETHOVEN, L.V.-SMITH.  TRIO (ABSCHIEDSGESANG)                D14
BEETHOVEN, L.V.-DELISSE.  TRIO                                B98
BENNETT, J.  SLIPPERY JOE                                     D14
BERGENFELD.  CHACONNE                                         F79
BERGENFELD, N.  DIVERSION                                     E80
BERLICZ, H.  AT THE STABLE                                    B85
BLAZHEVICH, V.M.  FIRST SUITE                                 M92
BLOCK.  INCANTATION & CANZONA                                 M79
BORRIS, S.  2 CANZONEN, OP. 92/3                              F53
BOYCE.  ALLEGRO                                               G78
BOYCE.  LARGO & ADAGIO                                        G78
BRIEGEL.  BURLESQUE ON "O DU LIEBER AUGESTINE"                A91
BRUCKNER, A.  AEQUALE                                         B98
CALDARA-DOCKSTADER.  ADAGIO                                   G78
CALDARA-DOCKSTADER.  ALLEGRO                                  G78
CHAGRIN, F.  FANFARE FOR ADAM                                 E41
CHASE, A.H.  8 TRIOS FOR 3 TRB                                B44
CORBEEL, R.  TRIO                                             D67
CORELLI, A.-DOCKSTADER.  ADAGIO                               G78
CORELLI, A.-DOCKSTADER.  LARGO & ADAGIO                       G78
CORELLI, A.-NETHERCUTT.  SONATA DA CHIESA, OP. 3/7            M80
CORELLI, A.-DOCKSTADER.  SONATA IV                            G78
CORELLI, A.-OSTRANDER.  2 TRANSCRIPTIONS FOR 3 TRB            B98
CORELLI, A.-OSBORN.  TRIO SONATA, OP.1/10                     B98
CORELLI, A.-OSBORN.  TRIO SONATA, OP.1/11                     B98
CORELLI, A.-OSBORN.  TRIO SONATA, OP.1/5                      B98
CORELLI, A.-MYERS.  TRIO SONATA, OP.3/2                       B98
CORELLI, A.-MYERS.  TRIO SONATA, OP.3/5                       B98
CORNETTE, V.  TRIO NO.1                                       B98
CORNETTE, V.  TRIO NO.2                                       B98
CORNETTE, V.  TRIO NO.3                                       B98
COSTANTINI.  RICERCAR                                         P19
CUOMO.  DRY RALPH                                             N29
DANDRIEU-DOCKSTADER.  VIVACE                                  G78
DESPREZ, F.  TRIPTIQUE                                        D67
DOCKSTADER (ARR).  SALZBURGER TRISONATE                       G78
DUNSTABLE, J.-SMELTEKOP.  3 PIECES                            E00
EHELLEMMES, R.  25 POLYPHONIQUES D'APRES LES GRAND MAITRES    D41
```

```
EHELLEMMES, R.  TRIOS MODERNES                                        B92
FRANCK, C.  PRELUDE ET DANSE                                         E80
FRANCO, J.  3 INVENTIONS FOR 3 TRB                                  E68
FRANCO, J.  3 INVENTIONS                                            A13
FRESCOBALDI, G.-FETTER.  CANZONA I                                  B98
FRESCOBALDI, G.-FETTER.  CANZONA II                                 B98
FUX, J.-DOCKSTADER.  TRIOSONATA I                                   G78
GEARHART, CASSEL, & HORNIBROOK.  BASS CLEF SESSIONS                 F43
GEMINIANI-MORRIS.  CONCERTO GROSSO                                  F43
GIBBONS, O.  SILVER SWAN, THE                                       P19
GREGORIEVA¬VOSTRYAKOVA.  TRIOS, BK 1                                N42
HAAN, S.D.  MARCH, WALTZ, QUASI ADAGIO                              C71
HANDEL, G.F.-PULIS.  ARIOSO                                         B98
HANDEL, G.F.-PULIS.  BOUREE                                         B98
HANDEL, G.F.-OSBORN.  GIGUE FR. SONATA IN F MAJOR, OP.2/5           B98
  2TRB, BTRB
HANDEL, G.F.-PULIS.  SARABANDE                                      B98
HANDEL, G.F.  SUITE OF 6 PIECES                                     B85
HANSEN, A.(ARR).  65 TRB TRIOS                                      B98
HARTZELL, C.  GRANDIOSO & ALLEGRO                                   F74
HAYDN, J.-JAMESON.  10 COMMANDMENT CANONS                           G78
HAYDN, J.-JAMESON.  5 CONONS                                        G78
HAYDN, J.-OSBORN.  PRESTO FR. QUARTET NO.17                         B98
HAYDN, J.-DOCKSTADER.  PRESTO                                       G78
HAYDN, J.  QUARTET NO.4, OP.33                                      B44
HAYDN, J.-SEAR.  QUARTET, OP. 33/4                                  B44
HAYDN, J.-SEAR.  QUARTET, OP. 75/1                                  B44
HAYDN, J.  TRB.TRIO FR. OP.75/1                                     B44
HAYDN, J.-DELISSE.  TRIO (PF SONATA #49 & STR QRT #63 & 73)         B98
HAYDN, J.-DELISSE.  TRIO (STR QUARTET #63 & 73)                     B98
HAYDN, J.-DELISSE.  TRIO(BARYTONE TRIO #123 & STR QUARTET #32)      B98
JACOBSON, I.D.  3 THOUGHTS FOR TRBS                                 D84
JAMESON (ARR).  SUITE OF OLD ENGLISH SONGS                          G78
JONES, R.  THREE BY THREE                                          F43
JOSQUIN-MORRIS.  MOTET                                             E80
KNAB, A.  16 CHORALE (2 VOL)                                        A90
KREISLER, A.V.  2 SKETCHES                                          F60
KUFELMANN ETC.  THREE-PART MUSIC FROM THE RENAISSANCE              M79
LASSO, C.  MOTET FOR 3 VOICES                                      N61
LASSUS, R.D.-MILLER.  ADORAMUS TE                                  B98
LEGRENZI, G.-DOCKSTADER.  SONATA A TRE                             G78
LO PRESTI, R.  TRIO                                                C11
LOTTI, A.-DEDRICK.  VERE LANGUORES NOSTROS                         D14
MATEJ, J.  10 TWO-PART & 3-PART INVENTIONS                          G81
MATTHESON, J.-DOCKSTADER.  SONATA IN B-FLAT MAJOR                  G78
2 MEDIEVAL MOTETS.                                                 D16
MORTARI.  ARIE (ON THE TOMB OF BEETHOVEN)                          N18
MOULAERT, R.  SUITE                                                B12
MOZART, W.A.-JAMESON.  CANONS FOR EQUAL VOICES, K. 229             G78
MOZART, W.A.  SUITE                                                B98
MOZART, W.A.-OSTRANDER.  SUITE                                     B98
MOZART, W.A.-DELISSE.  TRIO (STR QUARTET #4)                       B98
MULLER, R.(ARR).  AUSGEWAHLTE TRIOS                                G43
OSBORN, G.A.  4 TRANSCRIPTIONS.  2TRB, BTRB                         B98
OSTRANDER, A.(ARR).  2 TRANSCRIPTIONS                               B98
PALESTRINA, G.P.-SCHAEFFER.  RENAISSANCE BALLADE                   E80
PEDERSON, T.  BALANCE OF POWER, A                                  M93
PEDERSON, T.  BLACK LILAC                                          M93
PEDERSON, T.  3 BRIGHT KNIGHTS                                     M93
PEDERSON, T.  FRISKY MYSTERY, A                                    M93
PEDERSON, T.  IBERIAN ITCH                                         M93
PEDERSON, T.  MARSHMELLOW YELLOW                                   M93
```

PEDERSON, T. SPREE FOR THREE, A		M93
PEDERSON, T. THREE FACE PLACE, A		M93
PEDERSON, T. TRIED 'N TRUE 'N TRICKY		M93
PEDERSON, T. 5 TRIOS		F27
PEDERSON, T. TRIPLE JACK		M93
PORRET, J. EPICURE		D92
PORRET, J. FRAGONARD		D92
PREMRU, R.E. 2 PIECES FOR 3 TRBS		B98
PURCELL, H.-MILLER. 3 FANTASIAS. 2TRB, BTRB		B98
PURCELL, H.-OSBORN. TRIO SONATA		B98
RACUSEN, D. CANONIC ETUDES		F43
ROBINSON & GIOVANNINI. TRIPLE T'S		C25
RUGGIERI-DOCKSTADER. ADAGIO		G78
SCARLATTI, D.-PATCH. SONATA IN C MINOR		G78
SCHEIDT, S.-FETTER. GIB UNS HEUT		B98
SCHEIN, J.H. 4 WALD-LIEDERLEIN		E00
SCHIFFMAN, E. FANTASIE, OP.66. (OPT TIMP)		C75
SCHILLING, H.L. PARTITA		D98
SCHUMANN, R.-OSTRANDER. ALBUM FOR THE YOUNG		A56
SCHUMANN, R.-FOTE. FUGUE, OP.68. 2TRB, BTRB		D14
SKOLNIK. LITTLE SUITE IN F		F80
SMELTEKOP (ARR). 2 GERMAN RENAISSANCE PIECES		E00
SNOSKO-BOROVSKY, A.-GIBSON. SCHERZO, OP.13		C91
SPEER, D.-BAINES. SONATA IN E MINOR & SONATA IN A MINOR		E14
SPEER, D.-BAINES. 2 SONATAS		E14
STIEBER, H. TURMMUSIK NR.2		C75
TANNER, P. IMITATION		C77
TANNER, P. IMITATION		G21
TANNER, P. LARGHETTO		C77
TANNER, P. LARGHETTO		G21
THIELMAN. BONES A PLENTY		E80
TUTHILL, B.C. TROMBONE TROUBLE		F60
UBER, D.A. CARNIVAL FOR 3 TROBONES		A03
UBER, D.A. 3 CHORALES, OP. 55		B98
UBER, D.A. 5 CONCERT TRIOS, OP. 53		B98
UBER, D.A. CONTEMPORARY TRIOS, OP. 54		B98
UBER, D.A. MODERN TRIOS		B85
VIVALDI, A.-DOCKSTADER. ALLEGRO		G78
VIVALDI, A.-DOCKSTADER. PRESTO		G78
VOGLER-DE KLERK. ODE TO THE MIDNIGHT SUN		D92
VOGLER. TERZETTO		D92
WALTERS, H.L. 3 GAUCHOS		A91
ZNOSKO-BOROVSKY, A.F. SCHERZO, OP.13		D81

3 TUBAS

AMATO. PEZZETTO		N92
BLAIR. SERIOUS SUITE, THE		N78
CORELLI, A.-PITTS. SONATA DA CHIESA, OP. 3/7		B80
DAUGHTRY. PLAINS OF ESDRAELON, THE		N92
HASTINGS. LITTLE MADRIGAL		F60
LUPO. FANTASIA		P19
PRESSER, W.H. SUITE		F80
ROSS. FANCY DANCES		N92
STEWART, F. HEAVYWEIGHTS		G66

3 MIXED BRASS (BRASS-PERC)

```
ALBINONI, T.  ANDANTE DOLCE.  2TRB, TU                              G78
ARDEVOL, J.  SONATA A TRE NO.3 IN F#-MINOR.  2TPT, TRB             B43
ARDEVOL, J.  TERCERA SONATA.  2TPT, TRB                            F59
ARMSDORF-FRENCH.  ALLEIN GOTT IN DER HOH' SEI EHR'                 F60
   TPT, HN(TPT), TRB(HN)
AIKINS.  GIRL OF SHONAI, THE.  TPT, HN, TRB                        N10
AVRIL.  PETITE SUITE.  TPT, HN, TRB                                D16
BACH, J.S.-FRACKENPOHL.  5 PIECES.  TPT, HN, TRB                   B98
BACH, J.S.  THREE-PART INVENTION #1.  TPT, HN, TRB                 P19
BACH, J.S.  THREE-PART INVENTION #2.  TPT, HN, TRB                 P19
BACH, J.S.  THREE-PART INVENTION #3.  TPT, HN, TRB                 P19
BACH, J.S.  THREE-PART INVENTION #4.  TPT, HN, TRB                 P19
BACH, J.S.-MILLER.  THREE-PART INVENTION #4.  TPT, HN, TRB         B98
BACH, J.S.  THREE-PART INVENTION #5.  TPT, HN, TRB                 P19
BACH, J.S.  THREE-PART INVENTION #6.  TPT, HN, TRB                 P19
BACH, J.S.  THREE-PART INVENTIONS # 7 & 8.  TPT, HN, TRB           P19
BALDWIN.  THIS OLD MAN.  TPT, HN, TRB                              N42
BARK, J.  SIAMFONI.  TPT, HN, TRB                                  B90
BARTHOLOMEW.  ELIZABETHAN SUITE.  TPT, HN, TRB                     G78
BARTHOLOMEW (ARR).  (3 PIECES).  TPT, HN, TRB                      G78
BARTOK, B.  BAGATELLE OP 6/6.  TPT, HN, TRB                        N42
BARTOK, B.  BAGATELLE, OP. 6/6.  TPT, HN, TRB                      P19
BARTOK, B.-DISHINGER.  DANCE OF THE SLOVAKS.  TPT, HN, TRB         N61
BASSETT, L.R.  BRASS TRIO.  TPT, HN, TRB                           E68
BASSETT, L.R.  TRIO.  TPT, HN, TRB                                 D16
BECKWITH.  5 PIECES.  TPT, HN, TRB                                 G88
BEETHOVEN, L.V.-KING.  TRIO, OP.87.  TPT, HN(TPT), EU(HN)          D16
BENTLY, A.(ARR).  XVITH CENTURY TRIOS.  2TPT, HN(TRB)              B20
BENTZON, N.V.  TRIO, OP.82.  TPT, HN, TRB                          H30
BEYER, F.  CONVERSATIONS.  TPT, HN, TRB                            G83
BEZANSON, P.  DIVERSION FOR BRASS TRIO.  TPT, HN, TRB              E32
BIALOSKY, M.  2 MOVEMENTS.  TPT, HN, TRB                           D16
BOECK, I. & A.-JANETZKY.  10 STUECKE.  2HN, EU                     C75
BOHME, O.-WINICK.  PRELUDE & FUGUE IN C MINOR.  TPT, HN, TRB       G83
BOHME, O.-WINICK.  PRELUDE & FUGUE IN E-FLAT MAJOR                 G83
   TPT, HN, TRB
BORRIS, S.  SUITE.  2TPT, TRB                                      D98
BREHM, A.  DIVERTIMENTO.  TPT, HN, TRB                             D63
BREYDERT.  TRIO FOR MELODY INSTRUMENTS.  2TPT, TRB                 A38
BROWN, R.  6 FUGUES.  HN, TRB, TU                                  N96
BRUCKNER, A.  AEQUALE.  TPT, HN, TRB                               C11
BULL.  CONCERT.  TPT, HN, TRB                                      F87
BURGON.  TRIO.  2TPT, TRB                                          F65
BUTTS.  ODE FOR LOW BRASS.  2TRB, TU                               E80
BUTTS, C.M.  LATIN MUSIC BOX, A.  2TPT, HN(TRB)                    F27
BYRD.  ALMAN.  TPT, HN, TRB                                        N61
BYRD, W.  FANTASY TRIO #1.  TPT, HN, TRB                           P19
BYRD, W.  FANTASY TRIO #2.  TPT, HN, TRB                           P19
CABUS, P.N.  SONATE A TRE.  TPT, HN, TRB                           D67
CANIVEZ, L.  TRIO DE CONCERT, OP.121.  2TPT, EU                    F81
CHILDS, B.  BRASS TRIO.  TPT, HN, TRB                              G66
CHILDS, B.  BRASS TRIO, 1959.  TPT, HN, TRB                        G66
CLODOMIR, P.  1ST TRIO.  2TPT, HN                                  D92
COMPERE.  MOTET "O VOS OMNES".  2TPT, TRB                          P19
COPERARIO-BALDWIN.  FANTASIA.  TPT, HN, TRB                        N42
```

```
COWELL, J.   TRIO.  TPT, HN, TRB                                          B44
COX, H.   THEME ET VARIATIONS.  TPT, HN, TRB                              D67
DE JONG, C.   SUITE OF WISCONSIN FOLK MUSIC.   TPT, HN(TPT), TRB          F43
DE SCHRIJVER.   TRIO CLASSICO.  TPT, HN, TRB                              F81
DECKER (ED).   ENGLISH MADRIGAL SUITE.  TPT, HN(TPT), TRB                 D14
DEDRICK, A.   3 TO GO.  TPT, HN(TPT), TRB                                 D14
DESPREZ, F.   TRIPTIQUE.  2TRB, TRB(HN)                                   D67
DESPREZ, J.-LEE.  BERNARDINA, LA.  TPT, HN, TRB                           G78
DESPREZ, J.-DE JONG.  3 JOSQUIN PIECES.  TPT, HN, TRB                     B98
DESSAU.   3 STUECKE.  2TPT, TRB                                           B69
DIERCKS, J.   FIGURES ON CHINA.  HN, TRB, TU                              F80
DONAHUE.   LITTLE SUITE.  TPT, HN, TRB                                    G21
DUBOIS, R.   TRIO AGITATO.  HN, TRB, TU                                   B74
DUCKWORTH.   TRANSPARENT INTERLUDES.  TPT, HN, TRB                        B30
DVORACEK.   3 MINIATURES.  2TPT, TRB                                      G81
EHMANN, W.   WEIHNACHTSLIEDER.  2TPT, TRB                                 A51
FARNABY, G.-DISHINGER.  FAYNE WOULD I WEDD.  TPT, HN, TRB                 N61
FINK, R.   MODAL SUITE.  TPT, HN, TRB                                     B85
FLOTHUIS, M.   SONATINE, OP.26.  TPT, HN, TRB                             B74
FRACKENPOHL, A.R.  BRASS TRIO.  TPT, HN, TRB                              B98
GARDNER.   FOURSOME FOR THREE.  TPT, HN(TPT), TRB                         N58
GAY, P.   3 MOVEMENTS.  TPT, HN, TRB                                      D16
GEMINIANI-MORRIS.  CONCERTO GROSSO.  TPT, HN, TRB                         F43
GHISELIN, J.-LEE.  ALFONSINA, LA.  TPT, HN, TRB                          G78
GIBBONS, O.-ROSENTHAL.  2 FANTASIAS.  2TPT, TRB                          G21
GLASEL, J.   SIXTEENTH CENTURY CARMINA.  HN, TRB, EU(TU)                  B15
GLASSER, S.   TRIO.  2TPT, TRB                                            E14
GODEBRYE-GOLDSTEIN.  MADRIGAL ICH BIN VERWAIST.  TPT, HN, TRB             B44
GRAMATGES, H.   PRELUDE & INVENTION.  2TPT, TRB                           B91
HAAN, S.D.   TRIO.  HN(BSN), TRB(BSN), TU(BSN)                            C71
HANDEL, G.F.-ROSENTHAL.  SUITE FOR BRASS TRIO.  TPT, HN, TRB             G21
HANDEL, G.F.-WIENANDT.  SUITE.  TPT, HN, TRB                              E80
HARLAN, C.L.   TRIO FOR BRASS INSTRS.  TPT, HN, TRB                       B35
HARTLEY, W.S.   2 PASTICHES.  TPT, HN, BTRB                               G83
HASTINGS.   LITTLE MADRIGAL.  2EU, TU                                     F60
HAUBIEL, C.   ATHENAEUM SUITE.  TPT, HN, TRB                              B38
HAUBIEL, C.   ATHENEUM SUITE.  TPT, HN, TRB                               G66
HOGG, M.E.   3 SHORT PIECES.  TPT, HN, TRB                                B35
HOGG, M.E.   3 SHORT PIECES.  TPT, HN, TRB                                G83
HOGG, M.E.   VARIATIONS FOR BRASS TRIO.  TPT, HN, TRB                     B35
HOGG, M.E.   VARIATIONS.  TPT, HN, TRB                                    N59
HORUSITZKY.   CASSAZIONE.  2TPT, TRB                                      M98
HOVHANESS, A.S.   FANTASY #1.  TPT, HN, TRB                               E65
HOVHANESS, A.S.   FANTASY #2.  TPT, HN, TRB                               E65
HOVHANESS, A.S.   FANTASY #3.  TPT, HN, TRB                               E65
HUGHES, M.   DIVERTIMENTO.  TPT, HN, TRB                                  F80
ISAAC-DE JONG.   3 PIECES.  TPT, HN, TRB                                  B98
ISBELL (ARR).   DONA NOBIS PACEM.  EU, 2TU                                M80
ISBELL (ARR).   DONA NOBIS PACEM.  EU, 2TU                                P42
ISSAC, H.   DIGAU ALEZ DONZELLES.  TPT, HN, TRB                          N42
ISSAC, H.   4 PIECES.  HN, 2TRB                                           F59
IVES, C.E.   FROM THE STEEPLES & MOUNTAINS.  TPT, TRB, CHIMES             E61
JAGER.   VARIATIONS ON A MOTIVE BY WAGER.  EU, 2TU                        E77
JONG, DE.   SUITE OF WISCONSIN FOLK MUSIC.  TPT, HN(TPT), TRB            F43
JOSQUIN.   (SEE DES PREZ & DESPREZ)
JOSQUIN-SHOEMAKER.  BERNARDINA, LA.  TPT, HN(TPT), TRB                    N47
JOSQUIN.   3 PIECES.  TPT, HN, TRB                                        B98
KERLL, J.C.   CANZONE.  EU, 2TU                                          M80
KERLL, J.C.-LONG.  CANZONE.  EU, 2TU                                     P42
KING, R.D.(ED).   2 MEDIEVAL MOTETS.                                      D16
     HN(TPT, TRB), TRB(HN), EU-TU
KIRCHNER.   FANFARE.  2TPT, HN                                            A38
```

```
KNAB, A.   16 CHORALE (2 VOL).   2TPT(2TRB), TRB                          A90
KNIGHT.   CASSATION.   TPT, HN, TRB                                       F88
KNIGHT.   10 TRIOS.   2TPT, TRB                                           A35
KNIGHT, M.   CASSATION.   TPT, HN, TRB                                    F80
KOCSAR, M.   TRIO PER DUE TROMBE E TRB.   2TPT, TRB                       B84
KOCSAR, M.   TRIO.   2TPT, TRB                                            G39
KOHS, E.B.   BRASS TRIO.   TPT, HN, TRB                                   A13
KOX, H.   4 DIDACTISCHE STUKKEN.   2TPT, TRB                              B74
KOX, H.   KLEINE SUITE.   2TPT, TRB                                       B74
KREISLER, A.V.   TRIO.   2TPT, TRB                                        F60
KROEGER, K.   SONATA BREVE.   TPT, HN, TRB                                F88
KRUEGER, T.H.   TRIO FOR BRASSES.   TPT, HN, TRB                          E00
KUBIZEK, A.   4 STUECKE.   2TPT, TRB                                      A89
LASSO-MOORE.   CANTATE DOMINO.   TPT, 2TRB                                G21
LECLERCQ, E.   SUITE CLASSIQUE.   TPT, HN, TRB                            A96
LEMMON.   TRIO.   2TPT, TRB                                               N29
LESSARD.   QUODLIBETS.   2TPT, TRB                                        C40
LESTER.   3 PIECES.   2TPT, TRB                                           G21
LINKE, J.D.   KONKRETIONEN IV.   TPT, HN, TRB                             C41
LOTTI.   RICERCAR.   2TPT, TRB                                            P19
LOUEL, J.   TRIO.   TPT, HN, TRB                                          B12
LUENING.   TRIO.   TPT, HN, TRB                                           E65
LULLY, J.B.-MULLER.   AIRS DE TABLE.   TPT, HN(TPT), TRB                  D67
LUPO-BALDWIN.   FANTASIA.   TPT, HN, TRB                                  M82
LYON.   LITTLE SUITE.   TPT, HN, TRB                                      A35
MAILLOT.   TRIO.   TPT, HN, TRB                                           F87
MANIET, R.   TRIO #1.   TPT, HN, TRB                                      D67
MANIET, R.   TRIO #2 (A TROIS).   TPT, HN, TRB                            D67
MAREK, R.C.   TRIO.   TPT, HN, TRB                                        D16
MARTINI.   MOTET.   TPT, HN, TRB                                          B85
MARTINI.   2 PIECES.   2TPT, TRB                                          P19
MASSO, G.   TRIO FOR BRASS.   TPT, HN, TRB                                E83
MAYER.   COUNTRY FAIR.   2TPT, TRB                                        E77
MAYER, W.R.   COUNTRY FAIR.   2TPT, TRB                                   A78
MC BRIDE, R.   FOLKSONG FANTASY.   TPT, HN, TRB                           A13
MC BRIDE, R.   LAMENT FOR THE PARKING PROBLEM.   TPT, HN, TRB             A13
MC BRIDE, R.   RED RIVER VALLEY.   TPT, HN, TRB                           A13
MC GOVERN, M.   TRIPARTITE.   TPT, HN, TRB                                P49
MEULEMANS, A.   TRIO.   TPT, HN, TRB                                      A96
MEULEMANS, A.   2E TRIO.   TPT, HN, TRB                                   B12
MORLEY, T.-DISHINGER.   ALMAN.   TPT, HN, TRB                             N61
MOZART, W.A.-KING.   DIVERTIMENTO # 1, K.439B.   2TPT, EU(HN)             D16
MOZART, W.A.   5 TRIOS.   2TPT, TRB                                       B73
MUCZYNSKI, R.   VOYAGE.   TPT, HN, TRB                                    F23
MULLER, J.P.   SUITE NO.2.   2TPT, TRB(TPT)                               D67
MURZIN.   IMPROMPTU.   2TRB(EU), TU                                       P19
MUTTER, G.   KLEINES TRIO.   TPT, HN, TRB                                 C54
NAGEL, R.   BRASS TRIO #2.   TPT, HN, TRB                                 D73
NAGEL, R.   BRASS TRIO.   TPT, HN, TRB                                    E68
NANINO-LEE.   LAETANINI & SONNE SOAVE.   TPT, HN, TRB                     G78
NELHYBEL, V.   MUSICA FESTIVA.   3INST ?                                  B32
NELHYBEL, V.   TRIO FOR BRASS.   TPT, HN, TRB                             C40
NERIJNEN, J.V.   ANTIQUA.   2TPT, EU                                      D92
NERIJNEN, J.V.   2E SUITE VOOR KOPERBLAZERS.   2TPT, EU                   D92
NERIJNEN, J.V.   3E SUITE VOOR KOPERTRIO.   2TPT, EU                      D92
OROWAN.   TRIO OP.1.   2TRB, TU                                           B85
ORVAL.   PIECE EN RE.   TPT, HN, TRB                                      D67
OSTRANDER, A.   SUITE FOR 3 BRASS
     TPT(HN), HN(TPT), TRB(TPT, HN)                                       B85
OTT, J.   ENCORE SET.   TPT, HN, TRB                                      A65
OTT, J.   ENCORE SET.   TPT, HN, TRB                                      B53
PARKER.   RAG BAG.   TPT, HN(TPT), TRB                                    N58
```

```
PARRIS, R.   4 PIECES.  TPT, HN, TRB                                      A13
PARRIS, R.   4 PIECES.  TPT, HN, TRB                                      E68
PELEMANS, W.  KOPERBLAZERSONATE.  TPT, HN, TRB                            D67
PETERSEN, T.  DIVERTIMENTO.  TPT, HN, TRB                                 D14
PINKHAM, D.  BRASS TRIO.  TPT, HN, BTRB                                   E65
PINKHAM, D.  FANFARE, ARIA AND ECHO.  2HN, TIMP                           E65
POULENC, F.  SONATE.  TPT, HN, TRB                                        B23
PRESSER, W.H.  PRELUDE, FUGUE & POSTLUDE.  TPT, HN, TRB                   G83
PURCELL, H.-ELKAN.  FANFARE.  2TPT, TRB                                   B91
PURCELL, H.-ROSENTHAL.  FANTASIA #2.  TPT, HN, TRB                        G21
PURCELL, H.-ROSENTHAL.  FANTASIA NO.1.  HN, TRB, TU                       G21
PURCELL, H.  FANTAZIA 1.  TPT, HN, TRB                                    P19
PURCELL, H.  FANTAZIA 2.  TPT, HN, TRB                                    P19
PURCELL, H.  FANTAZIA 3.  TPT, HN, TRB                                    P19
PURCELL, H.-ENDSLEY.  FIFE AND HARMONY OF WAR.  2TPT, TIMP                M80
PURCELL, H.-LESTER.  LITTLE SUITE.  TPT, 2TRB                             G21
QUINET, M.  SONATE A TROIS.  TPT, HN, TRB                                 B12
RAPHLING, S.  3 PIECES.  TPT, HN, TRB                                     C40
REGNER, H.  3 SATZE FUR 3 BLECHBLASER.  2TPT, TRB                         C54
REGNER, H.  SPIELHEFT II FUR 3 BLASINSTRUMENTE.  2TPT, TRB                C54
REID, A.  NOVEMBER NOCTURNE.  TPT, HN(TPT), TRB                           D14
ROBB.  4 CONTRARY MOVEMENTS.  TPT, HN, TRB                                F27
ROBERTS, W.  DAY IN THE COUNTRY, A..  TPT, HN(TPT), TRB                   B44
ROBERTS, W.  MINIATURES FOR 3 WINDS.  TPT, HN, TRB                        B44
ROBERTS, W.  WALK IN THE COUNTRY.  TPT, HN, TRB                           E14
RODGERS, T.  3 PIECES FOR LOW BRASS TRIO.  2EU, TU                        M80
RODGERS, T.  3 PIECES FOR LOW BRASS TRIO.  2EU, TU                        P42
ROUSSAKIS.  COMPOSITION.  TPT, HN, TRB                                    B32
RUELLE, F.  TRIO, OP.147.  TPT, HN, TRB                                   D67
RUGGIERI-DOCKSTADER.  DOLCE.  TPT, HN, TRB                                G78
SANDERS, R.L.  TRIO FOR BRASS INSTRUMENTS.  TPT, HN, TRB                  D16
SCARLATTI-SCHMIDT.  SONATA (LONGO 104).  2TPT, TRB                        G21
SCHARFES, C.  DIVERTIMENTO.  TPT, HN, TRB                                 A96
SCHEIN, J.H.  WALDLIEDERLEIN, J.H..  HN, 2TRB                             E00
SCHILLING, H.L.(ARR).  BLASERSATZE DE SPATEN ...                          A90
    TPT, TRB, PERC
SCHMIDT.  SONATINA.  HN, TRB, TU                                          G21
SEAR, W.E.  BRASS DEMONSTRATION PIECE.  2TPT, TRB                         B44
SEEGER, P.  7 SPIELSTUCKE FUR 3 BLASINSTRUMENTE.  TPT, HN, TRB            C54
SHAW, I.E.  POCKET FULL OF WRY, A.  TPT, HN, TRB                          B98
SHINN, F.  CEREMONIAL FANFARE.  TPT, HN, BTRB                             G66
SMITH.  THEME & VARIATIONS.  TPT, HN, TRB                                 N85
SNYDER.  DANCE SUITE.  TPT, HN, TRB                                       M79
SPEZZAFERRI, G.  PRELUDIO E FUGA, OP.81.  2TPT, TRB                       G41
STREET.  POCKETFUL O' JINGLE.  TPT, HN(TPT), TRB                          N58
THIELMAN, F.  2 MOODS FOR BRASS.  2TPT, TRB (OPT HN, EU)                  D14
THILMAN, J.P.  TRIO-MUSIK & QUARTETT FUR BLECHBLASER                      C75
    2TPT, TRB
TULL, F.  TRIO.  TPT, HN, TRB                                             M96
TWO MEDIEVAL MOTETS.  HN(TPT, TRB), TRB(HN), EU(TRB)                      D16
TWO PIECES FROM GLOGAUER LIEDERBUCH.  TPT, HN, TRB                        B44
ULF, C.  6 ALTE TANZWEISEN.  2TPT, TRB                                    C54
VAN DE MOORTEL, L.  DIVERTIMENTO NO.2.  TPT, HN, TRB                      D67
VELLEFE, L.  2 ESSAIS.  TPT, HN, TRB                                      D67
VILLA-LOBOS, H.  CANCIONE.  TPT, HN, TRB                                  P19
VIVALDI, A.-DOCKSTADER.  ALLEGRO.  TPT, HN, TRB                           G78
VIVALDI, A.  SONATA DA CAMERA.  2TPT, TRB                                 B85
VOLLEMAN, A.  3 CROQUIS.  TPT, HN, TRB                                    D67
WALKER, J.  4 LITTLE DANCES.  TPT, HN(TPT), TRB                           N58
WALKER, R.  FALCONRY MATCH.  TPT, HN, 2TRB                                D14
WALTER.  CANON A DEPTIMI TONI.  TPT, HN, TRB                              P19
WALTON, W.T.-DEJONG.  6 PIECES, SET 1.  2TPT, TRB                         E51
```

WALTON, W.T.-DEJONG. 6 PIECES, SET 2. TPT, 2TRB		E51
WEELKES. GAY TUNE, A. 2TPT, TRB		B85
WEISSMAN. KFAR ATA. TPT, HN, TRB		M63
WERNER, J.J. CANZONI PER SONAR. TPT, HN, TRB		F87
WESTCOTT, F. PRELUDE, PAVAN & GALLIARD		C71
TPT, HN(TRB), TU (ALL PARTS IN TC)		
WIGGLESWORTH, F. TRIO SONATA. 2TPT, TRB		A13
WILBYE, J. MADRIGAL "FLY LOVE ALOFT". TP, HN, TRB		P19
WILBYE, J. MADRIGAL "WHAT SHALL I DOE?". TPT, HN, TRB		P19
WILLAERT, A.-WALDECK. RICERCAR. TPT, HN, TRB		B44
WILSON, D.M. STABILE II. 3INST ?		B36
WINICK. CONFRONTATION. TPT, HN, TRB		P19
WOOD, J. FUGUE IN E-FLAT MAJOR. 2TPT, TRB(EU)		P48
XENAKIS. LINAIA-AGON. HN, TRB, TU		F16
ZBINDEN, J.F. TRIO DE CUIVRES, OP.13. TPT, HN, TRB		C41
ZENONI-SMIM. SONFONIA A TRE. TPT, HN, TRE		E14

3 PARTS: HORN-WOODWIND

AMRAM, D.W. TRIO. HN, BSN, TSAX		E65
BENTLY, A.(ARR). 16TH CENTURY TRIOS		X97
HN(BSN, SAX), FL(OB, CL), OB(CL)		
COWELL, J. TRIO. HN, CL(TPT), BSN(TRB)		B44
DELMOTTE, C. TRIO. HN, OB, CL		D67
DEVIENNE, F.-LELOIR. TRIO NO.1 IN C. HN, CL, BSN		D11
DEVIENNE, F.-LELOIR. TRIO NO.2 IN F. HN, CL, BSN		D11
DEVIENNE, F.-LELOIR. TRIO NO.3 IN D MINOR. HN, CL, BSN		D11
DRESSEL, E. TRIO MINIATURE. HN, CL, BSN		E99
DUVERNOY, F.N.-LELOIR. TRIO NO.1 IN F. HN, CL, BSN		D11
DUVERNOY, F.N.-LELOIR. TRIO NO.2 IN E-FLAT. HN, CL, BSN		D11
DUVERNOY, F.N.-LELOIR. TRIO NO.3 IN F. HN, CL, BSN		D11
FUCHS, C.F. TRIO. HN, 2CL		E14
GEBAUER, F.R.-WEELINK. 3 WIND TRIOS. HN, CL, BSN		D11
GRAUN, K.H. TRIO SONATA. HN, OB D'AMORE, BSN		D55
HANDEL, G.F.-HAAS. OVERTURE (SUITE) IN D. HN, 2CL		F31
HANDEL, G.F.-COPPERSMITH & LARUE. SONATA IN D MAJOR		D74
HN(CL), 2CL		
HANDEL, G.F. SONATA IN D. HN, 2CL		D74
HAYDN, J.-WERNER. DIVERTIMENTO TRIO. HN, CL, BSN		B20
JACOBSOHN, G. ADAGIO & ALLEGRO. HN, CL, BSN		D71
KAUDER, H. TRIO I. HN, FL, OB		G66
KAUDER, H. TRIO II. HN, FL, OB		G66
LEVY, F. TRIO. HN, CL, BSN		B44
LEYE-LELOIR. SUITE. HN, BSN		D11
LYBBERT, D. TRIO FOR WINDS. HN, CL, BSN		E65
MAXWELL, C. TRIO. HN, FL, BSN		B38
MAYR, A. KLEINE SUITE. HN(VC), FL(VN), CL(VA)		E50
MICHALSKY, D.R. TRIO CONCERTINO. HN, FL, OB		G21
OTTEN, L. DIVERTIMENTO NO. 2. HN, FL, BSN		B74
PLATTI, G. SONATA. HN, CL, BSN		B44
REICHA, A.-LELOIR. TRIOS OP.92. 2HN, BSN		D11
REICHA, A.-LELOIR. TRIOS, OP. 92, VOL II. 2HN, BSN		D11
REICHA, A.-LELOIR. 12 TRIOS, OP. 93 (2BKS). 2HN, BSN		D11
ROBERTS, W. WALK IN THE COUNTRY, A. HN, CL, BSN		B44
SCHUMANN, G. MINIATURTRIO. HN, OB, BSN		F53
THURNER, E. TRIO, OP.56. HN, CL, BSN		C54
VIECENZ, H. TERZETT. HN, 2OB		C75

3 PARTS: BRASS-WOODWIND

```
BRINGS, A.  BURLETTE.  TRB, FL, CL                              G66
HORROD, N.S.  TRIO.  HN, TRB, BSN                               D11
KNIGHT, M.  SELFISH GIANT SUITE.  TRB(BSN), FL, CL             F80
MAES, J.  MINIATURE TRIO.  TPT, HN, BSN                        J39
PRUNTY, W.  TRIO ALLEGRIA.  TPT, TRB, CL                       A02
WILDER, A.  & KNIGHT, M.  SELFISH GIANT SUITE                  F80
  TRB(BSN), FL, CL
```

3 PARTS: TRUMPETS-KEYBOARD

```
ADAMS, S.  HOLY CITY, THE.  2TPT, *PF                          A78
ADAMS, S.-DEROOY.  HOLY CITY, THE.  2TPT, *PF                  D92
ALDROVANDINI, G.-VOISIN.  SONATA NO.1.  2TPT, *PF              C91
ALDROVANDINI, G.-VOISIN.  SONATA NO.2.  2TPT, *PF              C91
ALDROVANDINI, G.-VOISIN.  SONATA NO.3.  2TPT, *PF              C91
ALFORD, K.J.-WOOLDRIDGE.  COLONEL BOGEY.  2TPT, *PF           A78
ANDPIEU.  CONCERTINO.  2TPT, *PF                               A71
ARDITI, L.  BACIO, IL.  2TPT, *PF                             B13
ARNOLD, H.  SONATA.  2TPT, *PF                                F60
ARNOLD, J.  EVERBODY'S FAVORITE SERIES.  2TTPT, *PF           A18
ARNOLD, J.  MUSIC FOR MILLIONS SERIES: #15 EASY TRUMPET DUETS B41
  2TPT, *PF
ARNOLD, M.  SONATA.  2TPT, *PF                                F60
BARNARD.  PALS.  2TPT, *BAND, *PF                             C11
BARNHOUSE, C.L.  ADESTE FIDELIS.  2TPT, *PF                   A55
BARNHOUSE, C.L.  I LOVE TO TELL THE STORY.  2TPT, *PF         A55
BARNHOUSE, C.L.  ON THE MOUNTAIN TOP.  2TPT, *PF              A55
BARNHOUSE, C.L.  ROCK OF AGES.  2TPT, *PF                     A55
BEETHOVEN, L.V.  MINUET IN G.  2TPT, *PF                      B13
BEETHOVEN, L.V.-LEIDZEN.  RONDINO ON A THEME OF BEETHOVEN     C18
  2TPT, *PF
BELMANS, R.  JOHNNY'S LITTLE HORSE.  2TPT, *PF                F21
BENGER.  MINIATURE SUITE.  2TPT, *PF                          B23
BENT.  SWISS BOY.  2TPT, *PF                                  B53
BLAAUW, L.  FANTASIE CAPRICE.  2TPT, *PF                      F81
BLACK EYES.  2TPT, *PF                                        A91
BRAHE, M.H.-GLENN.  BLESS THIS HOUSE.  2TPT, *PF              A78
BRANDT, V.  2 PIECES, OP.15.  2TPT, *PF                       C91
BRIEGEL.  CATHEDRAL ECHOES.  2TPT, *PF                        A91
BRIEGEL.  LITTLE SHEPHERD.  2TPT, *PF                         A91
BRIEGEL.  SOLOETTE.  2TPT, *PF                                A91
BUCHTEL, F.I.  BONITA.  2TPT, *PF                             D84
BUSCH, C.  TRIO CONCERTANTE.  2TPT, *PF                       B53
CANIVEZ, L.  GRAND DUO BRILLANT & FACILE.  2TPT, *PF          F81
CANIVEZ, L.  GRAND DUO CONCERTANTE, OP.20.  2TPT, *PF         F81
CARAZO, C.  TANGO OF MEMORIES.  2TPT, *PF                     D84
CIRRI, G.B.  ARIOSO.  2TPT, *PF                               B85
CLARK, H.  PURCELL & HANDEL ALBUM.  2TPT, *PF                 E51
CLARKE, H.L.  COUSINS.  2TPT(2COR), *PF                       G31
CLARKE, H.L.  FLIRTATIONS.  2TTPT, *PF                        C09
CONTE, B.  ALPEN POLKA.  2TPT, *PF                            D80
```

```
CORELLI, A.  ALLEMANDA.  TPT, TPT(TRB), *PF                      B85
CORELLI, A.-OSTRANDER.  ALLEMANDA.  2TPT, *PF                    B85
COUNTRY GARDENS.  2TPT, *PF                                      B13
CURZON, F.  EUSYBODIES.  2TPT, *PF                               A78
CUSTER, A.R.  3 CANONS.  2TPT, *PF                               D33
DEARNLEY, C.H.  MORE EASY PIECES BY CLASSICAL COMPOSERS          B23
   2TPT, *PF
DENZA, L.  FUNICULI FUNICULA.  2TPT, *PF                         B13
DORADO, A.-WHEELER.  2 AMIGOS.  2TPT, *PF                        G10
DREISSEN, A.-OVERVELD.  ZANDMANNETJE.  2TPT, *PF                 F81
DRINK TO ME ONLY WITH THINE EYES.  2TPT, *PF                     A91
DVORAK, A.  HUMORESKE.  2TPT, *PF                                B13
DVORAK, A.  SONGS MY MOTHER TAUGHT ME.  2TPT, *PF               A91
EISENACH, J.J.L.V.  2 CAPRICCIOS.  2TPT, *CONTINUO               E14
ESTES, A.  CONCORDIANA.  2TPT, *PF                               D14
FABRE, C.  REVERIE.  2TPT, *PF                                   B53
FABRE, C.  2ND REVERIE.  2TPT, *PF                               B53
FERNANDEZ, O.L.  BEAUTIFUL HEAVEN.  2TPT, *PF                    A91
FORSTER, C.  SONATA A 7.  2CTT, PF                               E14
FOSTER, S.C.  JEANIE, WITH THE LIGHT BROWN HAIR.  2TPT, *PF     A91
FOTE, R.  AMIGOS.  2TPT, *PF                                     D14
FRANCESCHINI, P.-TARR.  SONATA IN D MAJOR.  2TPT, *PF, *ORCH    E14
FRANCK, C.-CLUWEN.  AUX PETITS ENFANTS.  2TPT, *PF              F81
FRANCK, C.  PANIS ANGELICUS.  2TPT, *PF                          A91
FRESCOBALDI, G.  CANZONAS 9-13.  2CTT(2OB), BC(HP)              E14
FRESCOBALDI, G.  CANZONAS 18-23                                  E14
   TPT, CTT(TPT, OB), OB, BC(ORG)
FRIML, R.-SEARS.  INDIAN LOVE CALL.  2TPT, *PF                   C58
GABRIELI, D.-VOISIN.  SONATA.  2TPT, *PF                         C91
GIORDANI, T.  EIGHTEENTH CENTURY AIR (CARO MIO BEN)             B85
   2TPT, *PF
GOSSEC, F.J.-ROCHON.  OUVERTURE.  2TPT, *PF                      D92
GRIEG, E.H.  TO SPRING.  2TPT, *PF                               B13
GROOMS.  DARK EYES.  2TPT, *PF                                   B13
GROOMS.  2 GUITARS.  2TPT, *PF                                   B13
HANDEL, G.F.-ORVID & OSTRANDER.  ADAGIO & ALLEGRO.  2TPT, *PF   C91
HANDEL, G.F.  TRUMPET SHALL SOUND, THE.  TRB, TU(EU), PF        B85
HARRIS, F.O.  2 LITTLE STARS.  2TPT, *PF                         D52
HARRIS, F.O.  WE 3 REVELERS.  3TPT, *PF                          A55
HAWTHORNE.  WHISPERING HOPE.  2TPT, *PF                          A91
HEUBERGER, R.-KREISLER-LEIDZEN.  MIDNIGHT BELLS.  2TPT, *PF     C18
HONEGGER-BOSWELL.  PETITE SUITE.  2TPT, *PF                      N42
HOWELL.  RUSTIC DANCE.  2TPT, *PF                                B13
JACCHINI-VOISIN.  SONATA #2.  2TPT, *PF                          C91
JACCHINI-VOISIN.  SONATA.  2TPT, *PF                             C91
JAKMA, F.  VROLIJKE BROEDERS, DE.  2TPT, *PF                     F81
JUNG.  KONZERTANTE SUITE.  2TPT, *PF                             C75
KALMAN, E.-SCHOENFELD.  PLAY GYPSIERS--DANCE GYPSIES            C58
   2TPT, *PF
KLEES, W.  CASTOR & POLLUX.  2TPT, *PF                           F10
KLING.  DEIDEN KLEINEN FINKEN, DIE.  2TPT, *BAND, *PF           E43
KLING.  DIE DEIDEN KLEINEN FINKEN.  2TPT, *PF                    D92
KLING.  PERLEN, DIE.  2TPT, *PF                                  E43
KLING.  VOGLEIN AUF DEM ZWEIGE.  2TPT, *PF                       E43
LABITZKY.  DREAM OF THE SHEPHERDESS.  2TPT, *PF                  B13
LEGRENZI, G.  SONATA "LA BUSCHA," OP. 8.  2CTT, PF              E14
LEIDZEN, E.W.G.  TRIFOLIUM.  2TPT, *PF                           C11
LEMARE, E.H.-LONG.  ANDANTINO.  2TPT, *PF                        G10
LESTER.  CRIMSON BLUSHES.  2TPT, *PF                             B13
LEYBACH.  FIFTH NOCTURNE.  2TPT, *PF                             B13
LOEILLET, J.B.  CONCERTO EN RE                                   A71
LONDONDERRY AIR.  2TPT, *PF                                      A91
```

```
LOSEY, F.H.  IDA & DOTTIE.  2TPT, *PF                             C11
LOTTI.  ARIETTA.  2TPT, *PF                                       B85
LOUMEY.  SHADOWS ON THE WATER.  2TPT, *PF                         B13
MANFREDINI, F.  CONCERTO IN B-FLAT MAJOR.  2TPT, *PF              D92
MANFREDINI, F.-THILDE.  CONCERTO IN D MAJOR.  2TPT, *PF           A71
MANFREDINI, F.-JOOSEN.  CONCERTO.  2TPT, *PF                      D92
MANFREDINI, F.-VOISIN.  CONCERTO.  2TPT, *PF                      C91
MANIET, R.  DUETTINO #2.  2TPT, *PF                               D67
MARCELLO, B.  PRELUDE & DANCE.  2TPT, *PF                         B85
MENDELSSOHN, F.-VEKEN.  EVENING SONG.  2TPT, *PF                  F81
MENDELSSOHN, F.-VEKEN.  ICH WOLLT'MEINE LIEB'ERGOSSE SICH         F81
    2TPT, *PF
MENDELSSOHN, F.-VEKEN.  MAIGLOCKCHEN & DIE BLUMELEIN              F81
    2TPT, *PF
MENDEZ, R.G.  CHIAPANECAS.  2TPT, *PF                             C11
MERTEN, P.  DUO VALSE.  2TPT, *PF                                 B85
MEYER, L.J.(ARR).  4 MOUNTAIN TUNES.  2TPT, *PF                   E77
MOZART, W.A.  AVE VERUM CORPUS.  2TPT, *PF                        B85
NAGEL, R.  REGAL TRUMPET.  2TPT, *PF                              D63
NELHYBEL, V.  SUITE FOR 2 TPTS & PA.  2TPT, *PF                   C40
NERIJNEN, J.V.  2ND CONTEST DUO.  2TPT, *PF                       D92
NERIJNEN, J.V.  DUO DE CONCOURS.  2TPT, *PF                       D92
NEVIN, E.W.-HARRIS.  ROSARY, THE.  2TPT, *PF                      D52
O'NEILL, C.  CHUMS.  2TPT, *PF                                    G13
O'NEILL, C.  PALS.  2TPT, *PF                                     G13
OSTRANDER, A.  DUET ALBUM.  2TPT, *PF                             B85
PANELLA.  2 BACHELORS.  2TPT, *PF                                 G10
PANELLA.  2 GNOMES.  2TPT, *PF                                    G10
PANELLA.  JOLLY TWO.  2TPT, *PF                                   G10
PANELLA.  2 LOVERS.  2TPT, *PF                                    G10
PANELLA.  TOM & JERRY.  2TPT, *PF                                 G10
PELZ, W.  HEROIC FANFARE.  2TPT, *PF                              A62
PELZ, W.  HONOR GUARD.  2TPT, *PF                                 A62
PETERSEN, T.  MEXICAN SUNDAE.  2TPT, *PF                          D14
PEZEL, J.C.  6 SONATINAS IN C.  2TPT, BC                          M80
PEZEL, J.C.  SONATINAS NOS. 61, 62, 65, AND 66.  2TPT, BC         F07
PEZEL, J.C.  SONATINAS NOS. 71 & 74.  2CLARINOS(2TPT), BC         F07
PORRET, J.  1ST CONTEST DUO.  2TPT, *PF                           D92
PORRET, J.  5TH CONTEST DUO.  2TPT, *PF                           D92
PORRET, J.  6TH CONTEST DUO.  2TPT, *PF                           D92
PORRET, J.  DUO DE CONCOURS #1                                    D92
PORRET, J.  DUO DE CONCOURS #2                                    D92
PORTER, C.-SEARS.  BEGIN THE BEGUINE.  2TPT, *PF                  C58
PUCCINI, G.-STEBBING.  MUSETTA'S WALTZ SONG.  2TPT, *PF           E98
PUCCINI, G.-STEBBING.  VISSI D'ARTE, VISSI D'AMORE.  2TPT, *PF    E98
PURCELL, H.  SOUND THE TRUMPETS.  2TPT, *PF                       B85
RAY-SEARS.  SUNSHINE OF YOUR SMILE.  2TPT, *PF                    C58
RICCIUS, R.A.-ROOY.  CONCERTINO.  2TPT, *PF                       D92
ROUGNON, F.-MAGER.  CONCERT POLONAISE.  2TPT, *PF                 F60
SAINT¬SAENS, C.  MY HEART AT THY SWEET VOICE.  2TPT, *PF          B13
SAVERIO-HARRIS.  FLOWER OF THE ORIENT.  2TPT, *PF                 D52
SCHAEFER, A.H.  FANCY FREE.  2TPT(2TRB), *PF                      C09
SCHAEFER, A.H.  TROUBADOURS.  2TPT(2TRB), *PF                     C09
SCHAEFFER, D. (ARR).  CHRISTMAS DUETS.  2TPT, *PF                 E80
SCHUBERT, F.P.  SERENADE.  2TPT, *PF                              B13
SIEBERT.  LATIN AMERICAN ALBUM.  2TPT, *PF                        A78
SMITH.  TRUMPETER'S FROLIC.  2TPT, *PF                            A91
SONG OF THE VULGAR BOATMEN.  2TPT, *PF                            A91
SUPPE, F.V.  POET & PEASANT OVERTURE.  2TPT, *PF                  B13
TARR (ARR).  SINFONIA A 2.  2TPT, BC                              M80
TARTINI, G.-ORVID & VOISIN.  ADAGIO & ALLEGRO.  2TPT, *PF         C91
TELEMANN, G.P.-THILDE.  CONCERTO IN C MINOR.  2TPT, *PF           A71
```

```
TELEMANN, G.P.-VOISIN.  CONCERTO.  2TPT, *ORCH, *PF              C91
TENAGLIA, A.F.-MAGANINI.  ARIA ANTICA.  2TPT, *PF               B85
TORELLI, G.-VOISIN.  CONCERTO IN C MAJOR.  2TPT, *ORCH, *PF     C91
TORELLI, G.  SINFONIA IN D, G.21.  2TPT, *ORCH, *PF            E14
TROTERE, H.  IN OLD MADRID.  2TPT, *PF                         B13
VANDERCOOK, H.A.  ARM IN ARM.  2TPT, *PF                       F07
VANDERCOOK, H.A.  FLAMINGOES.  2TPT, *PF                       F07
VANDERCOOK, H.A.  TRUMPET TWOSOME.  2TPT, *PF                  F07
VANDERMAESBRUGGE.  EN PETITS CARACTERES.  2TPT, *PF            D67
VEACH, D.  TWIN RIVERS.  2TPT, *PF                             C11
VEACH, D.  TWIN TORONADOS.  2TPT, *PF                          C11
VIVALDI, A.-GALAMBOS & NAGY.  CONCERTO IN C MAJOR.  2TPT, *PF  B84
VIVALDI, A.-GHEDINI.  CONCERTO IN C MAJOR.  2TPT, *ORCH, *PF   C91
VIVALDI, A.-IESKO.  CONCERTO IN C MAJOR.  2TPT, *PF            E98
VIVALDI, A.-THILDE.  CONCERTO IN C MAJOR.  2TPT, *PF           A71
VIVALDI, A.-GHEDINI.  CONCERTO IN E-FLAT MAJOR                 C91
   2TPT, *ORCH, *PF
WALLS, J.  2 CLOWNS, THE.  2TPT, *PF                           D80
WALTERS, H.I. (ARR).  AMAZING GRACE.  2TPT, *PF                F07
WATTERS, C.  DOUBLE OR QUITS.  2TPT, *PF                       A78
WENDLAND.  TWIN STARS.  TPT, TPT(TRB), *PF                     G10
WESTENDORF.  I'LL TAKE YOU HOME AGAIN KATHLEEN.  2TPT, *PF     A91
WILLIAMS, E.S.  LARBOARD WATCH.  2TPT, *PF                     B53
WOOD.  LET 'ER GO!.  2TPT, *PF                                 B13
ZIMMERMAN.  PLAY A SONG OF AMERICA (2 VOL).  2TPT, *PF         E77
```

3 PARTS: HORNS-KEYBOARD

```
BEETHOVEN, L.V.  SEXTET, OP.81B.  2HN, *PF                     B44
BEETHOVEN, L.V.  TRIO, OP. 81B.  2HN, *PF                      B44
BRAGA, G.  ANGEL'S SERENADE.  2HN, *PF                         B53
FIALA, J.  CONCERTO.  2HN, PF                                 E14
FRANZ, O.-SANSONE.  CONCERT PIECE, OP.4                       F60
   2HN(2TPT), *BAND, *ORCH, *PF
FRANZ, O.-SPIES.  KONZERTSTUCK, OP.4.  2HN, *PF               B99
HANSEL, A.  CONCERTINO, OP.80.  2HN, *PF                      F60
HARTZELL, D.  FRENCH PASTRY FOR 2 FRENCH HNS..  2HN, *PF      F79
HAYDN, J.-LELOIR.  CONCERTO IN E-FLAT MAJOR.  2HN, *PF        D11
HOFFMEISTER, F.A.-CHAMBERS.  CONCERTO.  2HN, *PF              C91
IVANOV.  DUET FOR 2 HNS.  2HN, *PF                            D71
KUHLAU, F.  CONCERTINO.  2HN, PF                             E14
MAHY, A.  CHANT DES VENEURS, LE.  2HN, *PF                   D92
MENDELSSOHN, F.-CLUWEN.  AUTUMN SONG.  2HN, *PF              D92
MOZART, L.  CONCERTO.  2HN, PF                               E14
MOZART, L.-LELOIR.  CONCERTO.  2HN, *PF                      D11
O'NEILL, C.  MISTS OF MORNING.  2HN, *PF                     G13
O'NEILL, C.  WINSOME FROLIC.  2HN, *PF                       G13
ROSETTI, F.A.-WEELINK.  CONCERTO #2.  2HN, *PF               D11
ROSETTI, F.A.-WEELINK.  CONCERTO #3.  2HN, *PF               D11
ROSETTI, F.A.-WEELINK.  CONCERTO #5.  2HN, *PF               D11
ROSETTI, F.A.-CHAMBERS.  CONCERTO IN E-FLAT MAJOR.  2HN, *PF C91
RUGOLO, P.  TILL WE SPIEGEL AGAIN.  2HN, *PF                 G21
SCHWARTZ, E.S.  DIVERTIMENTO #2.  2HN, *PF                   N91
TELEMANN, G.P.  CONCERTO IN D.  2HN, *PF                     D11
TELEMANN, G.P.-CHAMBERS.  SUITE IN F MAJOR.  2HN, *PF        C91
VIVALDI, A.-OUBRADOUS.  CONCERTO #20 IN F, P. 320.  2HN, *PF F87
VIVALDI, A.-CERMINARO.  CONCERTO IN F MAJOR, P. 320.  2HN, *PF C91
VIVALDI, A.-NAGY.  CONCERTO IN F MAJOR, P. 320.  2HN, *PF    B84
```

VIVALDI, A.-AMISANO. CONCERTO IN F, P. 320. 2HN, *PF   E98

3 PARTS: TROMBONES-KEYBOARD

ADAMS, S.-GLENN. HOLY CITY, THE. 2TRB, *PF   A78
ARNOLD, J. EVERBODY'S FAVORITE SERIES. 2TRB, *PF   A18
ARNOLD, J. MUSIC FOR MILLIONS SERIES: #20 EASY SOLOS OR DUETS B41
   2TRB, *PF
BELLINI, V.-LEWIS. DUET FROM NORMA. 2TRB, *PF   C11
BLACK EYES. 2TRB, *PF   A91
BRAHE, M.H.-GLENN. BLESS THIS HOUSE. 2TRB, *PF   A78
BRIEGEL, G.F. CATHEDRAL ECHOES. 2TRB, *PF   A91
CORELLI, A. SONATA IN G MINOR. 2TRB, *PF   B85
CORELLI, A.-BROWN. 3 SONATAS, OP.1. 2TRB, *PF   C91
DEARNLEY, C.H. MORE EASY PIECES BY CLASSICAL COMPOSERS   B23
   2TRB, *PF
DRINK TO ME ONLY WITH THINE EYES. 2TRB, *PF   A91
DVORAK, A. SONGS MY MOTHER TAUGHT ME. 2TRB, *PF   A91
FERNANDEZ, O.L. BEAUTIFUL HEAVEN. 2TRB, *PF   A91
FOSTER, S.C. JEANIE, WITH THE LIGHT BROWN HAIR. 2TRB, *PF   A91
FRANCK, C. PANIS ANGELICUS. 2TRB, *PF   A91
GODARD, B.I.E. BERCEUSE. 2TRB, *PF   B13
HARRIS, F.O. 2 BUCKAROOS. 2TRB, *PF   D52
HARTZELL, D. MEXICAN JUMPIN' BONES. 2TRB, *PF   F74
HAWTHORNE. WHISPERING HOPE. 2TRB, *PF   A91
LISZT, F. LIEBESTRAUM. 2TRB, *PF   B13
LONDONDERRY AIR. 2TRB, *PF   A91
MANFREDINI, F.-TONI. CONCERTO. 2TRB, *PF   B07
MARINI, B.-BASSETT. SONATA, OP. 8/9. 2BTRB, *PF   M80
MASSENET, J.-TRINKAUS. ELEGIE WITH ANDANTINO. 2TRB, *PF   C09
MENDELSSOHN, F.-TRINKAUS. ON WINGS OF SONG. 2TRB, *PF   C09
MOZART, W.A.-SMITH. ANDANTE FROM MOZART REQUIEM. 2TRB, *PF   E80
OFFENBACH, J. BARCAROLE FROM TALES OF HOFFMANN. 2TRB, *PF   C11
PELZ, W. SALUTE TO HONOR. 2TRB, *PF   A62
9 PIECES DE DIVERS COMPOSITEURS POUR 2 TRB ET PF. 2TRB, *PF   B17
PUCCINI, G.-STEBBING. MUSETTA'S WALTZ SONG FROM LA BOHEME   E98
   2TRB, *PF
PUCCINI, G.-STEBBING. VISSI D'ARTE, VISSI D'AMORE FROM TOSCA   E98
   2TRB, *PF
SCHAEFFER(ARR). CHRISTMAS DUETS. 2TRB, *PF   E80
SIBELIUS, J. VALSE TRISTE, OP.44. 2TRB, *PF   C09
SMITH, C. FAVORITE ENCORE FOLIO. 2TRB, *PF   C11
SONG OF THE VULGA BOATMEN. 2TRB, *PF   A91
TANNER, P. CONCERT DUET FOR TENOR & BASS TRBS   C77
   TRB, BTRB, *PF
TANNER, P. CONCERT DUET. 2TRB, PF   C77
TANNER, P. CONCERTO. 2TRB, *PF   C77
WALTERS, H.L. (ARR). AMAZING GRACE. 2TRB, *PF   F07
WESTENDORF. I'LL TAKE YOU HOME AGAIN KATHLEEN. 2TRB, *PF   A91
WHITNEY, M. DEM BONES. 2TRB, *PF   C11

3 PARTS: MISCELLANEOUS-KEYBOARD

AMBROSIO-WOLTAG. BARCAROLE FROM TALES OF HOFFMAN	C11
TPT, TRB, *PF	
BAUDONCK. DUO. TPT, EU, *PF	F81
BEETHOVEN, L.V.-TRINKAUS. MINUET. TPT, TRB, *PF	C09
BERKELEY, L. TRIO, OP.44. HN, VN, *PF	B23
BEZANSON, P. TRIO. HN, CL, *PF	B36
BLACHER, B. DIVERTIMENTO, OP.31. TPT, TRB, *PF	A83
BLACHER, B. DIVERTIMENTO, OP.31. TPT, TRB, *PF	F31
BOHM, K.-HUMMEL. CALM AS THE NIGHT. TPT, HN(TRB), *PF	F07
BUCHTEL, F.L. ROVING MINSTRELS. TPT, EU, *PF	D18
CASTEREDE, J. CONCERTINO. TPT, TRB, *ORCH, *PF	D36
CLEMENTI, A. SONATA. TPT, GUIT, *PF	G41
CORELLI, A.-OSTRANDER. ALLEMANDE. TPT, TRB, *PF	B85
CORELLI, A.-MORRIS. SONATA DA CHIESA. 2TU, *PF	D52
CORELLI, A. SONATA IN G MINOR. HN(TRB), TRB, *PF	B85
CORELLI, A.-OSTRANDER. SONATA IN G MINOR. TPT, TRB, *PF	B85
COWELL, J. TRIO FOR CL, HN, PA.. HN, CL, PA	B44
CROLEY, R. SONATA. TPT, TRB, PA	F88
DEDRICK, A. MARCH OF THE MISSILEMEN. 2TPT, *PF, *BAND	D14
DEDRICK, A. SPACE CADETS. 2TPT, *PF, *BAND	D14
DEFAY, J.M. CONCERTO. TPT, TRB, *ORCH, *PF	D36
DRIGO, R.-HUMMEL. SERENADE. TPT, HN(TRB), *PF	F07
DUVERNOY, F.N.-LELOIR. TRIO NO. 1 IN C. HN, PF, VN(FL)	D11
DUVERNOY, F.N. TRIO NO. 2 IN F. HN, PF, VN(FL, CL)	D11
DVORAK, A.-AMBROSIO. HUMORESKE. TPT, TRB, *PF	C11
ELGAR, E.W.-TRINKAUS. SALUT D'AMOUR. TPT, TRB, *PF	C09
ERICKSON, F. DOUBLE CONCERTO. TPT, TRB, *PF	A84
FRESCOBALDI, G. CANZONAS 18-23. TRB, OB(CTT), BC(ORG)	E14
FRESCOBALDI, G. CANZONAS 27-29	E14
TRB, 2CTT(2TPT, 2OB), BC(ORG)	
GARLICK, A. 2 PIECES FOR THREE PLAYERS. TPT, TRB, PF	G66
GOUNOD, C.F.-DEVILLE. FLOWER SONG FROM FAUST. TPT, TRB, *PF	C11
GOUNOD, C.F.-DEVILLE. SERENADE. TPT, TRB, *PF	C11
GRANT, P. CONCEPT DUO, OP. 48. 2TU, *PF	A13
HADRABA, J. POSAUNETTO. TRB, CL, *PF	D20
HADRABA, J. TAPFERE SCHNEIDERLEIN & DER RIESE, DAS	D20
TRB, CL, *PF	
HAMBRAEUS, B. MUSIQUE POUR TPT, VLN, & PA, CP.18/2	B90
TPT, VN, *PF	
HAMBRAEUS, B. MUSIQUE, OP. 18/2. TPT, PF, VN	B90
HANDEL, G.F.-SWAYZEE. TRUMPET SHALL SOUND, THE	B85
TRB, EU(TU), *PF	
HERTEL, J.W. DOUBLE CONCERTO IN E-FLAT. TPT, OB, PF	E14
HERZOGENBERG, H.V. TRIO D-DUR, OP. 91. HN IN D, OB, PF	N04
HINDEMITH, P. KONZERT FUR TPT & FAGOTT. TPT, BSN, *ORCH, *PF	F31
HOUDY, P. DIVERTISSEMENT. TPT, HN, *PF	D36
IRONS, E.D. PEDRO Y AMIGO. TPT, TRB, *PF	F07
JAMES. SCHERZO. TPT, TRB, *PF	P39
JOHNSON, C.W. SPRING ODYSSEY. TPT(COR), HN(TRB), *PF	F07
JOHNSON, R. TRIO. HN, CL, HPCD	B35
JOSEPHS. TRIO. HN, VN, PF	E41
KAUDER, H. TRIO #1. HN, OB, PF	G66
KAUDER, H. TRIO #2. HN, OB, PF	G66
KAUDER, H. TRIO. HN, VN, PF	A78
KAUDER, H. TRIO. HN, FL, PF	G66

```
KELLY, R.   INTRODUCTION & DIALOGUE.  HN, VC, *PF                       E68
KINYON, J.   BREEZE-EASY PROGRAM PIECES.  3INST ?                       H06
KLING.  ELEFANT & MUCKE (INTERMEZZO).  TPT(PIC), TRB, *PF               E43
KOEPKE, P.   GANDY DANCE.  TPT, HN(TRB), *PF                            F07
KOEPKE, P.   LONELY RIVER.  TPT, HN(TRB), *PF                           F07
LANCASTER, S.   PASTORALE.  TPT, TRB, *PF                               N66
LANG, P.J.   TRUMPET & DRUM.  TPT, SDR, *PF                             D84
LEMARE, E.H.-TRINKAUS.  ANDANTINO.  TPT, TRB, *PF                       C09
LUCAS, L.   AUBADE.  HN, BSN, *PF                                       B23
MALEZIEUX, G.   RELIGIOUS MELODY.  TPT, HN, *PF                         C38
MALEZIEUX, G.   ROMANCE SANS PAROLES.  TPT, HN, *PF                     C38
MALEZIEUX, G.   SUR LE LAC.  TPT, HN, *PF                               F16
MARCELLO, B.   PRELUDE & DANCE.  TPT, TRB, *PF                          B85
MENDELSSOHN, F.-YEREMIN.  SONG WITHOUT WORDS.  TPT, HN, *PF             D81
MOLINEUX.  BRIEF DIVERSION, A.  TPT, TRB, *PF                           F43
MOZART, W.A.-NAUMANN.  TRIO ES-DUR, KV.407                              A90
    HN(VA, VC), VN, *PF
OSTRANDER, A.   DUET ALBUM.  TPT, HN(TRB), *PF                          B85
PETERSON, H.   JB INTERLUDE.  HN, CL, PF                                P31
PEZEL, J.C.-TARR.  SONATA IN C.  TPT, BSN, BC                           M80
PHILLIPS, D.V.   A TRES.  HN, VN, *PF                                   B35
PORRET, J.   OVIDE.  TPT, TRB, *PF                                      D92
PORRET, J.   PETRARQUE.  TPT, TRB, *PF                                  D92
PRENTZEL-TARR.  SONATA IN C.  TPT, BSN, BC                              M80
PRENTZI, D.   SONATA A DUE.  TPT, BSN, BC                               E14
PRESSER, W.H.   RHAPSODY ON A PEACEFUL THEME.  HN, VN, *PF              F80
RACHMANINOFF, S.V.   VOCALISE, OP.34/14.  TPT, TRB, *PF                 B85
REINECKE, C.   TRIO A-MOLL, OP.188.  HN, OB, *PF                        A90
REINECKE, C.   TRIO IN A MINOR, OP.188.  HN, OB, *PF                    C91
REINECKE, C.   TRIO IN B-FLAT, OP. 274.  HN(VA), CL, PF                 E14
SCHMODT.  PIECE CONCERTANTE, OP. 19.  TPT, TRB, *PF                     H30
SCHUBERT, F.P.-JANETZKY.  AUF DEM STROM.  HN, S, PF                     E65
SCHUBERT, F.P.   WANDERING BROOKLET.  TPT, EU, *PF                      D18
SCHUMAN, W.   YOUNG DEAD SOLDIERS, THE.  HN, S, PF                      E77
SCHUMANN, R.-BUCHTEL.  VOICE OF LOVE.  HN, FL, *PF                      D18
SCHWARTZ, E.S.   DIVERTIMENTO.  HN, CL, PF                              C40
SCHWERTSIK, K.   TRIO.  HN, VN, *PF                                     D88
SIMONS, N.   FACETS 1.  HN, VN, *PF                                     E68
SMYTH, E.M.   TRIO.  HN, VN, *ORCH, *PF                                 G58
SPIEGLER, M.   CANZON A 2.  CTT(OB), BSN, BC                            E14
SPIEGLER, M.-VOISIN.  CANZONE I.  TPT, BTRE, *PF                        C91
STEINKE, G.   TRICINIUM.  TPT, PF, ASAX                                 G66
STEWART.  TOCCATA SONORE.  TRB, FL, PF                                  G66
STOUFFER, P.M.   CONCERTINO FOR TWO.  TPT, CL, *BAND, *PF               B91
STRAUSS, R.-FORST.  ZUEIGNUNG.  TPT, TRB, *PF                           B85
TANNER, P.   CONCERT DUET.  TRB, BTRB, *PF, *BAND                       G21
TELEMANN, G.P.-SCHROEDER.  CONCERTO A TRE                               C71
    HN, RCDR, *CONTINUO
TENAGLIA, A.F.-MAGANINI.  ARIA ANTICA.  TPT, TRB, *PF                   B85
TITL, A.E.   SERENADE.  HN, FL, *PF                                     D92
TITL, A.E.-BUCHTEL.  SERENADE.  HN, FL, *PF                             D18
TROTERE, H.-WALTERS.  IN OLD MADRID.  TPT, HN(TRB), *PF                 F07
UYTTENDOVE, Y.   TRIO POUR TPT, 4 TIMBALES ET PF                        D67
    TPT, 4TIME, *PF
WADOWICK, J.   TWO FOR THE TUBA.  2TU, *PF                              M87
WEBER, B.   IMAGE IN THE SMOW (FILM SCORE).  TRB, VC, CEL               E68
WEIGL, W.   CHERRY TREE, THE (VERSION II).  HN, OB(FL), *PF             B36
WEIGL, W.   ECHOES FROM POEMS BY PATRICIA BENTON.  HN, VN, *PF          E68
WEISGARBER, E.   DIVERTIMENTO.  HN, VA, *PF                             B44
WILDER, A.   SONATA FOR FRENCH HORN, TUBA & PA..  HN, TU, *PF           H09
WILDER, A.   SUITE.  HN, TU, *PF                                        C25
ZELENKA, I.   TRIO.  HN, VN, *PF                                        D88
```

3 PARTS: WIND(S)-STRING(S)

BALLIF, C. TRIO, OP.35/3. HN, CL, VN	A83
BERKELEY, L. TRIO, OP.44. HN, VN, PA	B23
BOECK, I. & A.-JANETZKY. 10 STUECKE. 2HN, VC(BSN)	C75
BORTOLOTTI, M. STUDI. HN, CL, VA	G41
BRAHMS, J. TRIO ES-DUR, OP.40. HN, VN, PA	A90
BRAHMS, J. TRIO IN E FLAT MAJOR, OP.40. HN, VN, PA	C91
BRAHMS, J. TRIO, E-FLAT MAJOR,OP.40. HN(VA, VC), VN, PA	C03
BRAHMS, J. TRIO, OP.40 IN E-FLAT MAJOR. HN(VA, VC), VN, PA	E65
BRAHMS, J. TRIO, OP.40 IN E-FLAT. HN, VN, PA	A42
DIJK, J.V. CONCERTO PER TRB,VIOLINO, EN VINCELLO	B74
TRB, VN, VC	
DUVERNOY, F.N.-LELOIR. TRIO NO. 1 IN C. HN, PF, VN(FL)	D11
DUVERNOY, F.N. TRIO NO. 2 IN F. HN, PF, VN(FL, CL)	D11
FELDMAN, M. DURATIONS III. TU, VN, PA	E65
HAMBRAEUS, B. MUSIQUE, OP. 18/2. TPT, PF, VN	B90
HAYDN, J.-IANDON. DIVERTIMENTO A TRE PER IL CORNO DA CACCIA	B73
HN, VN, VC	
KALLSTENIUS, E. TRIO SVAGANTE, OP.51. HN, CL, VC	B90
KAUDER, H. TRIO. HN, VN, PA	A78
KELLY, F. INTRODUCTION & DIALOGUE. HN, VC, PA	E68
LANGER, H.K. KONZERTANTE MUSIK NR. 5. TPT, MAR, DB	A39
MOZART, W.A.-NAUMANN. TRIO ES-DUR, KV.407	A90
HN(VA, VC), VN, *PF	
PERSICHETTI, V. SERENADE NO.6. TRB, VA, VC	B92
PHILLIPS, D.V. A TRES. HN, VN, *PF	B35
PRESSER, W.H. RHAPSODY ON A PEACEFUL THEME. HN, VN, *PF	F80
RAPHAEL, G. SONATINE, OP.65/4. HN, BSN, *PF	A90
SCHISKE, K. MUSIC FOR CL, TPT & VLA,OP.27. TPT, CL, VA	F97
SCHULLER, G. TRIO. HN, OB, VA	A38
SCHWERTSIK, K. TRIO. HN, VN, *PF	D88
SIMONS, N. FACETS 1. HN, VN, *PF	E68
SMYTH, F.M. CONCERTO FOR VLN, HN & ORCH. HN, VN, *ORCH, *PF	G58
SPERGER, J.M.-MALARIE. CASSATION NO.3 IN D. HN, VA, DB	D11
ULRICH, H.J. TRIO-PHANTASIE, OP.20. HN, VN, *PF	B73
WEBER, B. IMAGE IN THE SNOW (FILM SCORE). TRB, VC, CEL	E68
WEIGL, V. ECHOES FROM POEMS BY PATRICIA BENTON. HN, VN, *PF	E68
WEISGARBER, E. DIVERTIMENTO. HN, VA, *PF	B44
WOLFF, C. TRIO I. TPT, FL, VC	E65
ZELENKA, I. TRIO. HN, VN, *PF	D88

3 PARTS: BRASS-MISCELLANEOUS

BARBOTEU, G. ESQUISSE. HN, FL, PF(HP)	B24
BLANK, A. MUSIC FOR THREE PLAYERS. TPT, 2INST ?	G66
BUNJES, P. BUILT ON THE ROCK. 2TPT, *ORG, *CHORUS	B40
CHIHARA. WILLOW, WILLOW. TU, FL, PERC	E65
CZERNY, C. TRIO NO. 1 IN E-FLAT, OP. 105. HN, PF, VN	E14
DEPELSENAIRE, J.M. MATIN DE CHASSE. 2TPT, TIMP	B24
DEPELSENAIRE, J.M. POUR DES JEUX EQUESTRES. 2TPT, TIMP	B24
DIEMENTE, E. DIMENSIONS I. 3INST ?	G66
DIEMENTE, E. TRIO (1969). TPT, FL, PERC	G66

```
DIEMENTE, E.  TRIO.  TPT, FL, PERC                                      G66
DONOVAN, R.  SOUNDINGS.  TPT, BSN, PERC(4)                              E68
DUSSEK, F.  NOCTURNE CONCERTANTE.  HN, PF, VN                           E14
EISENACH, J.J.I.V.  PIECES.  2TPT, *CONTINUO                            E14
IVES, C.E.  FROM THE STEEPLES AND THE MOUNTAINS (ALLEGRO)              F59
   TPT, TRB, CHIMES(2PF)
KOHS, E.B.  NIGHT WATCH.  HN, FL, TIMP                                  E68
LA ROSA.  COMING IN GLORY.  TRB,VIB, ASAX                               G66
LUENING, O.  SUITE FOR DIVERSE HIGH & LOW INSTRS..  3INST ?            C33
MC BRIDE, R.  I RIDE OLD PAINT.  TPT, TRB, INST ?                       A13
NELHYBEL, V.  12 CONCERT PIECES.  3 TC INST                             B32
NELHYBEL, V.  MUSICA FESTIVA.  3INST ?                                  B32
PEZEL, J.C.  2 BICINA.  2TPT, *CONTINUO                                 E14
ROHLIG, H.  HOW LOVELY SHINES THE MORNING STAR                         B40
   2TPT, ORG, *CHORUS
ROSENBOOM, D.  TRIO.  TPT, CL, B                                        B35
SCHEIFES, H.M.  4 KLEINE STUKKEN VAN OUDE MEESTERS.  3 TC INST         F81
SCHUBERT, F.P.  AUF DEM STROM.  HN, PF, S                               B44
SCHUBERT, F.P.  AUF DEM STROM, OP. 119.  HN, PF, V                     A90
SCHWARTZ, E.S.  MUSIC FOR OBOE, TPT & CELLO.  TPT, OB, VC              C40
SYDEMAN, W.  TRIO FOR TREBLE INSTRUMENTS.  3INST ?                     G66
TAUTENHAHN, G.  TRIO #2.  TU, EH, GLOK                                  G66
TAUTENHAHN, G.  TRIO NO. 2.  TU, EH, GLCK                               G66
TAUTENHAHN, G.  TRIO.  TPT, VC, CHIMES                                  G66
VAN VACTOR, D.  ECONOMY BAND.  TPT, TRB, PERC                          C25
VAN VACTOR, D.  SONG & DANCE (ECONOMY BAND NO. 2)                      P44
   HN, TU, PERC
YANNAY, Y.  PREFIX-FIX-SUFFIX.  HN, BSN, VC                            N29
```

FOUR-PART MUSIC

4 TRUMPETS

ARENSKY, A.S. CUCKOO	A91
ARNOLD, J. EVERYBODY'S FAVORITE SERIES: #125 TRUMPET QUARTETS	A18
APTOT, A.J. 12 QUARTETTES	B53
BACH, J.S.-JOHNSON. 5 BACH CHORALES	F07
BACH, J.S.-MULLER. 3 CHORALES	D67
BACH, J.S.-DAVIDSON. FUGUE IN G MINOR	B31
BARATTO. BURLESKE	N40
BARATTO. TROMPETENGALOPP	N40
BARTH. FANFAREN MUSIK	E89
BARTSCH, C. FANFARE, CANTILENE, ET DANSE	D67
BEETHOVEN, L.V.-FRAKER. MINUET IN G	A55
BIZET, G. QUARTET	B44
BLOCH, W. PARTITA	B73
BOTTJE, W.G. CHORALE & ALLEGRO	B30
BRANDT, V. COUNTRY PICTURES	C91
BRIEGEL, G.F. FANFARE ON A MOUNTAIN TOP	A91
BRIEGEL, G.F. MORNING SONG & EVENING SONG	A91
BRIEGEL, G.F. 4 TRUMPETERS, THE	A91
BURGHAUSER. OLD CZECH FANFARES	A33
BUSCH, C. EVENING PROMENADE	C11
BUSCH, C. IN A PLAYFUL MOOD	C11
CASSEL, D. & GEARHART. TRUMPET SESSIONS	F43
CATELINET, P.B. 4 CEREMONIAL FANFARES	C71
CAZDEN, N. FANFARE NO.3, OP.40	F62
CROCE. RICERCAR	P19
DE ROYE, E. PAX	D80
DILLON, R.M. MARCH & CHORALE	A78
ELLMENREICH-IRONS. SPINNING SONG	F07
FITZGERALD, R.B. CAPRICE	A62
FITZGERALD, R.B. PRELUDE	C11
FITZGERALD, R.B. SCHERZINO	C11
FORESTIER, J.J.-COFIELD. SONATINA NO.1	F07
FRANCK, C.-STUBE. PANIS ANGELICUS	A62
FRANZ, O.-LA VIOLETTE. DEDICATION	A62
FRANZ, O.-WALTERS. QUARTETTO	F07
FRIESE, E.A. 5 TROMPETEN-QUARTETTE	C59
GANNE, L.G.-WRIGHT. GAVOTTE TENDRE	A78
GEARHART, L. & CASSEL. TRUMPET SESSIONS	F43
GILLIS, D. RUSHIN' TRUMPETEERS, THE	A62
GILLIS, D. RUSHIN' TRUMPETEERS, THE	A78
GILLIS, D. SONATINA	A78
GOEBERT. RHAPSODY	F60
GOLLER. FANFAREN ZU FESTLICHE ANLASSEN	B73
GUENTZEL, G. FESTIVAL DAYS	A55
HANDEL, G.F.-SCHAEFFER. HALLELUJAH CHORUS	E80
HAUGLAND, A.O. APOLLO	A38
HAVLICEK, L.C. TRUMPETERS POLKA FOR TRUMPET QUARTET	F79
HERVIG, R. ALLA MARCIA	F07
HESSEN, M.G.L.V.-MILLER. INTRADA A 4 CORNETTI	B98
HOFFMAN. 3 MOVIMENTI	F60
JOHNSON, W.S. FESTIVAL PRELUDE	A62
JOHNSON, W.S. IN THE FOREST	A62
JOHNSON, W.S. IN THE FOREST	A78
JOHNSON, W.S. OVERTURE "STREAMLINE"	C13
KAY, U.S. 3 FANFARES	D37

LA VIOLETTE, W.	COBBLER'S SONG	A62
LA VIOLETTE, W.	DEDICATION	A62
LA VIOLETTE, W.	EARLY STROLLING AT MY LEISURE	A62
LA VIOLETTE, W.	FOLLOW THE LEADER	A62
LA VIOLETTE, W.	QUARTET ALBUM	G85
LA VIOLETTE, W.	RAINBOW GODDESS	A62
LANGLEY.	SCHERZO	N58
LECAIL, C.	4 FANFARES	F81
LEIDZEN, E.W.G.	4 HERALDS	A84
LEONARD, B.	MOODS	C13
LISZT, F.-SMITH.	LIEBESTRAUME	D84
LODEON.	DIVERTISSEMENT	D36
LOTZENHISER, G.W.	MARCIA GRANDIOSO	F07
LOTZENHISER, G.W.	SCHERZETTO	F07
MAGANINI, Q.E.	FLOURISH FOR A HERO, A	B85
MANCINI, A.	SYMPHONIC BRASS QUARTETS	B31
MARSHALL-KLEIN.	TWO BY TWO	F43
MC KAY, G.F.	AMERICAN PANORAMA	C11
MC LIN.	INSTRUMENTAL ENSEMBLE BOOK FOR 4 TRUMPETS	E80
MENDELSSOHN, F.	NOCTURNE	A91
MENDELSSOHN, F.-SMITH.	WAR MARCH OF THE PRIESTS FR. "ATHALIA"	D84
MEULEMANS, A.	4 OPROEPEN	B12
MOHAUPT, R.	PARTITA	A84
MOLTER, J.M.	SYMPHONY IN C MAJOR	E14
MOZART, W.A.	ALLELUIA	B85
MOZART, W.A.-OSTRANDER.	ALLELUIA	B85
MOZART, W.A.-ROSENTHAL.	DIVERTIMENTI	E67
MOZART, W.A.-BIMBONI.	RONDO	F07
MOZART, W.A.-JOHNSON.	RONDO	F07
MULLER, B.E.	QUARTETTES (4 VOL)	F60
NELSON, H.T.	4 ACES	D18
NEUKOMM, S.R.V.-TOWNSEND.	3 FANFARES	D74
OSTRANDER, A.	BAROQUE SUITE	B85
OSTRANSKY, L.	DANCE SUITE	F07
OSTRANSKY, L.	FANFARE & ALLEGRO	F07
OSTRANSKY, L.	PAVANE & CANZONETTA	F07
PALESTRINA, G.P.-MOORE.	MADRIGAL	G21
PALESTRINA, G.P.	MOTET "CHRISTE, LUX VERA	P19
PEYSSIES, M.	PLEIN SOLEIL	B66
PORRET, J.	CALDERON	D92
PORRET, J.	DANTE	D92
QUARTET REPERTOIRE FOR CORNET OR TPT.		F07
RACUSEN, D.	CANONIC ETUDES	F43
RAPHLING, S.	CONCERT SUITE	B85
ROSSINI, G.	FANFARE DE CHASSE	D55
RUELLE, F.-REMA.	ETUDE A 4	D67
RUGOLO, P.	4 TRUMP	G21
RULST-REMA.	LITTLE FANFARE	A96
RULST & REMA.	INTRODUCTION & FANFARE	A96
SCHAEFFER.	LYRIC POEME	E80
SCHAEFFER, D.	15TH CENTURY MADRIGAL	E80
SCHAEFFER, D.	CONVERSATIONS	E80
SCHAEFFER, D.	IMPRESSIONS	E80
SCHEIDT, S.-KING.	CANZON	D16
SCHEIN, J.H.-MOORE.	INTRADA	G21
SCHUBERT, F.P.-LOTZENHISER.	MARCHE MILITAIRE	A62
SEMLER-COLLERY, J.	PIECE EN FORME DE MENUET	A71
SHERMAN.	3 EARLY MADRIGALS	B98
SIMPSON.	SONATINA FOR 4 TPTS	C11
SULLIVAN, A.S.-STUBE.	LOST CHORD	A62
TCHEREPNINE, N.N.	LA CHASSE	B53
TCHEREPNINE, N.N.-KARASICK.	6 PIECES	B85

TELEMANN, G.P. TOCCATA   M71
TELEMANN, G.P.-MOORE. TOCCATA   G21
THIBOUT-LA VIOLETTE. EARLY STROLLING AT MY LEISURE   A62
TIPPETT, M. FANFARE NR.2   F31
TIPPETT, M. FANFARE NR.3   F31
TITTEL. QUARTETTINO   C75
TROWBRIDGE, L. CHORALE   G66
TULL, F. CANONICAL TRILOGY   A43
TURINI-WIENANDT. FANFARE & PROCESSIONAL   F60
VECCHI, O. CRICKET, THE   B85
VERDI, G.-STUBE. TRIUMPHAL MARCH   A62
VIERDANCK, J.-ENGEL. CAPRICCI FUR 2-4 TPT OR FLUGELHORNER   A51
VON HESSEN. INTRADA   B98
WAIGNEIN, A. FLASCH   D67
WALTERS, H.L. TRUMPET FILIGREE   F07
WILLIAMS, E.S. BOLERO   B31
WILLIAMS, E.S. HALL OF FAME   B31
ZELENKA-JANETZKY. 6 REITERFANFAREN   C75

4 HORNS

ABT, F.-D'ARESE. SILENT WATER-LILY, THE   C11
ANGERER. HORNQUARTETT   B73
ARNELL, R. MUSIC FOR HORNS   F59
ARNOLD, J. EVERYBONDY'S FAVORITE SERIES   A18
ATTERBERG, K. SORGMARSCH FOR 4 HORN   B90
BACH, J.S.-THILDE. CANTATA # 29   A71
BACH, J.S.-LOCKWOOD. FUGUE IN A MINOR   C78
BACH, J.S.-TREAT. FUGUE IN B-FLAT   G31
BACH, J.S.-SHAW. FUGUE IN C MINOR   C78
BACH, J.S.-THILDE. GRANDE FUGUE IN C MAJOR   A71
BACH, J.S.-ROSENTHAL. 4 PIECES FOR 4 HNS   G21
BACH, J.S.-ROSENTHAL. 4 PIECES   A43
BACH, J.S.-ROSENTHAL. 4 PIECES   M63
BARBIER, R. QUATUOR, OP. 93   D67
BARBOTEU, G. 2 QUARTETTOS   B24
BECHER, H. SINFONIETTA   C54
BENNETT, D. FRENCH HORN FRAPPE   C11
BIZET, G.-ZAMECNIK. AGNUS DEI   C25
BODER. QUARTET #2   D11
BORRIS, S. CANZONA FUR 4 HN   F53
BORRIS, S. MUSIK FUR WALDHORN, OP.109   F53
BOUTRY, R. TETRACOR   D36
BOZZA, E. SUITE FOR 4 HORNS IN F   D36
BRAHMS, J.-WILCOX. FINALE FR. SYMPHONY NO.1   A62
BRAHMS, J.-WILCOX. FINALE FR. SYMPHONY NO.1   A78
BRANDT, V. COUNTRY PICTURES   C91
BURDICK, H. (ARR). TRANSCRIPTIONS FOR HORN QUARTET   P49
BUTTS, C.M. SUITE FOR 4 HNS   G90
BYRD, W. GAILIARDA   E00
CADOW, P. 3 PIECES   F62
CADOW, P. 3 STUCKE FUR 4 HNS IN F   C54
CASTELNUOVO-TEDESCO, M. CHORAL WITH VARIATIONS, OP.162   B91
CHAVEZ. SONATA   G85
CLARK, F.J. ST.HUBERT'S HUNTING SONG   B85
COFIELD, F.D. WINTER SUNSET   F07
COSCIA, S. CONCERT SUITE   N95
DAUPRAT, L.F. QUARTETS #5 & 6   C78

```
MAYER, R.   4 LITTLE PIECES                                          F60
MC KAY, F.H.   AMERICAN PANORAMA                                     C11
MC KAY, F.H.   MODERATO E CANTABILE                                  C11
MC KAY, F.H.   PETITE SUITE, OP.15                                   C11
MC KAY, F.H.   2 PIECES                                              E93
MC KAY, F.H.   2 PIECES                                              H06
MC KAY, F.H.   SUITE FOR 4 HORNS, OP.21                              A55
MC KAY, G.F.   NAUTICAL SCENE, BALLAD & CAPRICCIO                    A55
MENDELSSOHN, F.   NOCTURNE                                           A91
MENDELSSOHN, F.-ZAMECNIK.   NOCTURNE                                 C25
MICHIELS.   REVERIE                                                  F60
MITUSHIN, J.-LEUBA.   CONCERTINO                                     F60
MOLTER, J.M.   SYMPHONY IN C MAJOR                                   E14
MORLEY, T.-SCHAEFFER.   CONTRASTS                                    E80
MOULAERT, R.   ANDANTE                                               B12
MOZART, W.A.   ALLELUIA                                              B85
MOZART, W.A.-DUTSCHKE-LOCKWOOD.   MAGIC FLUTE, THE                   C78
MULLER, B.E.   QUARTETTES (4 VOL)                                    F60
MULLER, B.E.-POTTAG.   WALD LIED                                     B53
NELHYBEL, V.   QUARTET FOR HORNS                                     C40
NEULING, H.   JAGD-QUARTETT                                          E81
OSTRANDER, A.   BAROQUE SUITE                                        B85
OSTRANSKY, L.   AEOLIAN SUITE                                        F07
OSTRANSKY, L.   VELVET & TWEED                                       F07
OTEY, W.   SYMPHONIC SKETCHES                                        F60
PALESTRINA, G.P.-SCHULTZ.   CHRISTE, LUX VERA                        D14
PERILHOU, A.   CHASSE                                                C65
PIJLMAN, H.   4 DWERGEN, DE                                          F81
POLDINI, E.   SERENADE                                              F97
PORRET, J.   DANTE                                                   D92
POTTAG, M.P.   IN THE COUNTRY                                        C11
POTTAG, M.P.   QUARTET ON WAGNER MOTIVES                             G85
PRESSER, W.H.   HORN QUARTET                                         E77
PRICE.   OLD REFRAIN                                                 C11
PURCELL, H.-ROSENTHAL.   FANTASIA #9                                 G21
RACUSEN, D.   CANONIC ETUDES                                         F43
REICHE, H.   BREZEL-POLKA                                            G43
REICHE, H.   VIERSPANNNIG                                            G43
REIN, W.   DIVERTIMENTO                                              F31
REIN, W.   WALDMUSIK                                                 F31
REYNOLDS, V.   SHORT SUITE FOR HN QUARTET                            D16
RIMSKY-KORSAKOV, N.A.-GNESIN.   NOTTURNO                             E14
RIMSKY-KORSAKOV, N.A.-KING.   NOTTURNO                               D16
ROCHARD.   LE FOLKLORE DE LA CHASSE                                  D36
ROHNER.   50 CHRISTMAS CAROLS                                        D82
ROSSINI, G.   FANFARE FOR 4 HUNTING HORNS                            D55
POSSINI, G.   RENDEZ-VOUS DE CHASSE, LE                              F52
RUBANK(PUB).   QUARTET REPERTOIRE FOR HORN                           F07
SCARMOLIN, A.L.   ALBUM LEAF                                         A55
SCARMOLIN, A.L.   LENTO                                              C11
SCHAEFFER, D.   15TH CENTURY MADRIGAL                                E80
SCHEIDT, S.-KING.   CANZON FROM PADUANA ....                         D16
SCHEIN, J.H.   PADOUANA AUS BANCHETTO MUSICALE                       A89
SCHEIN, J.H.-PRUFER.   SUITE NR.22 AUS BANCHETTO MUSICALLE           A90
SCHMIDT.   VARIATIONS                                                A43
SCHMUTZ, A.D.   DIVERTIMENTO                                         A62
SERVAIS, T.   EN FORET D'ARDENNE                                     A96
SHAW, I.E.   FRIPPERIES FOR 4 HNS (5 VOL)                            C78
SHAW, L.E.   4 QUARTETS (BACH, TSCHAIKOWSKY, HANDEL)                 C78
SHAW, L.E.(ARR).   4 QUARTETS                                       C78
SMELTEKOP (ARR).   SUITE                                             E00
SNYDER.   RICERCAR                                                   D16
```

SOMBRUN. L'ART DE SONNER DE LA TROMPE, PT. 2	D36
STANHOPE, D. CORTETTES	C78
SUESSMUTH. SUITE FOR 4 WALDHORNER	A90
SUSATO, T.-MULLER. DANCERIES	D67
SUSSMUTH, R. SUITE, OP.32	A89
SWERT, J.D. PENSEE ELEGIAQUE, OP.47	D55
TCHAIKOVSKY, P.I. ANDANTE CANTABILE (5TH SYM)	A55
TCHEREPNINE, N.N. CHASSE, LA	B53
TCHEREPNINE, N.N.-MAGANINI. 6 PIECES	B85
TCHEREPNINE, N.N. QUARTET NO.5	D81
TCHEREPNINE, N.N. 6 QUARTETTE	C19
TCHEREPNINE, N.N. 6 QUARTETTE	C25
TIPPETT, M. SONATA	F31
TOMASI, H. PETITE SUITE	D36
UBER, D.A. SUITE	F59
VANINETTI-LELOIR. QUARTET	D11
VANINETTI, G.-LELOIR. QUARTET	D11
VECCHI, O. CRICKET, THE	B85
VICTORIA, T.L.D.-DONFRAY. AVE MARIA	N61
VICTORIA, T.L.D.-SCHULTZ. O SACRUM CONVIVIUM	D14
VINCZE, O. DIVERTIMENTO	P49
WAGNER, R.-SHAW. KING'S PRAYER (LOHENGRIN)	A62
WAGNER, R. PILGRIM CHORUS FROM TANNHAUSER	B53
WAGNER, R.-ZAMECNIK. PILGRIM'S CHORUS	C25
WAGNER, R.-POTTAG. QUARTET FOR HNS	A62
WAGNER, R.-WILCOX. SIEGFRIED'S FUNERAL MARCH	F60
WAGNER, R.-POTTAG. TANNHAUSER	A62
WAGNER, R. WALTHER'S PRIZE SONG	C25
WEBER, B. QUARTET #1	A90
WEBER, B. QUARTET #2	A90
WEBER, C.M.V. FREISCHUTZ, DER	B53
WEBER, C.M.V.-ZAMECNIK. FREISCHUTZ, DER	C25
WEBER, C.M.V.-POTTAG. HUNTING CHORUS	A62
WEBER, F.D.-JANETZKY. 3 QUARTETS	C75
WEISS, A.A. RHAPSODY	E68
WIENANDT (ED). PASTICCIO	E80
WILDER, A. SIX X FOUR	C78
WILDER, A. 4 STUDIES	F60
WINTER, J. SUITE FOR A QUARTET OF YOUNG HORNS	C78
WUNDERER, A. ORIG. WALDHORN QUARTETTE	A20
ZBINDEN, J.F. 3 PIECES, OP.20	A90

4 TROMBONES

AMELLER, A.A. CHORAL	C71
ARNOLD, J. EVERYBODY'S FAVORITE SERIES: #126 TRB QUARTETS	A18
ATHERTON. SUITE	N58
BACH, J.S.-MCCARTY. AIR	B98
BACH, J.S.-MCCARTY. ARIOSO	B98
BACH, J.S.-KING. 16 CHORALES	D16
BACH, J.S.-FETTER. 22 CHORALES	B98
BACH, J.S.-SMITH. CONTRAPUNCTUS I	E80
BACH, J.S.-KELLEHER. CONTRAPUNCTUS NO.14	B98
BACH, J.S.-ROCHUT. 3 DUOS FOR 2TRB & 2 FUGUES FOR 3 & 4 TRB	F16
BACH, J.S.-THILDE. FUGUE (1ST SONATE)	A71
BACH, J.S.-BARNES. FUGUE IN D MINOR	F79
BACH, J.S.-MYERS. FUGUE IN D MINOR	B98
BACH, J.S.-FETTER. FUGUE V FR. WTC	B98

```
BACH, J.S.-HANSON.  O SACRED HEAD (ST.MATHEW PASSION)        B98
BACH, J.S.-PULIS.  POLONAISE. 3TRB, BTRB(TU)                 B98
BACH, J.S.-FETTER.  PRELUDE & FUGUE (#16 OF WTC)             B98
BACH, J.S.-FETTER.  3 SHORT PIECES                          B98
BARK, J.-RABE.  BOLOS FOR 4 TROMBONER                       H30
BASSETT, L.R.  QUARTET FOR TRBS                             D16
BEETHOVEN, L.V.  3 EQUALE                                   A89
BEETHOVEN, L.V.  3 EQUALE                                   A91
BEETHOVEN, L.V.  3 EQUALI                                   B98
BEETHOVEN, L.V.-KING.  3 EQUALI                             D16
BEETHOVEN, L.V.-DEDRICK.  MISERERE-AMPLIUS                  D14
BERLIOZ, H.-LOTZENHISER.  RAKOCZY MARCH                     A62
BERLIOZ, H.-OSTRANDER.  SUITE (DAMNATION OF FAUST)          B85
BLAHNIK.  PRAGUE TROMBONES                                  N18
BLAZHEVICH, V.M.  VALSE DE CONCERT                          F07
BORODIN.  CHORALE (FR &PRINCE 2GOR)                         P19
BORRIS, S.  LARGO & PRESTO, OP.92/4)                        F53
BOTTJE, W.G.  VARIATIONS & FUGUE                            A13
BOUTRY, R.  5 PIECES A QUATRE                               D36
BOZZA, E.  3 PIECES                                         D36
BRAHMS, J.-KING.  CHORALE PRELUDE #9 & FUGUE(REQUIEM)       D14
BRAHMS, J.-POTE.  CHORALE PRELUDE NO.8 (OPT TU)             D14
BRAHMS, J.-WILLIAMS.  2 CHORALES                            D14
BRAHMS, J.-SAUER.  MARIENLIEDER                             M79
BRAHMS, J.-WILLIAMS.  MOTET BY BRAHMS                       D14
BRIEGEL.  MORNING SONG & EVENING SONG                       A91
BRITAIN, B.  RECESSIONAL                                    N07
BROWN.  SCHERZI                                             G21
BROWN, K.(CMPL).  ALBUM OF 17 PIECES (2 VOI)                C91
BRUCKNER, A.-FRIEDMAN.  ADAGIO FR. SYMPHONY NO.7            B98
BRUCKNER, A.-KING.  INVENI DAVID                            D14
BRUCKNER, A.-ROSE.  6 TANTUM ERGO                           B44
BURGSTAHLER.  12 QUARTETS                                   E80
BUSCH, C.  MEDITATION                                       C11
BUTTS, C.M.  SUITE FOR TRBS                                 F43
BYRD, W.  PAVANA & GALLIARDA                                E00
CARLES, M.  LAMENTO ET MARCHE                               D36
CASSEL, GEARHART, HORNIBROOK.  BASS CLEF SESSIONS           F43
CATELINET, P.B.  DIVERTISSEMENTS                            C71
CATELINET, P.B.  3 PIECES                                   C71
CEELY, R.  SLIDE MUSIC                                      A13
CHAPMAN, R.E.  SUITE OF 3 CITIES                            E65
CHARPENTIER, J.  QUATUOR DE FORME LITURGIQUE                D36
CHRISTENSEN, J.-MC DUNN.  COMEDY FOR TROMBONES              D18
CLAPP, P.G.  CONCERT SUITE FOR 4 TROMBONES                  P23
COFIELD, F.D.  LIGHT FANTASIC                               F07
COHEN, J.  RONDO                                            G70
CONLEY, L.  COLLOQUY                                        D14
COSTA, M.-IRONS.  I WILL EXTOL THEE                         F07
CROCE.  RICERCAR                                            P19
CROCE, G.-DISHINGER.  MOTET FOR 4 VOICES                    N61
DANIELSSON.  LITTLE SUITE                                   B90
DARCY, R.  SUITE                                            D67
DE JONG, M.  SUITE, OP.100                                  B12
DEFAY, J.M.  4 PIECES                                       D36
DEWIT, A.-TAILMADGE.  DIANA                                 B53
DONDEYNE, D.  SUITE                                         F87
DONIZETTI, G.  POLIUTO                                      F54
DOYLE & COONS-BULLA.  SCARLET TREE                          D14
DUBOIS, P.M.  QUATUOR                                       D36
DUFAY, G.-KELLEHER.  GLORIA                                 B98
EVERTSE, J.(ARR).  2 PIECES                                 F81
```

FAULDS, J. (ARR). EXCERPTS FROM TCHAIKOVSKY   A78
FAULDS, J. (ARR). EXCERPTS FROM WAGNER   A78
FETTER, D.J. 2 TRANSCRIPTIONS   B98
FIRST DIVISION BAND COURSE. DANCE & PRAYER   A62
FIRST DIVISION BAND COURSE. GILBERT AND SULLIVAN   A62
FIRST DIVISION BAND COURSE. MARCH OF THE PRIESTS   A62
FIRST DIVISION BAND COURSE. TRUMPET VOLUNTARY   A62
FRACKENPOHL, A.R. QUARTET   B98
FRANCISQUE, A.-RAPH. SUITE FROM LE TRESOR D'ORPHEE B98
FRANCK, C.-STUBE. PANIS ANGELICUS   A62
FUSS, H. 25 ERNSTE & RELIGIOSE STUCKE   G43
GABRIELI, A. RECERCARE DEL DUODECIMO TONO. 3TRB, BTRB   B98
GABRIELI, A.-ANDERSON. 2 RICERCARS   M79
GABRIELI, G. SONATA   C91
GEARHART, CASSEL, & HORNIBROOK. BASS CLEF SESSIONS F43
GERVAISE, C.-MULLER. 3 DANCES   D67
GERVAISE, C.-SMELTEKOP. SUITE   F00
GLASSER, S. 3 DANCES   E14
GODARD, B.L.P.-HOLMES. ADAGIO PATHETIQUE   A55
GOOSSEN, F. EQUALI   F59
GOUNOD, C.F.-LOTZENHISER. MARCH OF A MARIONETTE   F07
GOW, D. SUITE   E14
GRIEG, E.H.-LIAN. LANDSIGHTING   G96
HANDEL, G.F.-MILLER. 4 HANDEL CHORALES   B98
HANDEL, G.F.-WILLIAMS. LARGO FROM XERXES   F60
HANDEL, G.F.-BEELER. WHERE'ER YOU WALK   F07
HARDT, V.H. LULLABY & DANCE   F79
HARTZELL, D. BALLAD FOR BONES   F74
HARTZELL, D. BEGUINE FOR BONES   F74
HARTZELL, D. BO(NE)SSA NOVA   F74
HARTZELL, D. BONES OF CONTENTION   F74
HARTZELL, D. BOUNCIN' BONES   F74
HARTZELL, D. OH! MY ACHING BONES   F74
HARTZELL, D. TIEMPOS AZULES   F74
HARTZELL, D. WAILIN' WALTZ   F74
HASSLER, L. TRIPTYCH   E80
HAUBIEL, C. CLASICI   A62
HAUBIEL, C. CONSTRUCTION NO.1   B38
HAUBIEL, C. MODERNI   A62
HAUBIEL, C. PROCESSIONAL   B38
HAUBIEL, C. PROCESSIONAL   G66
HAUBIEL, C. RECESSIONAL   B38
HAUBIEL, C. ROMANTICO   A62
HAYDN, J. ACHIEVED IS THE GLORIOUS (THE CREATION)   B98
HAYDN, J.-MILLER. ACHIEVED IS THE GLORIOUS WORK   B98
HAYDN, J.-JAMESON. 5 CANONS   G78
HAYDN, J.-JAMESON. 10 COMMANDMENT CANONS   G78
HEMEL, O.V. DONQUICHOTTERIE   B74
HOFFMANN, E.A. LITTLE SUITE   F60
HORNIBROOK, GEARHART, & CASSEL. BASS CLEF SESSIONS F43
HORNOFF, G.A. SUITE   G47
HURRELL, C.E. 2 CHORALES   A91
HURRELL, C.E. ETUDE   A91
HYDE. SUITE   G21
JACOB, G.P.S. SUITE   A78
JOHNSON, C.W. CRAGGED PASS   F07
JOHNSON, C.W. PILGRIM ODE   F07
JOHNSON, W.S. MARCHE TRIUMPHALE   A62
JOHNSON, W.S. PRELUDE SOLENNELE   C13
JOHNSON, W.S. VIKING SAGA, A   A62
JOHNSON, W.S. VIKING SAGA, A   A78
JORDAHL, R. 4 SHORT DANCES   D14

```
KING, R.D.(ARR).  24 EARLY GERMAN CHORALES                        D16
KOEPKE, P.  ELIGIE HEROIQUE                                       F07
KOEPKE, P.  SCHERZO CAPRICE                                       F07
LA VIOLETTE, W.  COBBLER'S SONG                                   A62
LA VIOLETTE, W.  FOREST                                           A62
LA VIOLETTE, W.  HAPPY ISLES                                      A62
LA VIOLETTE, W.  PARADE                                           A62
LA VIOLETTE, W.  PROMETHEUS                                       A62
LA VIOLETTE, W.  ROCK-BOUND COAST                                 A62
LANGLEY, J.W.  SUITE                                              C71
LAUDENSLAGER, H.  3 PRELUDES & FUGUES                             B44
LAUER.  SUITE                                                     P36
LULLY, J.B.-DOCKSTADER.  4 DANCES                                 G78
MAAS, A.-TALLMADGE.  2 GROSSE QUARTETTE                           B53
MAES, J.  FRAGMENT                                                D67
MANIET, R.  DIVERTIMENTO                                          D67
MARINI, B.-SMITH.  CANZONA, OP.8/3                                B98
MC CARTY, R.P.  RECITATIVE & FUGUE                                D16
MC KAY, F.H.  FESTIVAL MARCH                                      A55
MC KAY, F.H.  FESTIVAL PRELUDE                                    A55
MC KAY, F.H.  PAGEANT MARCH                                       A78
MC KAY, G.F.  ALLEGRO SCHERZOSO                                   A55
MENDELSSOHN, F.-WHITTMAN-VOXMAN.  EQUALE NC.2                     F07
MENDELSSOHN, F.-WHITTMAN-SMITH.  EQUALE NO.3                      D52
MENDELSSOHN, F.-AGOUNOFF.  HUNTER'S FAREWEIL, THE                 B85
MENDELSSOHN, F.-SMITH.  2 PIECES                                  E80
MEULEMANS, A.  SUITE                                              B12
MILLER.  COMING OF THE WARRIOR, THE                               G70
MILLER.  MAIN STREET                                              G70
MILLER, D.G.  2 TRANSCRIPTIONS                                    B98
MORALES-DIDRICKSON.  MAGNUM MYSTERIUM, O                          M92
MORLEY, T.-MYERS.  MY BONNIE LASS                                 B98
MORLEY, T.-MYERS.  NOW IS THE MONTH OF MAYING                     B98
MOZART, W.A.-JAMESON.  CANONS FOR EQUAL VOICES, K. 553            G78
MOZART, W.A.-JAMESON.  CANONS FOR EQUAL VOICES, K. 554            G78
MOZART, W.A.-JAMESON.  CANONS FOR EQUAL VOICES, K. 555            G78
MOZART, W.A.-JAMESON.  CANONS FOR EQUAL VOICES, K. 557            G78
MOZART, W.A.-SHUMWAY.  FUGUE, K.401                               B98
MOZART, W.A.-ROSE.  MENUETTO (QUARTET #21)                        B44
MOZART, W.A.-THILDE.  PRESTO                                      A71
MOZART, W.A.-STEIMAN.  SONATA ALLEGRO FR. SYM.NO.13              B98
MULLER, J.P.  CHORAL ET VARIATIONS                               D67
MULLER, R.  AUSGEWAHLTE QUARTETTE FUR 4 ZUGPOSAUNEN (3 VOL)      G43
MULLER, R.  QUARTETTES FOR 4 TRBS, BK.1                          B53
NELHYBEL, V.  3 ORGANA FOR TRB QUARTET                           B32
NELHYBEL, V.  6 PIECES FOR 4 TRB                                 C40
OLANDER, E.P.-FERGUSON.  FIRST SUITE                             F23
ORR, R.  5 SKETCHES                                              D16
OSTRANSKY, L.  DONNYBROOK                                        F07
OSTRANSKY, L.  2 EPISODES                                        F07
OSTRANSKY, L.  PRELUDE & GALLIARD                                F07
OTTEN, L.  SUITE                                                B74
PALESTRINA, G.P.-SCHAEFFER.  ARCADIA                            E80
PALESTRINA, G.P.-READ.  HYMN-IN FESTO TRANSFIGURATIONIS DOMINI  B32
PEDERSON, T.  BALMY BELLS                                        M93
PEDERSON, T.  CAT NIP                                            M93
PEDERSON, T.  GOPHER SERENADE                                    M93
PEDERSON, T.  HOLLYWOOD HILLS                                    M93
PEDERSON, T.  PICNIC BEAR, THE                                   M93
PEDERSON, T.  5 QUARTETS                                         M93
PEDERSON, T.  SENOR AT THE DOOR                                  M93
PEDERSON, T.  SILHOUETTES                                        M93
```

PEDERSON, T. SPANISH WATERWHEEL	M93
PEDERSON, T. TIGER TAIL	M93
PEDERSON, T. WINES & CHIMES	M93
PEETERS, F. SUITE, OP.82	E65
PFLEGER, C.-TALLMADGE. HERTZENBESANG, OP.5	B53
PONCE, J.-KELLEHER. AVE, COLOR VINI CLARI	B98
PORRET, J. GALILEE	D92
PORRET, J. HERCULE	D92
PRAETORIUS, M.-MYERS. 2 ANCIENT CAROLS	B98
PRAETORIUS, M.-AMMERBACH. 2 SIXTEENTH-CENTURY GERMAN DANCES	E00
PREMRU, R.E. IN MEMORIAM	B98
PREMRU, R.E. TISSINGTON VARIATIONS	E14
PRESSER, W.H. CHACONNE & MARCH	F80
PURCELL, H.-THILDE. HORNPIPE	A71
PURCELL, H.-THILDE. PRELUDE	A71
RACUSEN, D. CANONIC ETUDES	F43
RAKSIN, D.-CHALLIS. LAURA	A70
RAPH, A. BURLESQUE FOR TRB QUARTET	B44
RAPHLING, S. QUARTET FOR TRBS	A03
REICHE, G.-DOCKSTADER. FUGA II	G78
REICHE, G.-DOCKSTADER. FUGA IV	G78
REICHE, G.-DOCKSTADER. FUGA V	G78
REICHE, G.-DOCKSTADER. SONATINA I	G78
REICHE, G.-DOCKSTADER. SONATINA III	G78
REICHEL. 3 PIECES	A71
RIDDLE. IN MEMORIAM	G66
ROSENTAHL(ARR). SACRED MUSIC FOR 4 TRBS	G21
RUBANK(PUB). QUARTET REPERTOIRE FOR TRB	F07
RUEFF, J. 2 PIECES BREVES	D36
SAINT¬SAENS, C.-MURLEY. ADAGIO FR. SYM. NO.3	B98
SANDERS, R.L. SCHERZO & DIRGE	A38
SCHEIDT, S. 7 CHORALS	E00
SCHEIDT, S.-KING. DA JESUS AN DEM KREUZE STUND	D16
SCHEIN-FATCH. INTRADA	G78
SCHEIN, J.H.-SMELTEKOP. 10 CHORALS	E00
SCHEIN, J.H.-STONE. PADOUANA	A82
SCHUBERT, F.P.-ROWELL. SUITE OF LIEDER	B98
SCHUMANN, G. 3 MINIATURES	D36
SCHUMANN, R.-LAFOSSE. SCENES D'ENFANTS	A56
SCOTT, L.J.-GUENTZEL. ANNIE LAURIE	A55
SEMLER¬COLLERY, J. 2 PIECES	F87
SEROCKI, K. SUITE FOR 4 TRBS	A31
SEROCKI, K. SUITE FOR 4 TRBS	D63
SMELTEKOP. SIXTEENTH-CENTURY GERMAN DANCES	E00
SMELTEKOP (ARR). ELIZABETHAN SUITE	E00
SMITH. 2 PIECES	E80
SOLOMON. FIESTA	F60
SPEER, D.-BROWN. SONATA FOR 4 TRB W/PF.	C91
SPEER, D.-MILLER. SONATA	B98
STEIN, L. PRELUDE, CHORALE & FUGUE	E68
SULLIVAN, A.S.-STUBE. LOST CHORD	A62
TALMADGE, J.I. LEGEND	G31
TANNER, P. JUST BACH	G21
TANNER, P. STUDY IN TEXTURE, A	G21
TAVERNER, J.-FETTER. AUDIVI	B98
TCHAIKOVSKY, P.I. ANDANTE CANTABILE	A55
TCHEREPNIN, A.N. QUARTET #2	P19
TCHEREPNINE, N.N.-HARRIS. CHASSE, LA	B53
TELEMANN, G.P.-LUMSDEN. CONCERTO A 4	E14
TISNE, A. ODE	D36
TULL, F. CONCERT PIECE	M96
UBER, D.A. 3 MINIATURES, OP.29	B98

```
VAN VACTOR, D.  CONTRAPUNCTUS, CANONE ET FUGUE              P44
VICTORIA, T.I.D.-MOORE.  AVE MARIA                          M71
VIVALDI, A.-THILDE.  CONCERT                                A71
WAGNER, R.-EVERTSE.  PELGRIMSKOOR                           F81
WIENANDT.  3 FESTIVE PIECES                                 F60
WRIGHT, D.S.  AGE OF CHIVALRY, THE                          G16
WUORINEN, C.  CONSORT OF 4 TROMBONES                        A13
```

4 TUBAS

```
BALL, E.  QUARTET                                          F54
COOK.  INTRODUCTION AND RONDINO.  (ALL TREBLE CLEF)        C71
HEUSSENSTAMM, G.  TUBAFOUR                                 G66
PALESTRINA, G.P.  MOTET "CHRISTE, LUX VERA"                P19
PAYNE.  QUARTET                                            F43
PRESSER, W.H.  SERENADE                                    F80
RICHARDSON, N.  3 STATEMENTS                               F60
UBER, D.A.  SUITE, OP. 67                                  D14
```

4 MIXED BRASS (BRASS-PERC)

```
ABACO, E.F.-WELSHMAN.  DOLCE.  2TPT, TRB, TU               G78
ADAMS, S.  HOLY CITY, THE.  2TPT, TRB, TRB(HN)             A91
ADAMS, S.-LEMARC.  HOLY CITY, THE.  2TPT, HN(EU), TRB      F81
ADDISON, J.  DIVERTIMENTO, OP.9.  2TPT, HN, TRB            G26
ALBINONI, T.-DOCKSTADER.  ALLEGRO.  2TPT, TRB, TU(BTRB)    G78
ALBUM OF FRENCH PIECES.  2TPT, HN, TRB                     C91
AMELLER.  EPIGRAPH.  3TRB, TU                              D36
ANDRES, D.  QUATUOR.  2TPT, 2TRB                           A71
ANDRIESSEN, H.  AUBADE.  2TPT, HN, TRB                     B74
ANDRIESSEN, H.  SUITE.  2TPT, HN, TRB                      B74
ANDRIESSEN, J.  INTRODUZIONE E ALLEGRO.  2TPT, HN, TRB     B74
ANERIO.  CANZONA I.  2TPT, 2TRB                            P19
ANTEGNATI, C.  CANZONA 9.  2TPT, TRB(HN), TRB              E14
ANTEGNATI, C.  CANZONA 20.  2TPT, TRB(HN), TRB             E14
AREND, A.D.  KWARTET VOOR BLAASINSTRUMENTEN.  2TPT, TRB, EU   F81
ARENSKY, A.S.  CUCKOO, THE.  2TPT, TRB, EU, *PF            A91
AUBER, D.F.E.-HEKKER.  PRIERE.  2TPT, HN(EU), TRB          F81
BACH, J.S.-JOHNSON.  BACH CHORALES FOR BRASS.  4INST ?     F07
BACH, J.S.-BENOY.  BACH SUITE.  TPT, TRB(HN), TPT(HN), TRB    E51
BACH, J.S.-SCHAEFER.  BRASS FUGUE.  2TPT, 2TRB            E80
BACH, J.S.-KING.  22 CHORALES                             D16
   TPT, TRB(HN), EU(TRB, TU), TPT(HN)
BACH, J.S.-MULLER.  3 CHORALS.  3TPT, TRB                 D67
BACH, J.S.-PETIT.  3 CHORALS.  2TPT, HN(TRB), TRB         A71
BACH, J.S.  CONTRAPUNCTUS I (ART OF FUGUE).  TPT, HN, TRB, TU   B44
BACH, J.S.  CONTRAPUNCTUS I.  2TPT, 2TRB                  P19
BACH, J.S.-WALDECK.  CONTRAPUNCTUS I(ART OF FUGUE)        B44
   TPT, HN, TRB, TU
BACH, J.S.-CAILLIET.  FERVENT IS MY LONGING.  2TPT, 2TRB    A62
BACH, J.S.-MAYES.  6 FOUR-PART CHORALES.  2TPT, 2HN(2TRB)   C33
BACH, J.S.-SNIECKOWSKI.  5 FOUR-PART FUGUES.  2TPT, HN, TRB   E72
BACH, J.S.-SMIM.  FUGUE #14.  2TPT, 2TRB                  E14
BACH, J.S.-PETIT.  FUGUE IN D MAJOR.  2TPT, HN(TRB), TRB    A71
```

BACH, J.S.-TAYLOR.   FUGUE IN G MINOR.   2TPT, 2TRB   C09
BACH, J.S.-SIEBERT.   FUGUE NO.I, II & III.   2TPT, HN, EU   E59
BACH, J.S.   FUGUE NO.7.   2TPT, TRB, EU, *PF   A91
BACH, J.S.-SCHMIDT.   FUGUE V.   2TPT, 2TRB   G21
BACH, J.S.-IRONS.   GAVOTTE FR. THE 6TH SONATA   F07
  2TPT, TRB(HN), TRB
BACH, J.S.-DE FILIPPI.   MARCH, CHORALE & BOURREE   B91
  2TPT, HN, TRB
BACH, J.S.-KING.   MARCH, CHORALE & FUGUE   D16
  TPT, TRB(HN), EU-TU, TPT(HN)
BACH, J.S.   ORGAN PRELUDE & FUGUE FR WTC.   2TPT, HN, TRB   C91
BACH, J.S.-SIMON.   PRELUDE & FUGUE.   2TPT, 2TRB   D63
BACH, J.S.-CORLEY.   SARABANDE & MINUET.   2TPT, TRB-TU, TRB(HN)   D16
BACH, J.S.-KING.   VOM HIMMEL HOCH DA KOMM' ICH HER   D16
  2TPT, TRB-TU, TRB(HN)
BACH, J.S.-DISHINGER.   VON HIMMEL HOCH DA KOMM' ICH HER   N61
  2TPT, HN, TRB
BACH, K.P.E.-SIMON.   MARCH.   3TPT, TIMP   D63
BADINGS, H.   FRIESE TRIJE.   TPT, HN, TRB, EU   F81
BADINGS, H.   GELDERSE PEERDESPRONG.   TPT, TRB, EU, TPT(HN)   F81
BADINGS, H.   HOLLANDSE BOERENPLOF.   TPT, HN, TRB, EU   F81
BADINGS, H.   KOPERKWARTET.   2TPT, HN, TRB   B74
BADINGS, H.   3 NEDERLANDSE DANSE   B74
  2TPT(2BGL, 2CL), HN(SAX), TRB(TU, BSN, SAX)
BAKER (ARR).   LUTE DANCES.   2EU, 2TU   M80
BAKER (ARR).   LUTE DANCES.   2EU, 2TU   P42
BAKER, D.   HYMN & DEVIATIONS FOR BRASS QUARTET.   2TPT, TRB, TU   D94
BANCHIERI, A.-THOMAS.   CANZONAS-L'ALCENAGINA, LA BANCHIERIANA   E14
  2TPT, HN(TRB), TRB
BANCHIERI, A.-KING.   2 FANTASIAS   D16
  TPT, HN(TPT), TRB(HN), TRB(EU)
BANCHIERI, A.-CRABTREE.   L'ALCENAGINA.   INST ?   N47
BANCHIERI, A.-SMITH.   SINFONIA #13.   2TPT, HN(TRB), TRB   E80
BARGAGNI, O.-THOMAS.   CANZONA "LA MONTEVERDE"   E14
  2TPT, HN(TRB), TRB
BARRELL.   SUITE OP 21.   2TPT, 2TRB   E98
BARTOK, B.-STRATTON.   BARTOK FOR CHILDREN.   2TPT, HN, TRB   A78
BARTOK, B.-GORDON.   3 FOLK DANCES.   2TPT, HN(TRB), TRB   F60
BATH, E.   SUNSHINE & SHADE.   2TPT, HN, EU   F54
BAVICCHI, J.   QUARTET #1.   2TPT, 2TRB   E51
BEADELL, R.   3 SKETCHES.   2EU, 2TU   M80
BECKERATH, A.V.   WEIHNACHTS-SINFONIA.   TPT, HN, TRB, EU   C54
BEETHOVEN, L.V.-KAHN.   3 EQUALE.   TPT, 3TRE   D63
BEETHOVEN, L.V.-KING.   3 EQUALI   D16
  TPT, TPT(HN), TRB(HN), EU-TRB
BEETHOVEN, L.V.-FRAKER.   MINUET IN G.   4 INST ?   A51
BEETHOVEN, L.V.-CORLEY.   4TH MVT. FR. QUARTET OP 18/2   D16
  2TPT, TRB, EU
BELIEVE ME IF ALL THOSE ENDEARING YOUNG CHARMS.   A91
  2TPT, TRB, EU, *PF
BENDUSI-MOENKEMEYER.   OPERA NOVA DE BALLI.   2TPT, 2TRB   D90
BENOIST, A.-TALLMADGE.   FANTAISIE L'AMERIQUE.   2TPT, 2TRB   C11
BERGER, J.   INTRADA.   2TPT, TRB(HN), TRB   D16
BERGSMA, W.L.   SUITE.   2TPT(2COR), TRB, EU   C11
BERLIOZ, H.   CHORUS OF THE JUGGLERS.   2TPT, HN(TRB), TRB   B85
BERNSTEIN, L.   FANFARE FOR BIMA.   TPT, HN, TRB, TU   M66
BEVERSDORF, T.   3 EPITAPHS.   2TPT, TRB(HN), TRB   F60
BIERSACK.   KONZERTANTE MUSIK.   2TPT, HN, TRB   C75
BIZET, G.   AGNUS DEI.   2TPT, TRB, EU, (OPT PF)   A91
BLAAUW, L.   CONCERTINO.   TPT, HN(TPT), TRB, EU(HN)   F81
BLAAUW, L.   HUMORESKE.   TPT, TRB, EU, TPT(HN)   F81
BLAAUW, L.   KWARTET.   2TPT, HN(EU), EU   F81

```
BLAAUW, L.  ROMANCE.  TPT, TRB, EU                                   F81
BLANK, A.  BRASS QUARTET.  2TPT, 2TRB                                A13
BODA, J.  PRELUDE, SCHERZO,POSTLUDE.  2TPT, HN, TRB                  G83
BOEDIJN, G.H.  KWARTET NO.2, OP.111.  2TPT, HN, TRB                  B74
BOEDIJN, G.H.  KWARTET, OP.95.  2TPT, HN, TRB                        D92
BOGAR.  3 HUNGARIAN FOLKSONGS.  2TPT, HN, TRB                        B84
BOGAR.  3 MOVEMENTS.  2TPT, TRB, TU                                  B84
BOHM, K.-HAMILTON.  CALM AS THE NIGHT.  2TPT, TRB(EU), TRB           C33
BOKHOVE, J.J.A.  PRO MUSICA.  2TPT, HN(EU), TRB                      F81
BONONCINI, G.-DOCKSTADER.  MODERATO.  2TPT, 2TRB(TU)                 G78
BONONCINI, G.-DOCKSTADER.  PRESTO.  2TPT, 2TRB                       G78
BOROWSKI, F.  MORNING SONG, A.  2TPT, HN, TRB                        A78
BOTTJE, W.G.  INCOGNITOS.  2EU, 2TU                                  M80
BOYCE-DOCKSTADER.  SYMPHONY IV, OP. 2.  2TPT, TRB, TU(BTRB)          G78
BOZZA, E.  3 PIECES.  3TRB, TU                                       D36
BREHM, A.  QUARTET.  2TPT, HN, TRB                                   D63
BRIEGEL, G.F.  EARLY MORNING SERENADE.  2TPT, TRB(HN), TRB(EU)       A91
BRIEGEL, G.F.  IN THE DEEP CELLAR.  3TPT, TU(TRB)                    A91
BRIEGEL, G.F.  REQUIEM.  2TPT, TRB(HN), EU, (OPT PF)                 A91
BRIGHT, H.  LEGEND & CANON.  2TPT(2COR), HN(TRB), TRB                A38
BROEKHUIJSEN, H.(ARR).  'S MORGENS VROEG.  2TPT, HN(EU), TRB         D67
BROEKHUIJSEN, H.  GLORIFICATIE.  2TPT, HN(EU), TRB                   F81
BROEKHUIJSEN, H.  OP DE HEIDE.  2TPT, HN(EU), TRB                    F81
BRUCKNER, A.  LOCUS ISTE.  2TPT, HN, TRB                             M71
BRUCKNER, A.-MOORE.  LOCUS ISTE.  2TPT, HN, TRB                      G21
BRUCKNER, A.-GORDON.  PRAYER & ALLELUIA                              F60
     2TPT, HN(TRB), TRB, TIMP
BRUGK, H.M.  4 KLEINE TURMMUSIKEN FUR 4 BLASER.  2TPT, 2TRB          C54
BRULL, I.-LEMARC.  BOERENDANS.  2TPT, TRB, EU(HN)                    F81
BRUNA.  FANTASIA.  2TPT, 2TRB                                        P19
BUBUIS.  ACCLAMATION.  2TPT, 2TRB                                    A71
BUCHTEL, F.L.  CANZONETTA.  2TPT, HN(EU), TRB(EU)                    D18
BUCHTEL, F.L.  CHORALE & PROCESSIONAL MARCH                          D18
     2TPT, HN(TRB, EU), TRB(EU)
BUONAMENTE, G.B.-SHOEMAKER.  CANZONA A 4 #13                         N47
     2TPT, HN(TRB), TRB
BURGHAUSER.  OLD CZECH FANFARES.  2TPT, 2TRB, TIMP                   A33
BURGON.  FANFARES & VARIANTS.  2TPT, 2TRB                            F65
BURGON.  5 STUDIES.  2TPT, 2TRB                                      B20
BURGON, G.  DIVERTIMENTO.  2TPT, HN, TRB                             B20
BURNETT.  SUITE BLAEN MAWRDIN.  2TPT, 2TRB                           E98
BUSCH, C.  SPRING IS HERE.  2TPT, TRB, EU                            B53
BUSCH, C.  TWILIGHT MEDITATION.  2TPT, TRB, EU                       C11
BUTTERWORTH.  4 MOTETS FOR BRASS.  2TPT, HN, TRB                     B20
BUTTERWORTH (ED).  NOBLE ERA, THE.  2TPT, HN, TRB                    B20
BUTTERWORTH, D.N.  SCHERZO (ALL PARTS IN TC).  2TPT, HN, TRB         C71
BUTTERWORTH, D.N.(ARR).  TUDOR SUITE FOR WIND INSTR.                 B20
     2TPT, HN, TRB(TU)
BUTTERWORTH, D.N.(ARR).  3 16TH CENTURY MOTETS                       E33
     2TPT, HN(TRB), TRB(TU)
BUTTS.  MARCH & CHORALE.  2TRB, EU(TU), TU                           F80
BYRD.  PIECE.  TPT, HN, 2TRB                                         N61
BYRD, W.  MEDLEY, A.  2TPT, 2TRB                                     E00
BYRD, W.-DISHINGER.  PIECE FOR BRASS.  TPT, HN, 2TRB                 N61
CABANILLES.  CORRENTE-FANTASIA.  2TPT, 2TRB                          P19
CABUS, P.N.  LENTO.  2TPT, 2TRB                                      D67
CAFARELLA, A.  MARCH, OP.62/1.  2TPT, 2TRB                           G31
CAILLIET, L.(ARR).  COLUMBIA THE GEM OF THE OCEAN.  2TPT, 2TRB       A62
CAILLIET, L.(ARR).  DEEP RIVER.  2TPT, 2TRB                          A62
CALABRO.  CEREMONIAL MARCH.  2TPT, 2TRB, PERC                        B92
CAMPRA, A.-KING.  RIGAUDON.  2TPT, TRB(HN), EU-TU                    D16
CARLE, R.-WHEELER.  ENCHANTMENT.  2TPT, 2TRB                         G10
```

```
CATELINET, P.B.  DIVERTISSEMENTS.  2TRB, TRB(HN), BTRB(TU)       C71
CAURROY, DE-MAGANINI.  LAMENT.  2TPT, 2HN                        B85
CAVACCIO, G.  2 CANZONAS.  2TPT, TRB, TRB(HN)                    E14
CAZDEN, N.  3 DIRECTIONS, OP.39.  2TPT, TRB, EU(TRB)             A38
CEULEMANS, I.  SUITE.  2TPT, HN, TRB                             D67
CHAILLEY.  SUITE DU XV SIECLE.  2TPT, HN, TRB                    D36
CHASE, A.H.  QUARTET NO.1 FOR BRASS.  2TPT, HN(TRB), TRB         B44
CHILESE, B.  CANZONA NO.22.  2TPT, TRB(HN), TRB                  E14
CHOPIN, F.  ANDANTINO FR. BALLAD & PRELUDE.  2TPT, TRB, EU       G10
CHOPIN, F.  POLONAISE MILITAIRE.  2TPT, 2TRB                     C33
CHOPIN, F.-FRANCK.  POLONAISE MILITAIRE.  2TPT, 2TPT(2TRB)       C33
CHRISTMAS CAROLS (3 VOL).  2TPT, TRB, EU, (OPT PF)               A91
CHRISTOPHE, J.  4 QUATORS.  2TPT, TRB, EU                        F81
CLARK, A.  HOEDOWN SHOWDOWN.  2TPT, 2TRB                         N32
CLARK, F.J.  ST.HUBERT'S HUNTING SONG.  3TPT, EU                 B85
CLEMENT (ARR).  NOVELTY BRASS QUARTET LIBRARY (3 VOL)            G10
     TPT(TRB), TPT(TRB), TRB(TPT, HN), TRB(TPT)-TU
COHEN, J.  RONDO.  3TRB, EU                                      B52
COHEN, S.B.  HOLIDAY FOR BRASS.  2TPT, HN, TRB                   F62
COHEN, S.B.  MARCHING MEN.  2TPT, HN, TRB                        F62
COHEN, S.B.  QUARTET FOR BRASS INSTR..  2TPT, HN, TRB            A62
COLE, G.  7 IMPRESSIONS.  3TRB, EU(TU)                           A38
CONE, E.T.  VARIATIONS ON A FAN-FAIR.  2TPT, 2HN                 D63
CONLEY, J.  3 EARLY SACRED PIECES.  2TPT, HN, TRB               M73
CONLEY, J.(ARR).  3 EARLY SACRED PIECES.  2TPT, HN, TRB          G21
CONLEY, L.  CONCERT POLKA.  2TPT, 2TRB                           D14
CORELLI, A.  ADAGIO & PASTORALE.  2TPT, HN, TRB                  C91
CORELLI, A.-ZABEL.  2 PIECES.  2TPT, HN, TRB                     C91
COSCIA, S.  CONCERT SUITE.  3HN, TRB                             N95
COSTELEY, G.-KEENAN.  CHANSON.  2TPT, TRB(HN), TRB               E80
COUPERIN, F.-KING.  FUGUE ON THE KYRIE                           D16
     TPT, TRB, TPT(HN), TRB-TU
COUPERIN, F.-KING.  2 PIECES.  2TPT, HN(TRB), TRB-TU             D16
COUPERIN, L.  SARABANDE & CARILLON.  2TPT, TRB(HN), TRB-TU       D16
COX, H.  2 HYMNES.  2TPT, TRB(HN), TRB                           D67
CRAWFORD, J.  RITORNELLO.  2TPT, 2TRB                            E68
CREUSOT-PETIT.  POCHADE.  2TPT, HN(TRB), TRB                     A71
CROCE.  CANZONA I.  2TPT, 2TRB                                   P19
CRUFT, A.F.  4 ENGLISH KEYBOARD PIECES.  2TPT, HN, TRB           G26
CUNDELL, E.  2 PIECES.  2TPT, HN, TRB                            G26
DAEMS, H.  GRIEKSE SUITE.  2TPT, HN, TRB                         D67
DANIELSSON.  LITTLE SUITE.  HN(TRB), 2TRB, TU(TRB)               B90
DE BOECK, M.  BOUFFON, LE-DE HOFMAR.  2TPT, HN, TRB(TU)          F21
DE FILIPPI, A.  SUITE.  2TPT, HN, TRB                            B91
DE JONG, C.  GRAB BAG.  2EU, 2TU                                 M80
DE SCHRIJVER.  DRIEDELIGE-SUITE.  2TPT, 2TRB                     F81
DE SCHRIJVER.  VIERDELIGE SUITE.  2TPT, HN(TPT), TRB             B91
DEDRICK, A.  3 HYMNS.  2TPT, 2TRB                                D14
DEDRICK, A.  WALTZ FOR 4.  2TPT, 2TRB                            D14
DEEP RIVER.  2TPT, TRB(HN), EU, (OPT PF)                         A91
DELIBES, L.-SIEBERT.  DANSE HONGROISE.  2TPT, HN, EU             E59
DEMPSTER, S.  QUARTET, OP.3/1.  2TPT, TRB, BTRB                  B98
DES PREZ, J.  MOTET & ROYAL FANFARE                             D16
     TPT, TRB(HN), TU-TRB, TPT(HN)
DESPRES, J.-SHOEMAKER.  VIVE LE ROY.  INST ?                     N47
DESPREZ, F.  DIVERTISSEMENT.  3TPT, TRB, (OPT PERC)              D67
DESPREZ, F.  JEUNESSE.  3TPT, TRB, (OPT PERC)                    D67
DIERCKS, J.  QUARTET.  2TPT, HN, TRB                             F80
DILLON, R.M.  MARCH & CHORALE.  3TPT, TRB(TPT)                   A78
DISHINGER, R.  HAVAH NAGILAH.  TPT, HN, 2TRB                     N61
DONAHUE.  5 PIECES.  2TPT, 2TRB                                  F80
DONATI & SCANDELLUS.  LENTO & ANDANTE.  2TPT, TRB, TU(BTRB)      G78
```

DONATO, A. SUITE FOR BRASS. 2TPT, HN, TRB   G70
DORSEY. BRASS MUSIC I. 2TPT, TRB, TU(TRB)   E00
DORSEY. BRASS MUSIC II. 2TPT, TRB, TU(TRB)   E00
DUBENSKY, A. CONCERTO GROSSO. 3TRB, TU(TRB), (OPT *ORCH)   E98
DUBOIS. MUSICA PER QUATTRO. 2TPT, HN, TRB   E65
DUBOIS, P.M. CINEMA MUET, LE. TPT, HN, TRB, TU   D36
DUBOIS, P.M. ILLUSTRATIONS. 2TPT, HN, TRB   D36
DUFAY. AGNUS DEI. TPT, HN, 2TRB   N61
DUFAY-KLAUSS. ET IN TERRA "AD MODUM TUBE". 2TPT, 2TRB, TIMP   F79
DUFAY, G.-DISHINGER. AGNUS DEI. TPT, HN, 2TRB   N61
DZHERBASHYAN. SCHERZO. 2TPT, HN, TRB   P19
EBERLIN-KLEIN. FUGUE 1. 2TPT, 2TRB(HN)   G78
EBERLIN-BARNES. TOCCATA & FUGUE #8. 2TPT, 2TRB   D14
EBERLIN, J.E.-BARNES. TOCCATTA & FUGUE NO.3. 2TPT, 2TRB   F79
EDMONDSON. HYMN AND BATTLE SONG. 2TPT, HN, TRB(EU)   D14
EHMANN, W.(CMPL). ALTE SPIELMUSIK FUR BLASER. 4INST ?   A51
EHMANN, W. BLASER-INTRADEN ZUM WOCHLIED FUR 4-6 BLASERCH.   A51
  4 INST?
ELGAR, E.W.-LEMARC. LAND OF HOPE & GLORY. 2TPT, HN, TRB   F81
EVERTSE, J.(ARR). CANON. 2TPT, HN(EU), EU   F81
EVERTSE, J.(ARR). CHANSON. 2TPT, HN(EU), EU   F81
EVERTSE, J.(ARR). KYRIE. TPT, HN, TRB, EU   F81
EVERTSE, J.(ARR). REGINA COELI. 2TPT, HN(EU), EU   F81
EVERTSE, J.(ARR). RESURREXIT. 2TPT, 2EU   F81
FARNABY, G.-SMELTEKOP. FARNABY SUITE. 2TPT, 2TRB   E00
FELDERHOF, J. DIVERTIMENTO. 2TPT, HN, TRB   B74
FELDSHER, H. LITTLE SUITE FOR BRASS QUARTET   F79
  2TPT, HN(TRB), TRB
FILIPPI, DE. QUADRIVIUM. 2TPT, HN, TRB   C40
FILIPPI, DE. SUITE. 2TPT, HN, TRB   B91
FINDLAY, F.M.(CMPL). BRASS CHOIR SERIES FCR JR.GROUPS   B53
  TPT, HN(TRB), TRB-TU, TPT(HN)
FIRST DIVISION BAND COURSE. ALLELUIA. 4 INST?   A62
FIRST DIVISION BAND COURSE. BLUE FLAME. 4INST ?   A62
FIRST DIVISION BAND COURSE. IRISH KISS. 4INST ?   A62
FIRST DIVISION BAND COURSE. MOTHER GOOFS. 4 INST?   A62
FISCHER-FRENCH. DER TAG, DER IST SO FREUDENREICH   F60
  2TPT(HN), 2TRB(HN)
FISCHER, J.-KLEIN. FUGA 1 & 2. 2TPT, 2TRB   G78
FISCHER, J.-KLEIN. FUGA 3 & 4. 2TPT, TRB, TU   G78
FISCHER, J.-KLEIN. FUGA 5 & 6. 2TPT, 2TRB   G78
FISCHER, J.-KLEIN. FUGA. 2TPT, 2TRB   G78
FISCHER, J.-MOORE. 2 MARCHES FOR BRASS QUARTET. 2TPT, 2TRB   G21
FISCHER, J. 2 MARCHES. 2TPT, 2TRB   M71
FISCHER, J.-SCHWADRON. 2 PIECES. 2TPT, HN, TRB   E83
FITZGERALD, R.B. ANDANTE CANTABILE. 2TPT, HN(TRB), TRB   A62
FITZGERALD, R.B. LENTO. 2TPT, HN(TRB), TRB   A62
FITZGERALD, R.B.-KRONE. PRO-ART EMSEMBLE SERIES (2 VOL)   C13
  2TPT, HN, TRB
FITZGERALD, R.B. TARANTELLA. 2TPT, HN, TRB   A62
FORESTIER, J.J. SYMPHONIC QUARTET. 2TPT, HN(TRB), TRB   B85
FORESTIER, J.J. TIRANNA. 2TPT, HN(TRB), TRB   B85
FOURMY. QUATUOR. 2TPT, HN, TRB   D67
FRACKENPOHL, A.R. POP SUITE. 2EU, 2TU   D14
FRACKENPOHL, A.R. QUARTET. 2TPT, TRB, EU(TRB)   D16
FRANCESCO. TU DISOIS. 2TPT, HN, TRB   E80
FRANCK-PETIT. PIECE INSTRUMENTALE. 2TPT, HN(TRB), TRB   A71
FRANCK, C. PANIS ANGELICUS. 2TPT, TRB, EU, (OPT *PF)   A91
FRANCK, C.-LEMARC. PANIS ANGELICUS. 2TPT, HN(TRB), EU   F81
FRANCK, C.-SIEBERT. SCHERZO FR. STRING QUARTET IN D MAJOR   E59
  2TPT, HN, EU
FRANCO, J. BRASS QUARTET. 2TPT, HN, TU   E68

```
FRANCO, J.  CHORALE & CONTEMPLATION.  2TPT, HN, TRB              E68
FRANCO, J.  QUARTET.  2TPT, HN, TU                              A13
FRANGKISER, C.  ROMANCE.  2TPT, 2TRB                            A62
FRESCOBALDI, G.-SMITH.  CANZON SESTA A 4.  2TPT, HN(TRB), TRB   E80
FRESCOBALDI, G.-SMITH.  CANZON TERZA.  2TPT, TRB, TRB(HN)       D14
FRESCOBALDI, G.  CANZONA QUARTA.  2TPT, 2TRB                    D92
FRESCOBALDI, G.  CANZONAS NO.13 & 21.  2TPT, TRB(HN), TRB       E14
FRESCOBALDI, G.-SCHWADRON.  CANZONE DOPO L'EPISTOLA             D14
   2TPT, 2TRB
FRESCOBALDI, G.-PETIT.  CAPRICE SUR LE CHANT DU COUCOU          A71
   2TPT, HN(TRB), TRB
FRESCOBALDI, G.-AARON.  GAGLIARDA.  2TPT, TRB, EU               F23
FRESCOBALDI, G.-CICHOWICZ.  GALLIARD & FUGUE                    M92
   2TPT, HN(TRB), TRB
FRESCOBALDI, G.-MOORE.  TOCCATA FOR BRASS QUARTET               G21
   2TPT, HN, TRB
FRESCOBALDI, G.  TOCCATA.  2TPT, HN, TRB                        M71
FROBERGER.  CAPRICCIO.  2TPT, HN(TRB), TRB                      N61
GABRIELI, A.  CANZONA NO.1.  2TPT, 2TRB                         E14
GABRIELI, A.  CANZONA NO.2.  2TPT, 2TRB                         E14
GABRIELI, A.  CANZONA NO.3.  2TPT, 2TRB                         E14
GABRIELI, A.  CANZONA NO.4.  2TPT, 2TRB                         E14
GABRIELI, A.-LUMSDEN.  RICERCAR DEL DUODECIMO TONI              E14
   TPT, TPT(HN), 2TRB
GABRIELI, A.-KING.  RICERCAR DEL DUODECIMO TUONO                D16
   2TPT(HN), 2TRB(HN)
GABRIELI, A.-LUMSDEN.  RICERCAR DEL SESTO TUONO                 E14
   TPT, TRB(HN), TPT(HN), TRB
GABRIELI, A.-SMITH.  RICERCAR.  3TPT, TRB                       B85
GABRIELI, A.-WALDECK.  3 RICERCARI.  2TPT, TRB, TU              B44
GABRIELI, G.-KING.  CANZONA PER SONARE #2                       D16
   TPT, HN(TRB), TRB(EU)
GABRIELI, G.  CANZONA PER SONARE NO.1.  2TPT, HN(TRB), EU-TRB   D16
GABRIELI, G.-KING.  CANZONA PER SONARE NO.3                     D16
   2TPT, HN(TRB), TRB(EU)
GABRIELI, G.-KING.  CANZONA PER SONARE NO.4                     D16
   2TPT, HN(TRB), TRB(EU)
GABRIELI, G.  CANZONI 1 & 2, 3 & 4.  2TPT, TRB(HN), TRB         E14
GABRIELI, G.-SMITH.  RICERCAR.  2TPT, HN(TRB), TRB              B85
GALLUS.  CANZONA I.  2TPT, 2TRB                                 P19
GALLUS.  CANZONA II.  2TPT, 2TRB                                P19
GARDNER, J.L.  THEME & VARIATIONS, OP.7.  2TPT, HN, TRB         E51
GARLICK, A.  ESSAY.  2TPT, HN, TU                               G66
GARLICK, A.  SUITE.  TPT, 2HN, TRB                              G66
GARRETT, J.A.  MYSTICAL MUSIC.  2EU, 2TU                        M80
GASSMANN, A.I.  SCHWEIZER QUARTETTE (35 QUARTETS)               C80
   EU, 2FLG, BARYTON
GAULT, G.C.  FRAGMENTS FR. STEPHEN FOSTER.  3TPT, TRB           H06
GAULT, G.C.  MELANGE.  3TPT, TRB                                H06
GENZMER, H.  MUSIK.  2TPT, 2TRB                                 E65
GERAEDTS, J.  KLEINE KOPERMUZIEK.  2TPT, HN, TRB                B74
GERIE, H.-WALDECK.  GAILLARDE & FUGUE.  TPT, HN, TRB, TU        B44
GERVAISE, C.-PETIT.  6 BRANLES.  2TPT, HN(TRB), TRB             A71
GIBBONS, O.  CORNET VOLUNTARY.  3TPT, EU                        B85
GILSON, P.  QUATUOR.  2TPT, 2TRB                                F81
GIUAMI, G.  CANZONAS NO.6 & 19.  2TPT, TRB(HN), TRB             E14
GLAZEL, J.  SIXTEENTH CENTURY CARMINA.  2TPT, HN, TRB(EU)       B15
GLAZUNOV, A.K.  IN MODO RELIGIOSO.  TPT, HN, 2TRB               C91
GLAZUNOV, A.K.  IN MODO RELIGIOSO                               D16
   TPT, HN(TPT), TRB(HN), TU-TRB
GLAZUNOV, A.K.-KAHN.  IN MODO RELIGIOSO, OP.38.  TPT, HN, 2TRB  D63
GLAZUNOV, A.K.-VOXMAN.  IN MODO RELIGIOSO.  TPT, HN, TRB, BTRB  F07
```

```
GLUCK, C.W.-PETIT.  MARCHE RELIGIEUSE D'ALCESTE                A71
   2TPT, HN(TRB), TRB
GOLDSTEIN, A.E. (CMPL).  FIRST BOOK OF BRASS QUARTETS, A       B44
   TPT,HN(TRB), TRB(TU), TPT(HN)
GORDON (ED).  4 CENTURIES FOR BRASS.  2TPT, HN(TRB), TRB       C11
GOULD, M.  SUITE.  3HN, TU                                     N01
GOUNOD, C.F.  MARCHE PONTIFICALE.  2TPT, TRB(HN), EU, *PF      A91
GOUNOD, C.F.-LEHRER.  SOLDIER'S CHORUS FR. FAUST.  2TPT, 2TRB  C09
GRAHN.  3 SKISSER.  2TPT, HN, TRB                             G66
GRANT, P.  BREVITIES, SUITE NO.3,OP.44.  2TPT, HN, TRB        E68
GRANT, P.  EXCURSIONS, SUITE NO.2,OP.38.  2TPT, HN, TRB       E68
GRANT, P.  LACONIC SUITE, SUITE NO.1,OP.31.  2TPT, HN, TRB    E68
GRESHAM.  4 CANZONAS.  2TPT, HN(TRB), TRB                     B40
GRETCHANINOFF-LESTER.  SUITE.  TPT, 2HN, TRB                  G21
GRIEG, E.H.-GORDON.  ALBUM LEAF.  2TPT, HN(TRB), TRB          D14
GRIEG, E.H.  ASE'S DEATH.  2TPT, TRB, EU, (OPT *PF)           A91
GRIEG, E.H.  WATCHMAN'S SONG & LYRICAL PIECES.  2TPT, TRB, EU G10
GRILLO, G.B.  CANZONA 16.  2TPT, TRB(HN), TRB                 E14
GRILLO, G.B.  CANZONAS NO.14 & 15.  2TPT, TRB(HN), TRB        E14
GUAMI, G.-CRABTREE.  CANZON A 4 #3.  2TPT, HN(TRB), TRB       N47
GUAMI, G.-BLOCK.  CANZON 17.  2TPT, TRB(HN), TRB              E14
GUAMI, G.-BLOCK.  CANZONA #6.  2TPT, TRB(HN), TRB             E14
GUAMI, G.-CRABTREE.  GRAVE, LA.  2TPT, HN(TRB), TRB           F60
GUAMI, G.-CRABTREE.  GRAVE, LA.  INST?                        N47
GUAMI, G.  GUAMINA, LA (1596).  2TPT, HN(TRB), TRB            E14
GUAMI, G.  GUAMINA, LA.  2TPT, HN(TRB), TRB                   F60
GUAMI, G.-CRABTREE.  GUAMINA, LA.  INST ?                     N47
GUAMI, G.-THOMAS.  GUAMINA, LA.  2TPT, HN(TRB), TRB           E14
GUENTZEL, G.  IMPROMPTU.  2TPT, HN, EU                        A55
GUERRERO.  MOTET.  2TPT, 2TRB                                 E80
HABICHT.  DIVERTIMENTO.  3TPT, TRB                            C75
HADDAD, D.  QUARTET.  2TPT, HN, TRB                           F43
HAHN.  QUARTETT-MINIATUREN.  2TPT, 2TRB(HN)                   D98
HAINES, E.  TOCCATA.  2TPT, TRB(HN), TRB                      D16
HANDEL, G.F.  BOURREE & MINUET FR. THE FIREWORKS MUSIC        D16
   2TPT, TRB(HN), TU-TRB
HANDEL, G.F.-AARON.  CHACONNE.  2TPT, TRB, EU                 F23
HANDEL, G.F.  DANCE SUITE.  2TPT, 2TRB                        N42
HANDEL, G.F.-KNIGHT.  HANDEL FOR BRASS.  2TPT, 2TRB           F84
HANDEL, G.F.-WILLIAMS.  LARGO FROM XERXES.  4INST ?           F60
HANDEL, G.F.-KING.  MARCH & GAVOTTE                           D16
   TPT, TPB(HN), TU-TRB, TPT(HN)
HANDEL, G.F.-GORDON.  SARABANDE.  2TPT, HN(TRB), TRB          F60
HARDT, V.H.  LULLABY & DANCE.  2HN, TRB, TU                   F79
HARTLEY, W.S.  SOLEMN MUSIC.  2TPT(HN), TRB(HN), EU(TRB)      F88
HASLAM.  ANTIMASQUE.  2TPT, 2TRB                              E77
HASSLER, L.  AGNUS DEI.  TPT, HN, 2TRB                        N61
HASSLER, L.-DISHINGER.  AGNUS DEI.  TPT, HN, 2TRB             N61
HASSLER, L.-DISHINGER.  GLORIA.  TPT, HN, 2TRB                N61
HAUSDOERFER, F.  BOERENDANS.  4INST ?                         D92
HAUSDOERFER, F.  NAPOLITAANSE SERENADE.  4INST ?              D92
HAWTHORNE-BAKER.  WHISPERING HOPE.  2TPT, TRB, EU, *PF        A91
HAYDN, J.-BENNETT.  FUGUE & ALLEGRO VIVACE, OP. 34            M91
   2TPT, 2TRB
HAYDN, J.-KING.  MENUETT FR. QUARTET OP.76/3                  D16
   2TPT, HN(TRB), TRB
HAYDN, J.-STRAUWEN.  QUATUOR.  4INST ?                        F21
HEISS, H.  TROMPETENMUSIK.  2TPT, TRB, BTRB(TRB)              A90
HELDENBERG, A.  QUARTET, OP. 7.  2TPT,HN(ASAX), TRB(TU)       A96
HEMEL, O.V.  4 KOPERKWARTETTEN.  2TPT, HN, TRB                B74
HENRY, M.E.  MOVEMENT FOR BRASS QUARTET.  2TPT, HN, TRB       B35
HERING, S. (CMPL).  EARLY CLASSICS FOR BRASS ENSEMBLES        C11
   2TPT, HN, TRB
```

HEWITT, H. BRASS QUARTET #2. 2TPT, TRB, TU	P48
HINDEMITH, P. MORGENMUSIK. 2TPT, HN(TRB), TRB(HN)-TU	F31
HOGG, M.E. TOCCATA FOR BRASS QUARTET. 2TPT, HN, TRB	B35
HOLLINGWORTH. NATIVE VALE. 2TPT, HN, EU	F54
HORSCH. SUITE #2. 2TPT, 2TRB	F31
HOSKINS, W.B. SONATA. 2TPT, HN, TRB	A13
HOVHANESS, A.S. CANZONA & FUGUE. 2TPT, HN, TRB	E65
HOVHANESS, A.S. FANTASY #4. 2TPT, HN, TRB	E65
HOVHANESS, A.S. FANTASY #5. 2TPT, HN, TRB	F65
HOVHANESS, A.S. SHARAGAN & FUGUE	D16
2TPT, HN(TPT, TRB), TRB(EU), -TU	
HUG, V. INTRADE & FUGUE. 2TPT, 2TRB	F10
HUME, J.O. INSPIRATION. 2TPT, 2TRB	C11
HUME, J.O. RUSTIC BEAUTY. 2TPT, 2TRB	C11
HUMPERDINCK, E.-FINDLEY. PRAYER FROM OPERA HANSEL & GRETEL	B53
4INST ?	
HUTCHINSON, T. TUBA JUBA DANCE. 2EU, 2TU	M80
HUTCHINSON, T. TUBA JUBA DUBA. 2EU, 2TU	P42
IANNACCONE, A. ANAMORPHOSIS. 2TPT, TRB, PERC	G66
IANNACCONE, A. 3 MYTHICAL SKETCHES. 2TPT, HN, TRB	F80
ISAAC, H.-WALDECK. CANZONA. 2TPT, TRB, TU	B44
JACOB, G.P.S. SCHERZO. 2TPT, HN, TRB	G26
JAKMA, F. (ARR). 8 BEROEMDE MELODIEN (2 VOL). 2TPT, TRB, EU	F81
JAKMA, F. HYMNE TRIOMPHALE. 4INST ?	D92
JAMES. QUARTET. 2TPT, HN(TRB), TRB	P39
JANETZKY, K.(CMPL). JAGERSTUCKLEIN	C75
JANETZKY, K. MUSIK. 2TPT, 2TRB	B69
JARZEBSKI, A. 4 CANZONI. 2TPT, 2TRB	A71
JENSEN, J. 3 MOVEMENTS FOR BRASS QUARTET. 2TPT, TRB, BTRB	B35
JOHNSON, C.W. CAPRICE IN G MINOR. 2TPT, TRB, EU	F07
JONES, E. SORIANO MARCH. 2TPT, 2TRB	G66
JOSQUIN. MOTET & ROYAL FANFARE. TPT, HN(TPT), TRB(HN), TRB	D14
JUNG. SUITE, OP. 5. 2TPT, HN, TRB	B69
KABALEVSKY, D.B. 2 DANCES. 2TPT, 2TRB	G21
KABALEVSKY, D.B.-LESTER. 2 PIECES. 2TPT, 2TRB, OPT SDR	P54
KAY, U.S. BRASS QUARTET. 2TPT, TRB, BTRB(TRB)	E61
KAYSER, L. VARIAZIONI SOPRA "IN DULCI JUBILO"	B34
TPT, HN, TRB, TU	
KEITH, G.D. 4 NURSERY RHYMES. 2TPT, 2EU(2HN)	H06
KELLER, H.I. QUARTET. 2TPT, HN, TRB	D16
KEMP, D.E.(ARR). 4 BRASS FOR CHRISTMAS. 2TPT, HN, EU	G27
KEMP, D.E.(ARR). CHRISTMAS IN BRASS. 2TPT, HN, EU	G27
KEMP, D.E.(ARR). EASTER IN BRASS. 2TPT, HN, EU	G27
KEMPTON. DIMENSIONS IN BRASS. 2TPT, 2TRB(HN)	D14
KERRY. FANFARE & MARCH. 2TPT, HN, TRB	B20
KESNAR, M. INTERMEZZO. 2TPT, HN, TRB	E77
KETTING, O. SONATE. 2TPT, HN, TRB	B74
KING, R.D. 3 NEW ENGLAND HYMNS	D16
TPT, HN(TPT), TRB(HN), EU(TU)	
KING, R.D. (CMPL). REFORMATION CHORALES	D16
TPT, TPT(HN), TRB(HN), EU-TU	
KIRNBERGER, F.-DISHINGER. GAVOTTE. 2TPT, HN, TRB	N61
KLEIN, J. SONATA. 2TPT, 2TRB	A38
KLEMM, G. AT THE CONSOLE. 2TPT, TRB, EU	A78
KNELLWOLF, J.B. QUARTETTE. EU, 2FLG, BAR	C80
KNIGHT, M. BRASS QUARTET NO.1. 2TPT, 2TRB	F88
KNIGHT, M. BRASS QUARTET NO.2. 2TPT, 2TRB	F88
KNIGHT, M. BRASS QUARTET NO.3. 2TPT, 2TRB	F88
KNIGHT, M. 6 BRASS QUARTETS. 2TPT, 2TRB	F80
KNOX, C. SOLO FOR TPT WITH BRASS TRIO(OR PA.). 2TPT, HN, TRB	G83
KNOX, C. SOLO FOR TUBA WITH BRASS TRIO. TPT, HN, TRB, TU	F80
KOELL. TURMQUARTET I & II. 2TPT, 2TRB	D98

KOETSIER, J.   KLEINE SUITE, OP.33/1B.   2TPT, 2TRB   B74
KOETSIER, J.   PETITE SUITE, OP.33/1A.   2TPT, HN, TRB   B74
KOETSIER, J.   QUARTETTINO, OP.33/2.   2TPT, HN, TRB   B74
KOMZAK-SHOEMAKER.   CZECH. FOLKSONG AND MARCH.   INST?   N47
KOMZAK.   CZECHOSLOVAKIAN FOLKSONG & MARCH.   2TPT, 2TRB   N47
KOUSEMAKER, A.   SONATINE VOOR KOPERKWARTET.   2TPT, TRB, EU   F81
KRAPF, G.   CHORALE INTRADAS (2 VOL).   2TPT, 2TRB   B40
KREISLER, A.V.   CONCERT PIECE.   2TPT, HN, TRB   F60
KREISLER, A.V.   MUSIC FOR BRASS QUARTET.   2TPT, HN, TRB   F60
KREMER.   3 APHORISMEN.   2TPT, 2TRB   A80
KRONE, M.T. & FITZGERALD.   PRO-ART ENSEMBLE SERIES   C13
   2TPT, HN, TRB
KUDO, E.T.   MUSIC FOR BRASS.   2TPT, 2TRB   B35
KUHNAU.   ALLEGRO.   2TPT, 2TRB   N61
KUHNAU, J.-DISHINGER.   ALLEGRO FOR BRASS.   TPT, HN, 2TRB   N61
KUPFERMAN.   MADRIGAL.   2TPT, 2TRB   C40
LALANDE, M.R.D.-PETIT.   FANFARE.   2TPT, HN(TRB), TRB   A71
LANDRE, G.   QUARTETTO PICCOLO.   2TPT, HN, TRB   B74
LANGLEY, J.W.   SUITE.   3TRB, TU(TRB)   C71
LANGSTROTH, I.S.(ARR).   5 DANCES OF THE 16TH & 17TH C.   E77
   2TPT, 2TRB
LAPPI, F.   CANZONA 11 & 12.   2TPT, TRB(HN), TRB   E14
LASSUS-DOCKSTADER.   ALLEGRETTO.   2TPT, TRB, TU(BTRB)   G78
LASSUS, R.D.-CHEYETTE.   MATONA, LOVELY MAIDEN.   2TPT, 2TRB   C33
LASSUS, R.D.-BUTTERWORTH.   4 TUDOR CANZONAS   B20
   2TPT, HN, TRB(TU)
LAVROV, G.(ARR).   5 PIECES BY WESTERN & RUSSIAN COMPOSERS   D81
   3TRB, TU(EU)
LAW & HEWITT & BILLINGS.   3 NEW ENGLAND HYMNS   D16
   TPT, TRB(HN), TRB-TU, TPT(HN)
LAWTON, S.M.   BRASS QUARTET, THE (2 VOL)   E51
   2TPT, HN(TRB), TRB, (OPT *PF)
LEAHY, M.   SUNDAY AFTERNOON.   2TPT, 2TRB   P48
LECUONA-GORDON.   COMPARSA, LA.   2TPT, HN(TRB), TRB(TU)   D63
LEIDZEN, E.W.G.   FOURSOME, THE.   4INST ?   A84
LEJEUNE-PETIT.   FANTAISIE.   2TPT, HN(TRB), TRB   A71
LEMARC, A.(ARR).   2 PIECES.   2TPT, HN(EU), EU   F81
LETHBRIDGE, L.   BRASS QUARTET, THE, BK 3.   2TPT, HN(TRB), TRB   E51
LETHBRIDGE, L.   BRASS QUARTET, THE, BK 4.   2TPT, HN(TRB), TRB   E51
LEVY, F.   CONCERTPIECE FOR BRASS QUARTET.   TPT, HN, TRB, BTRB   B44
LEWIS & ODE.   HYMNS, DESCANTS & FANTASIAS.   2TPT, HN, TRB   L74
LIEBERMAN.   LEAVES OF BRASS.   2TPT, 2TRB   B32
LIJNSCHOOTEN, H.V.   FUGHETTA VOOR KOPERKWARTET   F81
   TPT, HN(EU), TRB, TPT(HN)
LINDEN, N.V.D.-LEMARC.   CHINESE MARS.   2TPT, HN(EU), TRB   F81
LINKE, J.D.   KLEINE DRESDNER BLASERMUSIK.   2TPT, 2TRB   C75
LISZT, F.   DREAM OF LOVE.   2TPT, TRB, EU, (OPT *PF)   A91
LO PRESTI, R.   MINIATURE FOR BRASS QUARTET   F43
   2TPT, HN(TRB), TRB
LOACHER, E.   SORIANO MARCH.   2TPT, 2TRB   B38
LOCKE, M.-WALDECK.   SUITE NO. 1.   2TPT, TRB, TU   B44
LOCKE, M.-WALDECK.   SUITE NO. 2.   TPT, HN, TRB, TU   B44
LONG(ARR).   NOVELTY BRASS QUARTET LIBRARY (VOL 4-5)   G10
   TPT(TRB), TRB(TPT, HN), TPT(TRB, HN), TRB(TPT), -TU
LONG, N.H.   CHACONNE IN D MINOR.   2TPT, HN, TRB   F07
LOVELOCK, W.   3 PIECES.   2TPT, HN, TRB   B20
LOVREGLIO.   EVOCATION.   3TRB, TU, TIMP   F87
LUBIK, I.(ARR).   MADRIGALS & PRECLASSICAL DANCES.   2TPT, 2TRB   B84
LUDWIG BRASS QUARTETS (5 VOL).   4INST ?   D52
LUZASCHI, L.   CANZONA 10.   2TPT, TRB(HN), TRB   E14
MACHAUT, DE.   CONTREPOINT A 4.   2TPT, HN(TRB), TRB   A71
MACHAUT, M-DISHINGER.   AGNUS DEI.   TPT, HN, 2TRB   N61

MAGANINI, Q.E. DOUBLE-CANON. 2TPT, HN(TRB), TRB(HN)   B85
MAGANINI, Q.E. FLOURISH FOR A HERO, A. 2TPT, HN(TRB), TRB   B85
MAGANINI, Q.E. MEDEOVALE. 2TPT, HN, TRB   B85
MAGANINI, Q.E. MUSIC OF THE MIDDLE AGES. 2TPT, 2TRB   B85
MAGANINI, Q.E.(ARR). 3 ORIGINAL ENSEMBLES. 2TPT, HN, TRB   C11
MANCINI, A.(ARR). CONCERT HIGHLIGHTS. 3TPT, TRB   B31
MANCINI, A.(ARR). ENSEMBLE SERIES. 3TPT, TRB   B31
MARCELLO, B.-WIENANDT. FANFARE, FUGUE & FINALE. 2TPT, 2TRB   E80
MASCHERA, F.-LOTZENHISER. CANZONA NO.14   C11
    2TPT, HN(TRB), TRB(EU)
MASCHERA, F. CANZONA 7 & 8. 2TPT, TRB(HN), TRB   E14
MASCHERA, F.-WALDECK. CANZONA. 2TPT, TRB, TU   B44
MASCHERA, F.-THOMAS. CANZONAS-LA GIRELLA, L'UGGIERA   E14
    2TPT, HN(TRB), TRB
MASCHERA, F. CANZONAS-LA MAGGIA, AL S. POMPEO CORADELLO   E14
    2TPT, HN(TRB), TRB
MASSO, G. 4 HYMNS. 2TPT, HN(TRB), TRB   E83
MC CABE, J. FANTASY FOR BRASS QUARTET   E41
    2TPT, HN(TRB), TRB(HN)
MC CHESNEY (ARR). KING JAMES' MARCH & SARABANDE   E80
    2TPT, TRB, EU(TRB)
MC COY. MUSIC OF FAITH. 2TPT(HN), 2TRB(HN)   F60
MC KAY, F.H. ADAGIO ASSAI & ALLEGRO VIVACE. TPT, 2HN, TRB   H06
MC KAY, F.H. PAGEANTRY. 2TPT, TRB(HN), TRB   A55
MC KAY, F.H. 2 PIECES FOR BRASS QUARTET. 2TPT, TRB(HN), TRB   E77
MC KAY, F.H. SECOND SUITE. TPT, HN(TPT), 2TRB   H06
MC VEY, L. & MC KAY. TEN FOR BRASS. 4 INST ?   A81
MEIER, J. 2 CANZONEN. 2TPT, 2TRB   A71
MELLE, R.D.-SPEETS. LARGO RELIGIOSO. 2TPT, HN(EU), EU   F81
MENDELSSOHN, F. FAITH, OP.102/6   A91
    2TPT, TRB(HN), EU, (OPT *PF)
MENDELSSOHN, F.-GLUWEN. HERINNERINGEN AAN FELIX MENDELSSOHN   F81
    TPT, HN, TRB, TPT(HN)
MENDELSSOHN, F. SCHERZO. TPT, HN, TRB, TU(BTRB)   B44
MENDELSSOHN, F.-VOXMAN. SONG OF THE LARK. 4INST ?   F07
MERULO, C.-LUMSDEN. CANZON 5. 2TPT, HN(TRB), TRB   E14
MERULO, C. CANZONA 5, 18,23. 2TPT, TRB(HN), TRB   E14
MERULO, C.-CRABTREE. L'OLICA. 2TOT, HN(TRB), TRB   N47
MESANG, T.L. (ARR). QUARTETS FOR BRASS. 2TPT, 2TRB   F27
MEVER, P.V. SONATINE. 4INST ?   D92
MIHALY, A. KLEINE TURMMUSIK. 2TPT, 2TRB   B84
MILANO, F.D-WIEANDT. TU DISOIS. 2TPT, HN, TRB   E80
MINKLER, C. MADRIGAL FOR BRASS. 2TPT, 2TRB   D14
MITCHELL, L.C. FOLK SUITE. 2TPT, HN, TRB   F02
MOZART, W.A. AVE VERUM. 2TPT, TRB, EU, (OPT *PF)   A91
MOZART, W.A.-LEMARC. AVE VERUM. 2TPT, HN(EU), EU   F81
MOZART, W.A.-SIEBERT. EINE KLEINE NACHTMUSIK. 2TPT, HN, EU   E59
MOZART, W.A.-JAMESON. FUGUE IN G MINOR, K. 401   G78
    2TPT, TRB, TU(BTRB)
MOZART, W.A.-KING. FUGUE, K.401   D16
    TPT, HN(TPT), TPB(HN), EU-TU
MOZART, W.A.-ROSENTHAL. MOTET: JUSTUM DEDUXIT. 2TPT, HN, TRB   G21
MOZART, W.A.-KING. 2 THEMES. 2TPT, TRB(HN), TRB-TU   D16
MUFFAT-KLEIN. ALLEGRO. 2TPT, TRB, TU   G78
MUFFAT-KLEIN. ANDANTE. 2TPT, TRB, TU(BTRB)   G78
MULLER, B.E. QUARTETTES (4 VOL). 3HN, TRB   F60
MUNCASTER. BANBURY BRASS-4 MINIATURES. 2TPT, 2TRB   B20
MURPHY, L. ETUDE NO.1. 2TPT, HN(TRB), TRB   G21
MUSSORGSKY, M.P. CAPRICCIO. 2TPT, HN, TRB   C91
MYDDLETON, W.H.-WRIGHT. PHANTOM BRIGADE, THE. 2TPT, 2TRB   A78
NANIO. CANZONA I. 2TPT, 2TRB   P19
NANNINO. CANZONA I. 2TPT, 2TRB   N42

NORDEN, H. SOLEMNE MUSICK, A,OP.15. 2TPT, TRB, EU   A78
NUTEN, P. INTERMEZZO. 2TPT, HN, TRB   F81
O'NEILL, C. BY THE FIRESIDE. 4INST ?   G13
O'NEILL, C. EVENING SHADOWS. 4INST ?   G13
O'NEILL, C. FALLING LEAVES. 4INST ?   G13
O'NEILL, C. LEISURE HOURS. 4INST ?   G13
OBERHAEUSSER. OBERHAEUSSER QUARTET ALBUM. 2TPT, 2TRB   G10
OBRECHT, J.-KING. TSAT EEN MESKIN. TPT, 2TRB(2HN), TRB   D16
OFFENBACH, J.-LEHRER. BARCAROLLE FROM TALES OF HOFFMANN   C09
    2TPT, 2TRB
ORPHEUS. 3HN, TU   F54
ORREGO-SALAS. CONCERTINO. TPT, 2HN, TRB   E61
OSBORNE, W. CANZON FOR BRASS INSTR.. 2TPT, HN(TRB), TRB-TU D16
OSBORNE, W.(ARR). FANFARES (18TH C. FRENCHH HUNTING CALLS) D16
    3TPT, TIME
OSTRANDER, A. BAROQUE SUITE. 2TPT, HN(TRB), TRB   B85
OSTRANSKY, L. DONNYBROOK. 2TRB, EU(TRB), TU(TRB)   F07
OSTRANSKY, L. 2 EPISODES. 2TRB, EU(TRB), TU(TRB)   F07
OSTRANSKY, L. PRELUDE & GALLIARD. 2TRB, EU(TRB), TU(TRB)   F07
OTT, J. 3 LITTLE PIECES. 2EU, 2TU   A65
OTTEN, L. 2 SUITES FOR BRASS QUARTET. TPT, 2HN, TRB   B74
PACHELBEL, J.-KING. 2 MAGNIFICATS. TPT, HN(TPT), TRB, TRB-TU D16
PACHNICKE, B.(CMPL). KLINGENDE GRUSSE. 2TPT, HN, TRB   C75
PALESTRINA, G.P.-SPEETS. ADORAMUS TE. 2TPT, HN(EU), EU   F81
PALESTRINA, G.P.-WALDECK. ADORAMUS. TPT, HN, TRB, TU   B44
PALESTRINA, G.P.-GORDON. 3 CHANTS. 2TPT, HN(TRB), TRB   D14
PALESTRINA, G.P.-LEMARC. CHRISTE ELEISON. 2TPT, 2HN   F81
PALESTRINA, G.P.-CROLEY. DIES SANCTIFICATUS   D14
    2TPT, HN(TRB), TRB
PALESTRINA, G.P.-READ. HYMN-IN FESTO TRANSFIGURATIONIS DOMINI B32
    HN(TRB), 2TRB, EU
PALESTRINA, G.P.-KING. 3 HYMNS   D16
    TPT, TRB(HN), TU-TRB, TPT(HN)
PALESTRINA, G.P.-SCHULTZ. LAUDA SION. 2TPT, HN(TRB, EU), TRB D14
PALESTRINA, G.P.-WISE. 3 MADRIGALS. 2TPT, HN, EU   M79
PALESTRINA, G.P.-SCHULTZ. MASS "ISTE CONFESSOR"   D14
    2TPT, HN(EU), TRB
PALESTRINA, G.P. O BONE JESU. 2TPT, 2TRB   N61
PALESTRINA, G.P.-EVERTSE. PUERI HEBRAECORUM. 2TPT, HN, TRB F81
PALESTRINA, G.P.-KING. RICERCAR DEL PRIMO TUONO   D16
    TPT, HN(TPT), TRB(HN), EU-TU
PALESTRINA, G.P.-WALDECK. RICERCARI DEL PRIMO TUONO   B44
    2TPT, TRB, TU
PARSHALL, H.E. QUARTET IN B-FLAT MAJOR. 2TPT, HN, TRB   A62
PELZ, W.(ARR). 10 MASTERWORKS FOR BRASS CHOIR   F43
    TPT, TPT(HN), TRB(HN), TRB
PENA, A. PRELUDE AND FUGUE NO. 3. 2TPT, HN, TRB   F59
PERRIN, C. QUATUOR. 2TPT, 2TRB   A71
PETERSEN. ALLEGRO. 3TRB, TU   D14
PETERSEN. MAKE MUCH OF TIME. 3TRB, TU   D14
PETIT, P.Y.M.C. QUATRE VENTS, LES. TPT, 2HN, TU   D36
PETIT, P.Y.M.C. (ARR). DUMA A 4. 2TPT, HN(TRB), TRB   A71
PEUERL, P.-WITTNER. SUITE NR.10   C67
    TPT, HN(TPT), TRB-TU, HN(TRB)
PFOHL(ARR). MORAVIAN CHORALES. 4INST ?   A94
PHILLIPS, B. PRELUDE FOR BRASS QUARTET. TPT, 2TRB, TPT(HN) B92
PIKET, F. DANCE & MARCH. 2TPT, 2TRB   A38
PISK, P.A. QUARTET, OP. 72. 2TPT, HN, TRB   A13
PITONI, G.O.-HOUSEKNECHT. CANTATE DOMINO. 2TPT, HN(TRB), TRB F60
PITTS. CHURCH IN THE WILDWOOD, THE. 2TPT, TRB, EU, (OPT *PF) A91
PLONER, J. KLEINE BLECHBLAESER MUSIK. 2TPT, HN, TRB   C54
POLSON, R. SCHERZO. 2TPT, 2TRB   G70

POST (ARR). 2 TRANSCRIPTIONS. 4 INST ?   B85
PRAAG, H.C.V. SONATE. 2TPT, HN, TRB   B74
PRAETORIUS, M. BRANSLE DOUBLE. 2TPT, 2TRB   M71
PRAETORIUS, M.-MOENKEMEYER. FRENCH DANCES. 3TPT, TRB   D90
PRAETORIUS, M.-DOCKSTADER. MADRIGALE. 2TPT, 2TRB   G78
PRESSER, W.H. 5 SOUTHERN SONGS. TPT, 2TRB, TPT(HN)   B91
PRESSER, W.H. SUITE #2. 2TPT, HN, TRB   F80
PRESSER, W.H. SUITE. 2TPT, 2TRB   B98
PRICE, M. QUARTET FOR BRASS. 2TPT, HN, EU   F54
PROGRAM REPERTOIRE FOR BRASS QUARTET. 2TPT, HN(TRB), TRB   F07
PUCCINI, G.-LEIDZEN. MUSETTA'S WALTZ SONG   B32
   TPT, TRB(HN), TPT(HN), TRB
PUCCINI, G.-LEIDZEN. SI, MI CHIAMANO MIMI   B32
   TPT, TRB(HN), TPT(HN), TRB
PUCCINI, G.-LEIDZEN. UN BEL DI. TPT, TRB(HN), TPT(HN), TRB   B32
PUCCINI, G.-LEIDZEN. VISSI D'ARTE VISSI D'AMORE   B32
   TPT, TRB(HN), TPT(HN), TRB
PURCELL, H.-KING. ALLEGRO & AIR FROM KING ARTHUR   D16
   2TPT, TRB(HN), TRB-TU
PURCELL, H.-ROSENTHAL. FANTASIA. 2TPT, HN, BTRB   M71
PURCELL, H.-DART. MARCH & CANZONA...FUNERAL OF QUEEN MARY   E51
   2TPT, 2TRB, (OPT TIMP)
PURCELL, H.-KING. MUSIC FOR QUEEN MARY II   D16
   TPT, HN(TPT), TRB(HN), TRB-TU
PURCELL, H. PRELUDE TO FAIRY QUEEN. 2TPT, TRB(TPT), TRB   N42
PURCELL, H. THE FAIRY QUEEN: PRELUDE. 2TPT, TPT(TRB), TRB   P19
PURCELL, H. 2 TRUMPET TUNES & AYRE. 2TPT, TRB(HN), TRB-TU   D16
RAMSOE, W. MENUETTO FR. QUARTET NO.2. 2TPT, TRB(HN), EU   D16
RAMSOE, W.-MILLER. QUARTET NO.1. 2TPT, TRB, TU(BTRB)   B98
RAMSOE, W.-MILLER. QUARTET NO.2, OP.29. 2TPT, TRB, BTRB(TU)   B98
RAMSOE, W.-KING. QUARTET NO.3, OP.30, E-FLAT. 2TPT, TRB, EU   D16
RAMSOE, W.-KING. QUARTET NO.4, OP.37, A-FLAT MAJOR   D16
   2TPT, TRB, EU
RAMSOE, W.-KING. QUARTET NO.5, OP.38, B-FLAT MAJOR   D16
   2TPT(2COR), HN(TRB), EU
RAPHLING, S. SQUARE DANCE. 2TPT, HN(TPT, TRB), TRB   B85
RASMUSSEN, M. (ED). CHRISTMAS MUSIC FOR BRASS   D16
   2TPT, HN(TRB), TRB
RATHAUS, K. INVOCATION ET FANFARE. 2TPT, HN, TRB   A78
RAYMOND, L. SHORT SUITE. 2TPT, HN, TRB   G21
RAYNER, A.(ARR). 4 CELEBRATED MELODIES (2 SETS)   E59
   2TPT, HN, EU
REGER, M.-MOORE. ABSCHLIED. 2HN, 2TRB   M71
REGNER, H. MORGENRUF. 2TPT, TRB(HN), TRB   D98
REICHE, G.-DOCKSTADER. FUGA IV. 2TPT, TRB, TU(BTRB)   G78
REICHE, G.-LEMARC. FUGA OVER EEN BEKEND MOTIEF   F81
   TPT, EU, TU, TPT(HN)
REICHE, G.-DOCKSTADER. FUGA 5. 2TPT, TRB, TU(TRB)   G78
REICHE, G.-SEAR. FUGUE NO.18. TPT, HN, TRB, TU   B44
REICHE, G. HUNTING SCENE. 2TPT, HN(TRB), TRB   B85
REICHE, G.-MILLER. 24 NEUE QUATRICINIA. 2TPT, HN(TRB), TRB   B98
REICHE, G.-MULLER. 24 NEUE QUATRICINIA. TPT(COR), 3TRB   D78
REICHE, G. SONATA NO. 1. TPT, HN(TPT, TRB), TRB(HN), TRB-TU   D16
REICHE, G. SONATA NO. 7. TPT, HN(TPT, TRB), TRB(HN), TRB-TU   D16
REICHE, G.-FROMME. SONATA NO.11   C25
   TPT, HN(TPT, TRB), TRB(HN), TRB
REICHE, G.-FROMME. SONATA NO.12   C25
   TPT, HN(TPT, TRB), TRB(HN), TRB
REICHE, G.-KING. SONATA NO.15   D16
   TPT, TPT(HN, TRB), TRB(HN), TRB-TU
REICHE, G.-KING. SONATA NO.18   D16
   TPT, HN(TPT, TRB), TRB(HN), TRB-TU

```
REICHE, G.-KING.  SONATA NO.19.  TPT, HN(TRB), TRB, TU        D 16
REICHE, G.-SEAR.  SONATA NO.19.  TPT, HN, TRB, TU            B44
REICHE, G.-KING.  SONATA NO.24                               D 16
   TPT, HN(TPT, TRB), TRB(HN), TRB-TU
REICHE, G.-KING.  2 SONATAS (21 & 22)                        D 16
   TPT, HN(TPT, TRB), TRB(HN), EU-TU
REICHE, G.-DOCKSTADER.  SONATINA 10.  2TPT, TRB, TU(TRB)     G78
REICHE, G.-DOCKSTADER.  SONATINA 15.  2TPT, TRB, TU          G78
REICHE, G.-MULLER.  TURMSONATE.  2TPT, TRB(HN), TRB          D67
REMA & PULST.  INTRODUCTION & FANFARE.  2TPT, HN, TRB        A96
REMA & RULST.  LITTLE FANFARE.  2TPT, HN, TRB                A96
RIMSKY-KORSAKOV, N.A.-KING.  NOTTURNO                        D 16
   TPT(HN), HN(TPT), TRB(HN), TRB-TU
RIVERS.  12 CHRISTMAS HYMNS & CAROLS                         E41
   TPT, HN(TPT), TRB-TU, TPT(HN)
ROBERTS & GOLDSTEIN & SCHOALES.  1ST BOOK OF BRASS QUARTETS, A  B44
   TPT, TPT(HN), HN(TRB), TRB(TU)
ROHNER & CHRISTIE.  50 CHRISTMAS CAROLS.  2TPT(2HN), 2TRB(2HN)  D82
ROIKJER.  VARIATIONS OG FUGA.  2TPT, TRB, TU                 H30
ROSSINI, G.-BARNES.  QUANDO CORPUS.  2TPT, TRB, EU           F79
RUBANK.  RUBANK PROGRAM REPERTOIRE.  2TPT, HN(TRB), TRB      F07
RUFFO.  RICERCAR.  2TPT, 2TRB                                P19
RUGOLO, P.  RAZING THE 7TH.  2TPT, 2TRB                      G21
RULST & REMA.  INTRODUCTION & FANFARE.  2TPT, HN, TRB        A96
RULST & REMA.  LITTLE FANFARE.  2TPT, HN, TRB                A96
SABATINI, G.  BRASS QUARTET.  2TPT, HN, TRB                  B44
SANDERS, R.L.  SUITE FOR BRASS QUARTET.  2TPT, 2TRB          D 16
SCANDELLUS & DONATI.  LENTO & ANDANTE.  2TPT, TRB, TU(BTRB)  G78
SCARLATTI & MUFFAT-KLEIN.  LARGO & ADAGIO.  2TPT, TRB, TU    G78
SCARMCLIN, A.L.  IMPROVISIO.  2TPT, HN, TRB                  C11
SCHAEFFER, D.(ARR).  CONCERT CLASSICS.  3TPT, TRB            E80
SCHAEFFER, D. (ARR).  HAVA NAGILA.  2TPT, 2TRB              E80
SCHARWENKA, F.X.-CAFARELLA.  MARCH, OP.62/1.  2TPT, 2TRB     H06
SCHEIDT, S.-KING.  3 CHRISTMAS CHORALES                      D 16
   TPT, HN(TPT, TRB), TRB(HN), TRB-TU
SCHEIDT, S.-KING.  DA JESUS AN DEM KREUZE STUND             D 16
   HN(TRB), 2TRB, TU(TRB)
SCHEIN & HANDEL-SEAR.  PADUANA FOR 4 KRUMMERHORNER          B44
   TPT, HN, TRB, TU
SCHEIN, J.H.-BECK.  INTRADA & PADUANA.  2TPT, 2TRB          D74
SCHICHT-SURTEES.  GREAT IS THE LORD.  2TPT, HN(TRB), TRB    B20
SCHILLING.  SUITE EN TRIO.  2TPT, 2TRB                      D98
SCHLAG, E.  HEITERES DIVERTIMENTO.  2TPT, HN, TRB(EU)       E03
SCHLAG, E.  JOYFUL DIVERTISEMENT.  2TPT, HN, TRB            C11
SCHMUTZ, A.D.  AIR & SCHERZO.  2TPT, HN, TRB                C11
SCHMUTZ, A.D.  CHORAL PRELUDE ON "INTEGER VITAE"            A62
   2TPT, HN, TRB
SCHNEIDER, W.  TURMMUSIK I.  2TPT, TRB(HN), TRB             C60
SCHOALES, GOLDSTEIN & ROBERTS.  1ST BOOK OF BRASS QUARTETS  B44
   TPT, TPT(HN), HN(TRB), TRB(TU)
SCHONBERG, S.G.  MADRIGAL.  2TPT, 2TRB                      B90
SCHONBERG, S.G.  TORNMUSIK.  2TPT, 2TRB                     B90
SCHOOLEY.  PARTITA.  2TPT, TRB, TU                          D 14
SCHUBERT, F.P.-MOORE.  6 ANTIPHONAL CHORUSES.  2TPT, 2TRB   M71
SCHUBERT, F.P.-CAFARELLA.  LAST WALTZ, OP.127/3            G 10
   2TPT, HN, TRB
SCHUBERT, F.P.-SPEETS.  SALVE REGINA.  2TPT, HN(EU), EU    F81
SCHULLER, G.  LITTLE BRASS MUSIC.  TPT, HN, TRB, TU        D73
SCHUMANN, R.-DEDRICK.  CHORAL & MARCH.  2TPT, 2TRB          D14
SCHUMANN, R.-WILLIAMS.  SEHR LANGSAM, OP.68/30             F60
   2TPT(2COR), HN, TRB
SCHUMANN, R.-NAGLE.  SONG, CHORALE & MARCH                 D73
   2TPT, HN(TRB), TRB(TU)
```

SCHUSTER, G. INTERMEZZI FOR BRASS QUARTET. 2TPT, HN, TRB   C94
SCIORTINO, P. SUITE EN ROUGE. 2TPT, HN, TRB   F87
SEAR, W.F. QUARTET FOR BRASS. 4INST ?   B44
SEEGER, P. KLEINE JAGDGESCHICHTE. TPT, 3INST ?   C54
SEEGER, P. TOCCATA FOR BRASS. 2TPT, 2TRB   E80
SEHLBACH, E. KLEINE TURM-MUSIKEN. 2TPT, 2TRB   D98
SEMLER¬COLLERY, J. OFFRANDE. 2TPT, 2TRB   A71
SERTL, F.(ED). MUNCHENER PETERSTURMMUSIKEN (4 VOL)   C67
    2TPT, 2TRB
SHELUKOV, V.-BEELER. FANFARE MARCH. 2TPT, HN(TRB), TRB   F07
SHOSTAKOVITCH, D.D. PRELUDE, OP.34/6. 2TPT, HN, TRB   P19
SHUMWAY, S. INTRADA, CANZONET & FUGUE. 2TPT, 2TRB   B98
SIBELIUS, J.-BEELER. ANDANTE FESTIVO. 2TPT, HN(TRB), TRB   F59
SIBELIUS, J. FINLANDIA. 2TPT, TRB, EU, (CPT *PF)   A91
SIEBERT, E. BEES-A-BUZZIN. 2TPT, TRB, EU   D16
SIEBERT, E. SUNDAY MORNING. 2TPT, HN, EU   E59
SIMON, A.Y.-SEAR. QUARTET IN 8 MVTS., OP.26. 2TPT, HN, TRB   B44
SIMON, A.Y. QUARTOUR EN FORME DE SONATINE. 2TPT, HN, TRB   F60
SMELTEKOP (ARR). SUITE OF ELIZABETHAN DANCES. 2TPT, 2TRB   E00
SMITH. SINFONIA NO. 13. 2TPT, 2TRB   E80
SMITH, F. 3 CHORALE SETTINGS. TPT, HN(TPT), TRB(HN), EU-TU   M98
SNYDER. RICERCAR. 2HN, 2TRB(2HN)   D16
SODERMANN, A.J.-LEMARC. BROLLOPS-MARSCH   F81
    2TPT, HN(TPT, TRB), TPT(HN)
SOLOMON. FIESTA. 2TPT(2TRB), 2TRB(EU, TU)   F60
SORCE. FANTASIA FOR BRASS. 2TPT, HN, TRB   N81
SORCE, F. FANTASIA FOR BRASS. 2TPT, HN, TRB   N59
SOURIS, A. CHORAL, MARCHE ET GALOP. 2TPT, 2TRB   B12
SOUSA, J.P.-MORRIS. CAPITAN, EL. 2EU, 2TU   M80
SPEER, D. 2 SONATAS. TPT, 3TRB, (OPT *PF, *ORG)   C91
SPEER, D.-MILLER. 2 SONATAS. TPT, TRB(TPT), 2TRB   B98
SPEETS, D. (ARR). CANTATE DOMINO. 2TPT, HN(EU), TRB   F81
SPEETS, D. KLASSIEK KWARTET. TPT, HN(EU), TRB, TPT(HN)   F81
STABILE. SUITE. 2TPT, 2TRB   G21
STARER, R. DIRGE. 2TPT, 2TRB   E77
STARER, R. PROFILES IN BRASS. 2TPT, 2TRB   G85
STEFFE, W.-ISBEN. BATTLE HYMN. 2EU, 2TU   P42
STEIN, L. PRELUDE, CHORALE & FUGUE. 2TPT, 2TRB   N98
STEPHENSON. INTRADAS. 2TPT, HN(TRB), TRB   B20
STIEBER, H. TOWER MUSIC. 2TPT, 2HN   E14
STOKER, R. LITANY, SEQUENCE & HYMN. TPT, HN(TPT, TRB), 2TRB   C71
STOKES, F. PRELUDE & RONDO. 2TPT, HN, EU   F54
STONE (ARR). MINSTRELS' GALLERY, THE   A78
    TPT(OB, CL), TPT(CL), HN(CL, EU), TRB(BSN, BCL)
STORL, J.G.C.-KING. SONATA NO.1   D16
    TPT, HN(TPT, TRB), TRB(HN), TRB-TU
STORL, J.G.C.-BROWN. 6 SONATAS. TPT, 3TRB   C91
STORL, J.G.C.-MILLER. 6 SONATAS   B98
    TPT, TRB(TPT, HN), TRB, BTRB
STOUFFER, P.M. PARADE OF THE LITTLE GREEN SPACEMEN   B91
    3TPT, TRB
STRAESSER, J. MUSIC FOR BRASS. 2TPT, HN, TRB   B74
STRAUSS, J.-GAULT. PIZZICATO POLKA. 3TPT, TRB   E11
STRAVINSKY, 2. BERCEUSE DU CHAT. 2TPT, 2TRB   P19
STROUD, R. ARTICULATION FOR BRASS. TPT, HN, TRB, TU   B35
SUSATO, T. 3 DANCES. TPT, HN(TPT, TRB), TRB(HN), TRB-TU   D16
SWEELINCK, J.P. OR SUS, SERVITEURS, DU SEIGNEUR   B40
    TPT, HN, 2TRB
SYDEMAN, W. FANFARE AND VARIATIONS. 2TPT, 2TRB   G66
SYDEMAN, W. MUSIC FOR LOW BRASS. 3TRB, TU   G66
SZELENYI. SUITE. 2TPT, 2TRB   F23
TANEYEV, A.S.-AGCUNOFF. ROME AT NIGHT. 2TPT, HN(TRB), TRB   B85

```
TAYLOR.  ANDANTE.  2TPT, 2TRB                                          C09
TAYLOR.  SCHERZO.  2TPT, 2TRB                                          C09
TCHAIKOVSKY, P.I.-CAFARELLA.  CHANSON TRISTE, OP.40/2                  G10
   2TPT, TRB, EU
TCHAIKOVSKY, P.I.-HAMILTON.  CHANSON TRISTE.  2TPT, 2TRB               C33
TCHAIKOVSKY, P.I.-FITZGERALD.  HUMORESQUE, OP.10/2                     E77
   2TPT, HN, TRB
TCHAIKOVSKY, P.I.  HUNTING(THE SEASONS, OP. 37A)                       C91
   2TPT, HN, TRB
TCHAIKOVSKY, P.I.-SIEBERT.  SLEEPING PRINCESS, THE                    E59
   2TPT, HN, EU
TCHEREPNINE, N.N.  CHASSE, LA.  2TPT, 2TRB                            B53
TCHEREPNINE, N.N.  6 PIECES.  3TPT, TRB                               B85
TENAGLIA, A.F.-CHEYETTE.  ARIA.  2TPT, HN(TRB), TRB                   C33
THILMAN, J.P.  TRIO-MUSIK FUR BLECHBLASER & QUARTETT...               D85
   2TPT, HN, TRB
TICE, D.  4 PIECES.  2TPT, 2TRB                                       G01
TOMASI, H.  ETRE OU NE PAS ETRE.  3TRB, TU(TRB)                       D36
TOMKINS-BUTTERWORTH.  3 PIECES.  2TPT, HN, TRB                        B20
TOMKINS, T.  MR. CURCH'S TOYE.  2TPT, HN, TRB(TU)                     B20
TRABACI-PETIT.  GAILLARDE.  2TPT, HN(TRB), TRB                        A71
TREVARTHEN, R.  SONATA.  2TPT, HN, TRB                                G83
TRINKAUS, G.J.(ARR).  DEEP RIVER.  2TPT, 2TRB                         G31
TRINKAUS, G.J.  G.SCHIRMER'S SELECT ALBUM FOR WIND QUARTET            F23
   2TPT(2CL, 2HN), 2TRB(2HN, 2BSN)
TURNHOUT, G.-EVERTSE.  MOTET.  2TPT, TRB, EU(HN)                      F81
TUTHILL, B.C.  FUGUE FOR 4 BRASSES, OP.10/3.  2TPT, 2TRB              C11
UBER, D.A.  2 COMPOSITIONS FOR BRASS QUARTET.  2TPT, 2TRB             A03
UBER, D.A.  2 COMPOSITIONS-EVENTIDE, FLIGHT INTO SPACE                A62
   2TPT, 2TRB
UBER, D.A.  MINIATURE SYMPHONY.  2TPT, 2TRB                           F23
UBER, D.A.  3 MINIATURES, OP.29.  3TRB, TU(BTRB)                      B98
UBER, D.A.  2 PIECES.  2TPT, HN(TPT, TRB), TRB                        B85
UBER, D.A.  PROFILES IN BRASS.  2TPT, HN(TPT, TRB), TRB(HN)           A94
ULF, O.  2 CANZONEN ALTER MEISTER.  TPT, HN, TRB, EU                  C54
ULF, O.  2 CANZONEN VON C.ANTEGNATI.  2TPT, HN, TRB                   C54
URAY.  FANFARE.  2TPT, 2TRB                                           B73
VAN DE VATE.  SHORT SUITE.  2TPT, 2TRB                                F80
VAN DE VATE, N.  DIVERSION.  2TPT, HN, TRB                            P48
VAN VACTOR, D.  QUARTETTO.  2EU, 2TU                                  F60
VANDRE.  5 CHOICE SELECTIONS.  2TPT, 2TRB(HN)                         F79
VERDI, G.-LEMARC.  SLAVENKOOR.  4INST ?                               F81
VERDI, G.-STUBE.  TRIUMPHAL MARCH.  2TPT, 2TRB                        A62
VERDI, G.-HEKKER.  VERDI-KLANKEN.  2TPT, HN(EU), TRB                  F81
VICTORIA, T.L.D.-PRICE.  3 MOTETS                                     C78
VILLA¬LOBOS, H.  CHOROS NR.4.  3HN, BTRB                              F31
VITALI, G.B.-FITZGERALD.  CAPRICCIO.  2TPT, HN(TRB), TRB-TU           E77
VIVALDI, A.  SONATA DA CAMERA.  2TPT, HN(TPT, TRB), TRB               B85
VOXMAN, H.(ARR).  ENSEMBLE CLASSICS FOR BRASS QUARTET                 F07
   VOL 1: 2TPT, HN TRB, VOL 2: 2 TPT, 2TRB
WAGNER, I.L.  EVERY TIME I FEEL THE SPIRIT.  4TRB(2HN, TU)            N83
WAGNER, I.L.  ROLL, JORDAN, ROLL.  4TRB(2HN, TU)                     N83
WAGNER, I.L.  SWING LOW, SWEET CHARIOT.  4TRB(2HN, TU)               N83
WAGNER, R.  PILGRIM CHORUS.  2TPT, TRB, EU, (OPT *PF)                A91
WAGNER, R.-HUME.  QUARTET "WAGNER".  2TPT, 2EU                       A78
WAGNER, R.-STUBE.  WAGNER MELODIES.  2TPT, 2TRB                      D84
WALKER.  CANTICLE.  2TPT, HN, TRB                                    F60
WALKER, R.  BADINERIE.  2TPT, HN, TRB                                A38
WALKER, R.  PRELUDIO & RONDINO FOR BRASS QUARTET                     F79
   2TPT, HN, TRB
WALTON, W.T.-DE JONG.  6 PIECES IN 2 SETS, SET 3.  2TPT, 2TRB        E51
WALTON, W.T.-DE JONG.  6 PIECES IN 2 SETS, SET 5                     E51
   2TPT, HN(TRB), TRB
```

WERLE, F.C. MARCH, CHORALE,FUGUE. 2TPT, HN(TRB), TRB		B85
WESTCOTT, F. SUITE FOR BRASS. TPT, TRB(HN), TPT(HN), TRB(TU)		C71
WHEAR, P.W.(ARR). 3 CHORALES. 2TPT, 2TRB		D52
WHEAR, P.W. PRELUDE & RONDO. 2TPT, 2TRB		A55
WHITE, D. SERENADE NO.3. 2TPT, HN, TRB		F43
WHITNEY, M.C. BRASS QUARTET NO.1. 2TPT, HN(TRB), TRB(EU)		C11
WIENANDT. 10 MASTERWORKS. 2TPT, HN(TRB), TRB		E80
WIENANDT. TU DISOIS. 2TPT, HN, TRB		E80
WILLIS. HYMN. 2TPT, 2TRB		E80
WOHLFART, F. FANFAREN-MUSIK. 2TPT, 2TRB		F50
XARAVA. FANTASIA. 2TPT, 2TRB		P19
YODER, P.(ARR). PRELUDE(CHOPIN) & CHORALE(SIBELIUS) 3TRB, TU		D18
YOUMANS, V.-HEYMAN. THROUGH THE YEARS. 2TPT, 2TRB		P40
ZABEL-OSTRANDER. 4 FRENCH PIECES. 2TPT, HN, TRB		C91
ZAGWIJN, H. ENTRATA GIOCOSA. 2TPT, HN, TRB		B74
ZAGWIJN, H. PRELUDE ET CHORAL. 2TPT, HN, TRB		F81
ZANETTOVICH. SUITE POUR QUATRE. 2TPT, HN, TRB		D36
ZEHM. NEUE ELASERSTUCKE. 2TPT, 2TRB		F31
ZIELENSKI, N.-SPEETS. DA PACEM DOMINE. 2TPT, HN(EU), EU		F81
ZIELINSKI. CANZONA. 2TPT, 2TRB		P19
ZINDARS. CHORAL. 2TPT, TRB, TU(TRB)		B04
ZINGARELLI, N.A.-WIENANDT. ADAGIO & ALLEGRO 2TPT, HN(TRB), TRB		F60
ZINGARELLI, N.A.-CARLSTON. ADAGIO & PRESTO... 2TPT, TRB(HN), TRB		A55
ZINGARELLI, N.A. GO NOT FAR FROM ME, O GOD. 4INST ?		B40

4 PARTS: HORN-WOODWIND

APOSTEL, H.E. QUARTET IN 5 SATZEN, OP.14. HN, FL, CL, BSN		F97
BACH, J.S.-CATELINET. CONTRAPUNCTUS I A 4 VOCI HN, OB, CL, BSN		E65
BACH, J.S.-HIRSH. FUGUE IN E-FLAT. HN, OE(FL), CL, BSN		C11
BOUSTEAD, A. 3 MADRIGALS. HN, FL, CL, BSN		D36
BUTT, J.B. WINSOME'S FOLLY. HN, OB, CL, ESN		A78
BUTTERWORTH, D.N. TUDOR SUITE FOR WIND INSTRS. HN(SAX), FL(OB, CL), OB(CL), BSN		B20
ELER, A.-LELOIR. QUARTET #1. HN, 2CL, BSN		D11
ELER, A.-LELOIR. QUARTET #2. HN, 2CL, BSN		D11
ELER, A.-LELOIR. QUARTET #3. HN, 2CL, BSN		D11
EROD, I. RICERCARE ED ARIA. HN, FL, OB, BCL		B73
FRESCOBALDI, G.-AARON. GAGLIARDA. HN, OB(CL), CL, BSN(BCL)		F23
GEISER, W. DIVERTIMENTO, OP. 55. HN, OB, CL, BSN		H03
GRIEG, E.H.-CAFARELLA. NORWEGIAN DANCE, OP.47/28 HN, FL, OB, CL		G10
HANDEL, G.F.-AARON. CHACONNE. HN, OB, CL, BSN		F23
HAYDN, J.-AARON. CAPRICCIO. HN, OB, CL, ESN		F23
HAYDN, J.-LANDON. DIVERTIMENTO NR.4 IN C, H.II:14. 2HN, 2CL		B73
HAYDN, J.-LAUSCHMANN. DIVERTIMENTO, D MAJOR. HN, FL, OB, BSN		C75
HAYDN, J. DIVERTIMENTO, HII K5. 2HN, 2CL		H30
HAYDN, J.-PATTERSON-MOORE. LARGO FR. QUARTET, OP.76/5 HN, 2CL, BSN		G26
HAYDN, J.-JANETZKY. 12 NOCTURNOS, D MAJOR. 2HN, 2FL		E81
HAYDN, J.-PATTERSON-MOORE. POCO ADAGIO CANTABILE, OP.76/3 HN, 2CL, BSN		G26
HAYDN, M. DIVERTIMENTO. HN, FL, OB, BSN		C75
HENNEBERG, A. LITEN KVARTETT, OP.36. HN, FL, OB, BSN		B90

```
HERTEL, J.W.-SALLAGAR.  SONATA A QUATTRO ES MAJOR.  2HN, 2BSN        E37
HOVHANESS, A.S.  DIVERTIMENTO, OP. 61/5                               E65
   HN(CL), OB(CL), CL, BSN(BCL)
JADIN, L.E.  NOCTURNE NO.3 EN SOL MINOR.  HN, FL, CL, BSN            D21
KARKOFF, M.  DIVERTIMENTO, OP.29.  HN, FL, OB, BSN                   B90
KAUDER, H.  QUARTET.  HN, OB, CL, BSN                                E30
KREISLER, A.V.  SARABANDE.  HN, 2CL, BSN(VC)                         F60
MOZART, W.A.  ADAGIO, K. 580A.  2HN(2BSTHN), EH, BSN                 D21
MOZART, W.A.  CASSAZIONE.  HN, OB(FL), CL, BSN                       F60
MOZART, W.A.-JENSEN.  DIVERTIMENTO.  HN, FL, OB, BSN                 G70
MOZART, W.A.-SCHNEIDER.  KEGEL-DIVERTIMENTO.  HN, OB, CL, BSN        E37
NORDGREN, E.  6 MOVEMENTS, OP. 64.  HN,FL, BSN, TAM                  B90
NOWAK, L.  SUITE.  HN, FL, OB, CL                                    A13
PADOVANO, A.  RONDO FUR 4 BLASER.  HN, OB(FL), CL, BSN               G38
PALESTRINA, G.P.-CATELINET.  RICERCARE.  HN, OB, CL, BSN             C71
PEARSON, W.D.  HUNT, THE.  HN(BSN), FL, OB, CL                       B20
PETYREK, F.  GUTE NACHT, O WELT.  HN, OB, CL, BSN                    B73
PLACHETA, H.  QUARTETT, OP.10.  HN, OB, CL, BSN                      B73
PURCELL, H.-BUTTERWORTH.  LITTLE SUITE, A                            E33
   HN(CL), OB, CL, BSN
REGNER, H.  SERENADE.  HN, OB, CL, BSN                               E37
REICHEL, B.  ANDANTE AMABILE.  HN, FL, CL, BSN                       H03
RIISAGER, K.  DIVERTIMENTO.  HN, FL, OB, BSN                         C17
ROSSINI, G.  QUARTET NO.1.  HN, FL, CL, BSN                          F87
ROSSINI, G.-ZACHERT.  6 QUARTETS (2 VOL).  HN, FL, CL, BSN           F31
SCHNEIDER, W.  LITTLE QUARTET.  HN, FL, OB, CL                       D98
SCHNEIDER, W.  VARIATIONS ON A SUMMER-SONG.  HN, OB, CL, BSN         D98
SCHUBERT, F.P.  WALTZ IN A MINOR.  HN, FL, CL, BSN                   C11
SCHURTZ, F.  DIVERTIMENTO.  HN, OB, CL, BSN                          D98
SCHURTZ, F.  KLEINE MUSIK IN 3 MVTS..  HN, OB, CL, BSN               D98
SCHWEGLER, J.D.  QUARTET IN E-FLAT, OP.3/2.  2HN, 2FL                G21
STAMITZ, K.-WEIGELT.  BLASERQUARTET ES-DUR, OP.8/2                   D44
   HN, OB, CL, BSN
STRINGFIELD, L.  OLD BRIDGE, AN                                      D71
   HN(EH), OB(FL), CL, BSN, (OPT *PF)
TCHAIKOVSKY, P.I.-AARON.  HUMORESQUE.  HN,OB,CL,BSN(BCL)             F23
VELLERE, L.  PRELUDE.  HN, OB, CL, BSN                               D67
WOOD, J.  FUGUE IN C MINOR.  HN, OB, EHN, BSN                        P48
```

4 PARTS: BRASS-WOODWIND

```
CARTER.  CANON FOR 3.  2TPT, OB, CL                                  A38
CHAVEZ, C.  SOLI.  TPT, OB, CL, BSN                                  A78
DIAS.  MEU BEM.  TPT, TRB, PERC, SAX                                 E83
DOBROWOLSKI, A.  8 STUDIES.  TPT, OB, BSN, DB                        A31
HAYDN, J.-AARON.  CAPRICCIO.  TRB,2CL, BCL                           F23
KORDA, V.  ETUDE.  HN, TRB, FL, CL                                   B73
KREJCI, I.  DIVERTIMENTO.  TPT, FL, CL, BSN                          A33
KREJCI, I.  DIVERTIMENTO.  TPT, FL, CL, BSN                          A51
SUTERMEISTER, H.  SERENADE.  TPT, 2CL, BSN                           F31
```

4 PARTS: TRUMPETS-KEYBOARD

ABBOTT, G.J. TRUMPETERS 3. 3TPT, *PF		E77
AGOSTINI, G.-BAINUM. 3 TRUMPETERS. 3TPT, *PF		A62
ALFORD, K.J.-WCOLDRIDGE. COLONEL BOGEY. 3TPT, *PF		A78
ANDERSON, L. BUGLER'S HOLIDAY. 3TPT, *PF		D84
ANDERSON, L. TRUMPETER'S LULLABY. 3TPT, *PF		D84
BARNES, C.P. 3 DEBONAIRS. 3TPT(3TRB), *BAND, *PF		G10
BARNES, C.P. 3 GAYBRIELLOS. 3TPT, *BAND, *PF		D52
BEETHOVEN, L.V.-LEIDZEN. RONDINO ON A THEME OF BEETHOVEN		C18
3TPT, *PF		
BERLINSKI, H. THREE (& FOUR) PART CANONS AND ROUNDS		D74
3TPT, *PF		
BRIEGEL, G.F. CATHEDRAL ECHOES. 3TPT, *PF		A91
BRIEGEL, G.F. SOLOETTE. 3TPT, *PF		A91
BRIEGEL, G.F. 3 STARS. 3TPT, *PF		A91
BUCHTEL, F.L. AZURE SKIES. 3TPT(3FL), *PF		D18
BUCHTEL, F.L. 3 CHUMS. 3TPT, *PF		A55
BUCHTEL, F.L. COMRADES. 3TPT(3COR, 3CL), *PF		A55
BUCHTEL, F.L. COQUETTE. 3TPT(3CL), *PF		D18
BUCHTEL, F.L. DANCING NYMPHS. 3TPT, *PF		D18
BUCHTEL, F.L. 3 OF A KIND. 3TPT(3TRB), *PF		A55
BUCHTEL, F.L. POLKA DOTS. 3TPT(3TRB), *PF		A55
BUCHTEL, F.L. 3 PUCKS, THE. 3TPT, *PF		C09
BUCHTEL, F.L. ROSARY, THE. 3TPT, *PF		D18
BUCHTEL, F.L. 3 SERENADERS. 3TPT, *PF		A55
BUCHTEL, F.L. SOFT SHOE DANCE. 3TPT, *PF		D18
BUCHTEL, F.L. THEMES FROM "LES PRELUDES". 3TPT, *PF		D18
BURKE, J.F. MAGIC TRUMPET. 3TPT, *BAND, *PF		C11
BUSCH, C. CONTENTMENT. 3TPT, *PF		C11
BUSCH, C. FROLIC. 3TPT, *PF		C11
BUSCH, C. JOYFULNESS. 3TPT, *PF		C11
BUSCH, C. 4 MINIATURES. 3TPT, *PF		C11
BUSCH, C. ON HEARING AN AUTOMOBILE HORN. 3TPT, *PF		A62
BUSCH, C. SOLITUDE. 3TPT, *PF		C11
BUSCH, C. THREE OF US. 3TPT, *PF		A62
BUSCH, C. TRIO CONCERTANTE. 3TPT, *PF		B53
CATIZONE, J. JEMEZ. 3TPT, *PF		E80
CATIZONE, J. VALVETTE. 3TPT, *PF		G10
CLARKE, H.L. 3 ACES. 3TPT, *PF		C09
CLARKE, H.L. FLIRTATIONS. 3TPT, *PF		C09
CLARKE, H.L. FLIRTATIONS. 3TPT, *PF		C11
COHEN, S.B. FUN FOR 3. 3TPT, *PF		A62
COHEN, S.B. SCHERZO. 3TPT, *PF		A62
DAVIS, A.O. THREE CARDINALS, THE. 3TPT, *BAND, *PF		D52
DEDRICK, A. MARCH OF THE MISSILE MEN. 3TPT, *PF		D14
DEDRICK, A. NORTHWEST SAGA. 3TPT, *PF		D14
DEDRICK, A. SPACE CADETS. 3TPT, *PF		D14
DEEMER, C. (ARR). LITTLE BROWN JUG. 3TPT, *PF		A62
DELAMATER, E. CRACKER JACKS. 3TPT, *BAND, *PF		F07
DENZA, L. FUNICULI FUNICULA. 3TPT, *PF		B13
ERICKSON, F. TRIONATA. 3TPT, *PF		B53
ESTES, A. TRICMODE. 3TPT, *PF		D14
FEASEL, R.M. 3 BROTHERS. 3TPT, *PF		C09
FINLAY, G. TRUMPETER'S CARNIVAL. 3TPT, *BAND, *PF		B52
FINLAY, G. TRUMPETER'S CARNIVAL. 3TPT, *EF, *BAND		G70
FINLAYSON, W.A. BRIGHT EYES. 3TPT, *BAND, *PF		A78

```
FIRST DIVISION BAND COURSE.  FANFARE AND AIR.  3TPT, *PF          A62
FIRST DIVISION BAND COURSE.  HUNGARIANA.  3TPT, *PF               A62
FIRST DIVISION BAND COURSE.  MARCH FR "FRENCH SUITE"              A62
  3TPT, *PF
FIRST DIVISION BAND COURSE.  MARCH MILATAIRE.  3TPT, *PF          A62
FOTE, R.  SMOOTH FLIGHT.  3TPT, *PF                               D14
FRANK, F.L.  MINKA, MINKA.  3TPT, *BAND, *PF                      F07
FRANK, F.L.  TRIPLE PLAY.  3TPT, *PF                              F07
GABRIELI, A.-TOLMAGE.  MARCH FOR ST. MARK'S.  3TPT, *PF           F64
GABRIELI, G.-BOSWELL.  SONATA CON TRE TROMBE.  3TPT, *PF          N42
GOLDMAN, E.F.  ECHO WALTZ.  3TPT, *PF                             C11
GOLDMAN, F.F.  EXULTATION WALTZ.  3TPT, *PF                       C11
HANDEL, G.F.-GOLDMAN.  AIR & VARIATIONS IN B-FLAT.  3TPT, *PF     C11
HANDEL, G.F.-HANSON.  SONATA #2.  3TPT, *PF                       D52
HANDEL, G.F.-ORVID.  SONATA NO.2.  3TPT, *PF                      D81
HANDEL, G.F.-GARDNER.  WHERE'ER YOU WALK.  3TPT, *PF              F64
HARRIS, F.O.  3 CADETS.  3TPT, *PF                                D52
HARRIS, F.O.  3 CUBS.  3TPT, *PF                                  D52
HARRIS, F.O.  3 FOR THE SHOW.  3TPT, *PF                          D52
HARRIS, F.O.  GALLANT BRIGADIERS.  3TPT, *PF                      A55
HARRIS, F.O.  3 SYNCOPATORS.  3TPT, *PF                           D52
HAUBIEL, C.  ACCLEERATION.  3TPT, *PF                             A62
HAVLICEK, L.C.  3 PALS FOR TRUMPET TRIO.  3TPT, *PF               F79
HAYDN, J.-BRAHMS & POLLOCK.  CHORALE ST. ANTONI.  3TPT, *PF       F64
HENNEBERG, P.  TRIPLETS OF THE FINEST.  3TPT, *PF, *BAND          C11
HERBERT, V.-HARRIS.  GYPSY LOVE SONG.  3TPT, *PF                  D52
HERBERT, V.  3 SOLITAIRES.  3TPT, *PF                             E11
HERBERT, V.  3 SOLITAIRES.  3TPT, *BAND, *PF                      G31
HEUBERGER, R.-LEIDZEN.  MIDNIGHT BELLS.  3TPT, *PF                C18
HOPKINS.  TRIUMPHAL MARCH.  3TPT, *PF                             B13
HUBER, F.J.  THREESOME.  3TPT, *PF                                A55
HUFFMAN, C.H.  TRUMPET TRILOGY.  3TPT, *PF                        G13
HURRELL, C.E.  BOY FRIENDS, THE.  3TPT, *PF                       F07
JACOBSON, I.D.  3 CANTOS FOR CORNETS.  3TPT, *PF                  D84
JOHNSON, C.W.  TRIPLETEERS.  3TPT, *PF                            F07
JOHNSON, C.W.  TRUMPETERS 3.  3TPT, *PF                           F07
KIEFER-HOLMES.  ELENA POLKA.  3TPT(3TRB), *PF                     A55
KISER, J.A.  VANGUARD.  3TPT, *PF                                 B31
KLEES.  EIGER MONCH JUNGFRAU.  3TPT, *PF                          F10
KLEFFMAN, E.  MY BUDDY POLKA.  3TPT, *PF                          F07
KLEFFMAN, E.  RUBATO CAPRICE.  3TPT, *PF                          F07
KREISLER-VAN HOESEN.  LIEBESFREUD.  3TPT, *PF                     C18
KREISLER-VAN HOESEN.  OLD REFRAIN.  3TPT, *PF                     C18
KREISLER-VAN HOESEN.  SCHOEN ROSMARIN.  3TPT, *PF                 C18
KREISLER, F.-LEIDZEN.  MIDNIGHT BELLS.  3TPT, *PF                 C18
LEMARE, E.H.-LONG.  ANDANTINO.  3TPT, *PF                         G10
LEMGSFELDER.  TROPICAL TRUMPETS.  3TPT, *PF                       C25
LEONARD, C.H.  TRIOLET.  3TPT, *PF                                E93
LEONCAVALLO, R.-SCARMOLIN.  SONG OF THE BOHEMIANS.  3TPT, *PF     E80
LITTLE, L.  3 MODERNAIRES.  3TPT, *PF                             D52
LOESSER-LANG.  3 CORNERED TUNE.  3TPT, *PF                        C27
LOTTI.  ARIETTA.  3TPT, *PF                                       B85
LOTZENHISER, G.W.  JUNIOR TRUMPETEERS, THE.  3TPT, *PF            A62
MANIET, R.  TRIADE.  3TPT, *PF                                    D67
MARQUINA-MENDEZ.  POR LA ESPANA CANI.  3TPT, *PF                  C11
MARTIN.  BETTY'S WALTZ.  3TPT, *PF                                B13
MARTIN.  SKYROCKET.  3TPT, *PF                                    B13
MC KAY, F.H.  ANITA.  3TPT, *PF                                   A55
MC KAY, F.H.  3 CADETS.  3TPT, *PF                                A55
MC KAY, F.H.  CARMELA.  3TPT, *PF                                 A55
MC KAY, F.H.  CHIQUITA.  3TPT, *PF                                A55
MC KAY, F.H.  3 JESTERS.  3TPT, *PF                               A55
```

MC KAY, F.H. TRES AMIGOS. 3TPT, *PF		A55
MENDEZ, R.G. ANNIVERSARY POLKA. 3TPT, *PF		C11
MENDEZ, R.G. CHIAPENECAS. 3TPT, *PF		C11
MENDEZ, R.G. CHUNCA. 3TPT, *PF		C11
MENDEZ, R.G.-LOPEZ. ENCINO-POLKA. 3TPT, *PF		C11
MENDEZ, R.G. FLIRTATIONS OF A TRUMPET. 3TPT, *PF		C11
MENDEZ, R.G. GIRL FROM CHIHUAHUA, THE. 3TPT, *PF		C11
MENDEZ, R.G. 3 MENDEZ POLKA. 3TPT, *PF		C11
MENDEZ, R.G. NENA. 3TPT, *PF		C11
MENDEZ, R.G. POLKA IN-THE-BOX. 3TPT, *PF		C11
MERETTA, L.V. AURORA. 3TPT, *PF		D84
MERETTA, L.V. HOLIDAY POLKA. 3TPT, *PF		D84
MOZART, W.A. AVE VERUM CORPUS. 3TPT, *PF		B85
MOZART, W.A.-OSTRANDER. AVE VERUM. 3TPT, *PF		B85
NAGEL, F. TRUMPETS OF SPAIN. 3TPT, *PF		D84
O'NEILL, C. ALL TOGETHER. 3TPT, *PF		G13
O'NEILL, C. 3 FRIENDS. 3TPT, *PF		G13
O'NEILL, C. LAKE GOODWILL. 3TPT, *PF		G13
OERTEL, A. VIRTUOSO TRIO, A,OP.36. 3TPT, *PF		B53
OSTRANSKY, L. DIVERTISSEMENT. 3TPT, *PF		F07
OTTO, R.A. 3 PIECES OF BRASS. 3TPT, *PF		C11
OWEN, F. FANTASIES ON MEXICAN TUNES. 3TPT, *PF		A43
OWEN, H. FANTASIES. 3TPT, *PF		G21
PELZ, W. ROMANCE. 3TPT, *PF		A62
PILLIN. 4 SCENES. 3TPT, *PF		N43
PURCELL, H.-GARDNER. ANTIPHONAL VOLUNTARY. 3TPT, *PF		F64
PURCELL, H.-OSTRANDER. SOUND THE TRUMPETS. 3TPT, *PF		B85
PURCELL, H.-GARDNER. TRUMPET FANFARE & TUNE. 3TPT, *PF		F64
PURCELL, H.-GARDNER. TRUMPET VOLUNTARY. 3TPT, *PF		F64
RICHARDS, J.J. TRIAD. 3TPT, *PF		A55
RICHTER. MAN FROM MARS. 3TPT, *PF		B13
RICHTER. VAGABONDIA. 3TPT, *PF		B13
ROGERS, W. ECHOES OF THE CATSKILLS. 3TPT, *PF		B31
ROGERS, W. LASCA. 3TPT, *PF		B31
ROSSELL, J.D. ANDANTE & POLKA. 3TPT, *PF		G10
RUBARDT, P.(ARR). 3 TROMPETENSTUCKE. 3TPT, *PF		E65
SARTORIUS, H. BUMPY ROAD, THE. 3TPT, *PF		B13
SARTORIUS, H. CAPE COD CHANTY. 3TPT, *PF		B13
SARTORIUS, H. EASTWARD HO!. 3TPT, *PF		B13
SARTORIUS, H. ROMANY DANCE. 3TPT, *PF		B13
SCARMOLIN, A.L. POLKA ARABESQUE. 3TPT, *PF		A55
SCARMOLIN, A.L. 3 SWINGSTERS. 3TPT, *BAND, *PF		D52
SCHAEFER, A.H. FANCY FREE. 3TPT, *PF		C09
SCHAEFER, A.H. TROUBADOURS, THE. 3TPT, *PF		C09
SCHOLTES(ARR). FANTASIE. 3TPT, *PF		G13
SHEPPARD, W.S. MERRY MOMENTS. 3TPT, *PF		G13
SMITH, W.M. BOLERO. 3TPT, *PF		C09
SMITH, W.M. 3 KINGS. 3TPT, *PF		C09
SMITH, W.M. THREE KINGS, THE. 3TPT, *PF		C11
STAIGERS, D. 3 STARS, THE. 3TPT, *PF		C11
STORM, C.W. SILVER BELLS. 3TPT, *PF		F07
STORM, C.W. 3 STARS. 3TPT, *PF		F07
STORM, C.W. WINGS IN THE WIND. 3TPT, *PF		F07
SUPPE, F.V. POET & PEASANT. 3TPT, *PF		B13
TCHAIKOVSKY, P.I. SWEET DREAMS FR. "ALBUM FOR THE YOUNG" 3TPT, *PF		D52
TCHAIKOVSKY, P.I. TOY SOLDIER FR. "ALBUM FOR THE YOUNG" 3TPT, *PF		D52
TCHEREPNIN, A.N. MARCH OF 3 TPTS. 3TPT, *PF		D63
TROTERE, H. IN OLD MADRID. 3TPT, *PF		B13
VAN HOESEN-KREISLER. LIEBESFREUD. 3TPT, *PF		C18
VAN HOESEN-KREISLER. OLD REFRAIN, THE. 3TPT, *PF		C18

VAN HOESEN-KREISLER. SCHON ROSMARIN. 3TPT, *PF		C18
VANDERCOOK, H.A. ACES OF THE AIR. 3TPT, *PF		F07
VANDERCOOK, H.A. WHIP-POOR-WILLS. 3TPT, *PF		F07
WALKER, R. EABILLAGE. 3TPT, *PF		A55
WALTERS, H.L. 3 JACKS, THE. 3TPT, *BAND, *PF		D52
WALTERS, H.L. JIM DANDIES. 3TPT, *PF		F07
WALTERS, H.L. LATE ONE EVENING. 3TPT, *PF		F07
WALTERS, H.L. TRUMPET FILIGREE. 3TPT, *PF		F07
WALTERS, H.L. TRUMPETS WILD. 3TPT, *PF		F07
WILLIAMS, E. ORION. 3TPT, *BAND, *PF		B31
WILLIAMS, E. TRIUMVIRATE. 3TPT, *PF		B31
WILLIAMS, E.S. 3 BLUEJACKETS. 3TPT, *BAND, *PF		B31
YODER, P. BRILLIANTE. 3TPT, *PF		D18
YODER, P. CUCARACHA, LA. 3TPT, *PF		D18

4 PARTS: HORNS-KEYBOARD

BREHM-LEIDZEN. HORNS A-HUNTING. 3HN, *PF		C25
HANISCH-PETIT. CONCERTO. 3HN, *PF		D11

4 PARTS: TROMBONES-KEYBOARD

BARNES, C.P. 3 DEBONAIRS. 3TRB(3TPT), *BAND, *PF		G10
BENNETT, J. SLIPPERY JOE. 3TRB, *PF		D14
BUCHTEL, F.L. 3 OF A KIND. 3TRB(3TPT), *PF		A55
BUCHTEI, F.L. POLKA DOTS. 3TRB(3TPT), *PF		A55
BUTTS, C.M. SWINGIN' SLIDES. 3TRB, *PF		D52
CLOUGH, T.H. 3 TROMBONISTS, THE. 3TRB, *PF		A78
CORELLI, A.-BROWN. 3 SONATAS, OP.1. 3TRB, *PF		C91
GIFFEN, H.-HUME. TRIO FOR 3 TRBS. 3TRB, *PF		A78
HARTZELL, D. MINOR BIT. 3TRB, *PF		F74
HURRELL, C.E. LONGHORNS, THE. 3TRB, *PF		F07
HURRELL, C.E. MEN ABOUT TOWN. 3TRB, *PF		F07
JACOBSON, I.D. 3 THOUGHTS FOR TROMBONES. 3TRB, *PF		D84
JOHNSON, C.W. AZURE SKIES. 3TRB, *PF		F07
JOHNSON, C.W. CAVALIERS, THE. 3TRB, *PF		F07
JOHNSON, C.W. PURPLE VALE. 3TRB, *PF		F07
JOHNSON, C.W. SILVER LAKES. 3TRB, *PF		F07
JOHNSON, C.W. 3 SLIPPERS. 3TRB, *PF		F07
KIEFER-HOLMES. ELENA POLKA. 3TRB(3TPT), *PF		A55
KOEPKE, P. RHAPSODIC INTERLUDE. 3TRB, *PF		F07
MOECKEL, H. SCHNELLE ZUGE. 3TRB, *PF		F10
MOZART, W.A. AVE VERUM. 2TPT, TRB, *PF		E14
OSTRANSKY, L. CONTEST TRIO NO.1. 3TRB, *PF		F07
OSTRANSKY, L. CONTEST TRIO NO.2. 3TRB, *PF		F07
SCHMIDT. CHAMBER MUSIC. TPT, HN, TRB, *PF		G21
SIMEONE, H. SLIDE KICKS. 3TRB, *BAND, *PF		F43
STOUTAMIRE. FLEDGLING FLIGHT. 3TRB, *PF		E80
TUTHILL, B.C. TROMBONE TROUBLE. 3TRB, *PF		F60
WALTERS, H.L. 3 GAUCHOS. 3TRB, *PF		A91
WALTERS, H.L. SLIPPERY GENTLEMEN. 3TRB, *PF		F07
WALTERS, H.L. TROMBONE CONTRASTS. 3TRB, *PF		F07

4 PARTS: MISCELLANEOUS-KEYBOARD

```
BERGHMANS, J.   CONCERTO GROSSO.   TPT, HN, TRB, *ORCH, *PF        D36
BERWALD, F.A.   KVARTETT ESS.   HN(VA), CL(VN), BSN(VC), PF        C39
BOWLES, P.F.   MUSIC FOR A FARCE.   TPT, CL, PERC, PA             G17
BREVAL, J.   CONCERTANTE, OP. 38 IN F.   HN, CL, BSN, PF         D11
CASELLA, A.   SINFONIA, OP.54.   TPT, CL, VC, PA                 B07
CLAFLIN, A.   RECITATIVO, ARIA & STRETTA.   HN, VA, VC, PA       E68
CRUSELL, B.H.   CONCERTANTE.   HN, CL, BSN, FF                   D11
CRUSELL, B.H.   CONCERTANTE, OP. 3 IN B-FLAT.   HN, CL, BSN, PF  D11
CRUSELL, B.H.   CONCERTINATE IN B-FLAT                          D11
   HN, FL, BSN, *ORCH, *PF
DEPELSENAIRE, J.M.   CONCERTO GROSSO.   2TPT, TRB, *ORCH, *PF    B24
DOMENICA, R.D.   QUARTET.   HN, VN, FL, PA                      D63
DREW, J.   COLLAGE I.   TPT, TRB, FL, PA                        B36
FOSTER, S.C.-WALTERS.   COME WHERE MY LOVE LIES DREAMING        F07
   2TPT, HN(TRB), *PF
FRESCOBALDI, G.   CANZONAS 1 & 5.   TRB, 2CTT(2TPT), BC         E14
FRESCOBALDI, G.   CANZONAS 27-29.   TRB, 2OB(2CTT), BC(ORG)     E14
GABAYE, P.   RECREATION.   TPT, HN, TRB, *PF, *BAND             D36
HAMBRAEUS, B.   TRANSIT NR. 2.   HN,TRB, PF, GUIT               B90
HOEFFNER-BLOCK.   SONATA A 8 IN C.   2TPT, BSN, PF              E14
HUBEAU, J.   SONATINE.   HN, FL, CL, PA                         A71
JOHNSON, C.W. (ARR).   SONGS OF THE RANGE.   2TPT, HN(TRB), *PF F07
KLEBE, G.   GRATULATIONS-TANGO.   TPT,ASAX, HPCD, ORG           A83
KOEPKE, P.   CANZONA.   2TPT, HN(TRB), *PF                      F07
KOEPKE, P.   FANFARE PRELUDE.   2TPT, HN(TRB), *PF              F07
KOEPKE, P.   GANDY DANCE.   2TPT, HN(TRB), *PF                  F07
LEGRENZI, G.-BLOCK.   SONATA, OP. 8 "LA BUSCHA"                 E14
   2TPT, BSN(VC), PF
LEICHTLING, A.   RUBAIYAT FRAGMENTS, OP. 55.   HN, EU, CL, PF   G66
NELHYBEL, V.   PIANO-BRASS QUARTET.   TPT, HN, TRB, PF          C40
PERUTI, C.   AUTUMN.   TRB, FL, CL, PF                          P48
PERUTI, C.   LEFTOVERS.   TRB, CL, BCL, PF                      P48
PERUTI, C.   3 SUNDAY PIECES.   TRB, CL, BCL, PF                P48
PFEIFFER, J.-LAUSCHMANN.   SONATA.   HN, FL, OB, CL, BSN        C75
PIER, G.   3 ETUDEN.   TPT, CL, PERC, PA                        B73
POGLIETTI, A.   SONATA A TRE.   TPT, FL, BSN, *CONTINUO         E62
POGLIETTI, A.-GOEBELS.   SONATA A TRE                           C71
   TPT(COR), FL, BSN, *CONTINUO
RIEGGER, W.   MOVEMENT.   2TPT, TRB, *PF                        F59
SCHENK, J.   SINFONIA CONCERTANTE.   HN, OB, CL, PF             E14
SKALKOTTAS, N.   QUARTET.   TPT, OB, BSN, PA                    F97
SMITH, L.C.   QUARTET.   HN, VN, VC, PA                         E68
SPIEGLER, M.   CANZONE II.   2TPT, BTRB, PA                     C91
STARER, R.   CONCERTO A TRE.   TPT, TRB, CL, PF                 D71
SUBOTNICK, M.   SERENADE NO.2.   HN, CL, PA, PERC               D55
TELEMANN, G.P.-GREBE.   KONCERT IN D MAJOR                      F50
   TPT, 2OB, *CONTINUO
WELIN, K.E.   MANZIT.   TRB, CL, VC, PA                         B90
WOLPE, S.   QUARTET NO. 1.   TPT, TSAX, PERC, PF                D55
```

4 PARTS: WIND(S)-STRING(S)

```
AMON, J.A.-LELOIR.  QUARTET FOR HN & STRGS, NO.1 IN F,OP.20/1      D11
   HN, VN, VA, VC
BECKERATH, A.V.  DIVERTIMENTO FUR HN & STREICHTRIO                 C60
   HN, VN, VA, VC
BERTALI, A.  SONATA FOR SOLO TROMBONE.  TRB, 2VN, BC              E14
BIBER, H.I.F.-JANETZKY.  SONATA A TRE.  TRB, 2VN, *CONTINUO       E14
BUTTERWORTH, A.  ROMANCE.  HN, 2VN, VA, (OET VC)                  C71
CASELLA, A.  SINFONIA, OP.54.  TPT, CL, VC, PA                    B07
CLAFLIN, A.  RECITATIVO, ARIA & STRETTA.  HN, VA, VC, PA          E68
CORELLI, A.  SONATA, D.  TPT, 2VN, *CONTINUO                      E14
CZERNY, C.  SERENADE.  HN, EFCL, VC, PF                           E14
DOMENICA, R.D.  QUARTET.  HN, VC, FL, PA                          D63
EDER, H.  DIVERTIMENTO.  TPT, VN, VC, RCDR                        C60
FASCH, J.F.-TOTTCHER.  SONATA A 4.  HN, OB, VN, *CONTINUO         F50
KRUYF, T.D.  QUARTET.  TPT, FL, BSN, VN                           B74
KUBIZEK, A.  VERGNUGLICHE MINIATUREN, OP.28A.  TRB, VN, VC, DB    B73
MC CARTY, R.P.  SONATA FOR BASS TRB                               B98
   BTRB, VN, VA, VC (OR BTRB, *ORCH)
MENGAL, J.B.  QUARTET FOR HN & STRG, NO.1 IN F,OP.8.  HN, STR     D11
RATTENBACH, A.  SERENATA.  TPT, FL, CL, VC                        E53
SCHAT, P.  2 STUKKEN.  TPT, FL, VN, PERC                          B74
SMITH, L.C.  QUARTET.  HN, VN, VC, PA                             E68
SOURILAS, T.  SUITE.  HN, OB, VC, HP(PF)                          D41
STAMITZ, C.P.-UPMEYER.  QUARTET IN D MAJOR                        A53
   HN(VA), VN, VC, FL
STAMITZ, C.P.  QUARTET IN F, OP.8/3.  HN(VA), VN, VC, OB(CL)      E14
STAMITZ, K.-UPMEYER.  QUARTETT D-DUR.  HN(VA), FL(OB), VN, VC     A51
STAMITZ, K.-WINSCHERMANN.  3 QUINTETTE, OP. 11, NR. 3, ES-DUR     F50
   HN, VN, VA, VC
STICH, J.V.-GOTTRON.  QUARTET , OP.2/1 IN F MAJOR                 A53
   HN, VN, VA, VC
STICH, J.V.-GOTTRON.  QUARTET, OP.18/1 IN F.  HN, VN, VA, VC      A51
STICH, J.V.-GOTTRON.  QUARTETT, OP.2/1 IN F MAJOR                 A51
   HN, VN, VA, VC
STOLZEL, G.H.-HAUSSWALD.  SONATE, F-DUR                           A90
   HN, OB, VN, *CCNTINUO
TOWNSEND, D.  EIGHT BY EIGHT, OP. 3/1                             E65
   TPT(CL, OB), RCDR(FL, PIC), VC(BSN, PF
WELIN, K.E.  MANZIT.  TRB, CL, VC, PA                             B90
WINTER, P.-STEFAN.  CONCERTINO.  HN, CL, BSN, VA                  D11
```

4 PARTS: BRASS-MISCELLANEOUS

```
BERTALI, A.  SONATA FOR SOLO TROMBONE.  TRB, 2VN, BC             E14
COLDING-JORGENSEN.  INTRADA.  2TRB, VC, ORG                      C17
CZERNY, C.  SERENADE.  HN, PF, VC, EFCL                          E14
DEMANTIUS, C.-DEGEN.  DEUTSCHE TANZE.  4INST ?                   C17
DIEMENTE, E.  QUARTET.  TRB, PERC, DB, ASAX                      G66
FASCH, C.F.C.  TRIPLE CONCERTO IN E                             E14
   TPT, PF, VN, OB D'AMORE (OB)
FUX, G.G.-BARROLL & LANE.  SONATA A 3.  TRB, 2VN, BC            M80
```

```
GASSMANN, A.L.   BIM CHRONEWIRT....  TPT, 2CL, HAND ORG          C80
GASSMANN, A.L.   D'LANDLERMUSIK.  TPT,  CL, DB, ORG              C80
KAM, D.  GO.  TRB, VC(DB), CL, CONDUCTOR                         N91
KUBIZEK, A.  QUARTETTO DA CAMERA, OP. 24.  TRB, OB, CL, GUIT     B73
LE MIEUX, D.  CONTINUUM.  TPT, VIB, MARIMBA, PF                  B35
PORRET, J.  CALDERON.  4 EQUAL TC                               D92
SCHMELZER, J.H.  SONATA PASTORALIS.  TRB, 2VN, BC               E14
SHEINKMAN, M.  DIVERTIMENTO.  TPT, TRB, CL, HP                  D48
SHEINKMAN, M.  DIVERTIMENTO.  TPT, TRB, CL, HP                  E65
```

FIVE-PART MUSIC

5 EQUAL BRASS INSTRUMENTS

```
BACH, J.S.   CHORALE PRELUDE-"WIR GLAUBEN ALL'AN EINEN GOTT"      C78
   5HN
BACH, J.S.-SHAW.   2 CHORUSES (JESU, MEINE FREUDE)               C78
BACH, J.S.-HALVERSON.   JESU, MEINE FREUDE.   3TRB, 2BTRB        B98
BONELLI, A.-FALCONE & CRAMER.   ITALIAN MARCH.   5TRB           F60
BOTTJE, W.G.   ESSAY, MUSIC FOR LIKE INSTRUMENTS NO. 5.   5HN   A13
CHOPIN, F.-SHINER.   2 PRELUDES.   5TRB                         D14
DORSAM.   FANFARE & FUGUE.   5TPT                               N03
FRANK, M.   LYRIC POEM.   5TU                                   C25
GLOBOKAR, V.   DISCOURS II.   5TRB                              E65
GRIEG, E.H.-LIVELY.   LAST SPRING, THE.   5HN                   F60
HANDEL, G.F.-LIVELY.   EXCERPTS FROM WATER MUSIC.   5HN         F60
HAYDN, J.-JAMESON.   10 COMMANDMENT CANONS                      G78
HESSEN, M.G.L.V.-MILLER.   PAVANA.   5TRB                       B98
LEITERMEYER.   3 STUDIEN.   5HN                                 B73
LO PRESTI, R.   FANTASY FOR HORN QUINTET.   5 HN                P49
LO PRESTI, R.   SUITE.   5TPT                                   F43
MENDELSSOHN, F.   FUGUE.   5TPT                                 M71
MENDELSSOHN, F.-MOORE.   FUGUE.   5TPT                          G21
MENDELSSOHN, F.-SHINER.   SCHERZO.   5TRB                       D14
MONTEVERDI, C.   SINFONIA & CHORUS OF SPIRITS.   5TRB           D14
NASH.   SUITE.   5TRB                                           M96
OTT, J.   SUITE.   5TU                                          B53
PEDERSON, T.   BANANA BOAT.   5TRB                              M93
PEDERSON, T.   CHRISTMAS CAROLS.   5TRB                         D14
PEDERSON, T.   DUENA, LA.   5TRB                                M93
PEDERSON, T.   JOGGER, THE.   5TRB                              M93
PEDERSON, T.   LAUGHING FACE OF THE OLD, UGLY, ORNERY OGRE      M93
   5TRB
PEDERSON, T.   LEPRECHAUN LULLABY.   5TRB                       M93
PEDERSON, T.   PORTUGESE PASSPORT.   5TRB                       M93
PEDERSON, T.   SEVERAL ANNOUNCEMENTS.   TRB                     M95
PEDERSON, T.   WALTZ OF THE DIRTY SHIRTS.   5TRB                M93
PEDERSON, T.   WHAT ELSE.   5TRB                                M93
PEDERSON, T.   WISHING WELL, THE.   5TRB                        M93
PRESSER, W.H.   SUITE.   5TU                                    F80
PURCELL, H.-MILLER.   LAMENT FROM DIDO & AENEAS                 B98
   4TRB, BTRB(TU)
REYNOLDS, V.   MUSIC FOR 5 TPTS.   5TPT                         D16
RILEY, J.   3 ACTS.   5TRB                                      M80
RYKER.   SHORT FANFARE.   5TPT                                  D94
SCHUBERT, F.P.-SMITH.   LOVE'S LONGING (SEHNSUCHT).   5TRB      B98
SCHULLER, G.   5 PIECES FOR 5 HORNS.   5HN                      B00
SEVERSON.   VINCENTIAN FANFARE & ST.JUSTIN CHORALE.   5TRB      F27
SHELUKOV, V.   MOVEMENT.   5TU                                  N42
SHELUKOV, V.   MOVEMENT.   5TU                                  P19
SHELUKOV, V.   QUINTET.   5TPT OR 5 HN                          P19
SHINER, M.   MEXICAN CARNIVAL.   5TRB                           D14
SOMBRUN.   L'ART DE SONNER DE LA TROMPE, PT. 2.   5HN           D36
STEIN, A.   QUINTESSENCE.   5TRB                                N29
STOLZER, T.A.-KING.   FANTASIA.   5TRB                          D16
TCHAIKOVSKY, P.I.-SHINER.   DANCE OF THE REED PIPES.   5TRB     D14
TCHAIKOVSKY, P.I.-SHINER.   DANCE OF THE SUGAR PLUM FAIRY       D14
   5TRB
WAGNER, R.-SHINER.   PILGRIM'S CHORUS.   5TRB                   D14
```

WAGNER, R.-KING. WALKURE, DIE(ACT 2, SCENE 4). 4TRB, BTRB   B98

5 MIXED BRASS (BRASS-PERC)

ABACO, DALL-DOCKSTADER. ADAGIO & ALLEGRO   G78
  2TPT, HN, TRB, TU(BTRB)
ACKER. CANTUS DURIUSCULUS. 2TPT, HN, TRB, TU   C51
ADLER, S. 5 MOVEMENTS. 2TPT, HN, TRB, TU   D16
ADSON, J. 2 AYRES. 2TPT, HN(TRB), TRB, TU-TRB   D16
ADSON, J.-GREER. 3 COURTLY MASQUING AYRES. 2TPT, 3TRB   F31
ALBENIZ. TANGO. 2TPT, HN, EU, TU   B44
ALBINONI, T.-DOCKSTADER. ALLEGRO. 2TPT, HN, TRB, TU   G78
ALBINONI, T.-THILDE. SUITE IN A. 2TPT, HN, TRB, TU   A71
ALCHINGER-ROSENTHAL. 3 RENAISSANCE MADRIGALS   G21
  2TPT, HN, TRB, TU
ALEXANDER. 4 FOR FIVE. 2TPT, 2HN, TRB(TU)   F59
ALFORD, K.J.-STRATTON. COLONEL BOGEY. 2TPT, HN, TRB, TU   A78
ALIABIEV, A.N. KVINTET. 2TPT, TRB, 2EU   E14
AMES, W. BRASS QUINTET. 2TPT, HN, TRB, TU   B04
AMES, W. QUINTET. 2TPT, HN, TRB, TU   A13
AMRAM, D.W. FANFARE & PROCESSIONAL. 2TPT, HN, TRB, TU   E65
ANDRIESSEN, H. AUBADE. 2TPT, HN, 2TRB   B74
ANDRIESSEN, H. SUITE. 2TPT, HN, 2TRB   B74
ANDRIESSEN, J. QUATTRO MADRIGALI. 2TPT, HN, 2TRB   B74
ANTEGNATI, C. CANZONA 20. 2TPT, 2TRB, TRB(HN)   E14
ARCHER, V. DIVERTIMENTO FOR BRASS QUINTET. 2TPT, HN, TRB, TU   D94
ARNE, T.A.-DOCKSTADER. ADAGIO & VIVACE   G78
  2TPT, HN, TRB, TU(BTRB)
ARNE, T.A.-WELSHMAN. VIVACE. 2TPT, HN, TRB, EU   G78
ARNELL. VARIATIONS ON WAYFARING STRANGER. 2TPT, HN, TRB, TU   F59
ARNELL, R. QUINTET. 2TPT, HN, TRB, TU   F59
ARNOLD, M. QUINTET, OP.73. 2TPT, HN, TRB, TU   E58
ASOLA, J.-WALDECK. DIES IRAE. 2TPT, HN, TRB, TU   B44
AVARMAA, O. SUITE FOR BRASS QUINTET. 2TPT, HN, TRB, TU   D94
AVARMAA, O. THEME & VARIATIONS FOR BRASS QUINTET   D94
  2TPT, HN, TRB, TU
BABER. THEME AND FANTASIA. 2TPT, HN, TRB, TU   F43
BACH, J.S.-ROSENTHAL. AIR POUR LES TROMPETTES   G21
  2TPT, HN, TRB, TU
BACH, J.S.-CHRISTENSEN. 3 BACH CHORALES. 2TPT, TRB, EU, TU   D14
BACH, J.S.-TAYLOR. CANZONA IN D MINOR. 2TPT, HN, 2TRB   M79
BACH, J.S.-ADLER. CAPRICCIO. 2TPT, HN, TRB, TU   F60
BACH, J.S.-FOTE. CHORALE & FUGHETTA. 2TPT, HN, TRB, EU   D14
BACH, J.S.-KLEIN. CHORALE PRELUDE. 2TPT, HN, TRB, TU   G78
BACH, J.S.-ROSENTHAL. CHORALE PRELUDE:WIR GLAUBEN ALL   G21
  2TPT, HN, TRB, TU
BACH, J.S.-UBER. 2 CHORALES. 2TPT, HN, TRB, TU   B85
BACH, J.S.-SHAW. 2 CHORUSES FROM JESU, MEINE FREUDE. 4HN, TU   C78
BACH, J.S.-KING. CONTRAPUNCTUS I   D11
  2TPT, HN(TPT), TRB(HN), TRB-TU
BACH, J.S.-MORRIS. CONTRAPUNCTUS I. 2EU, 3TU   M80
BACH, J.S.-MORRIS. CONTRAPUNCTUS I. 2EU, 3TU   P42
BACH, J.S.-KING. CONTRAPUNCTUS III   D16
  2TPT, HN(TPT), TRB(HN), TU-TRB
BACH, J.S.-NAGEL. CONTRAPUNCTUS IV. 2TPT, HN, TRB, TU   D73
BACH, J.S.-GLASEL. CONTRAPUNCTUS IX FROM ART OF THE FUGUE   C25
  2TPT, HN, TRB, TU
BACH, J.S.-FOTE. CONTRAPUNCTUS IX. 2TPT, HN, TRB, TU   D14

```
BACH, J.S.  CONTRAPUNCTUS NO.IX.  2TPT, HN, TRB, TU                    D73
BACH, J.S.  CONTRAPUNCTUS NO.4.  2TPT, HN, TRB, TU                     D94
BACH, J.S.-KING.  CONTRAPUNCTUS V.  2TPT, HN(TRB), TRB, EU-TU          D16
BACH, J.S.-ROSENTHAL.  FANTASIE.  2TPT, HN, TRB, TU                    G21
BACH, J.S.  2 FUGARE.  2TPT, HN, TRB, TU                               D94
BACH, J.S.-SEAR.  FUGUE IN D MINOR.  2TPT, HN, TRB, TU                 B44
BACH, J.S.-DECKER.  FUGUE IN G MINOR.  2TPT, HN, TRB, TU               D14
BACH, J.S.-BROCKWAY.  FUGUE IV A5.  2TPT, HN, TRB, TU(TRB)             E61
BACH, J.S.  FUGUE NO.14.  2TPT, 2TRB, TU                               B85
BACH, J.S.-SEAR.  FUGUE XXII FROM WTC.  2TPT, HN, TRB, TU              B44
BACH, J.S.-BEELER.  IF THOU BE NEAR.  2TPT, HN, TRB, TU                F07
BACH, J.S.-SEAR.  IN DULCI JUBILO.  2TPT, HN, TRB, TU                  B44
BACH, J.S.-KLEIN.  JESU.  2TPT, HN, TRB, TU                            G78
BACH, J.S.-SEAR.  MY SOUL LONGETH & MARCH.  2TPT, HN, TRB, TU          B44
BACH, J.S.-GORDON.  5 PIECES FOR BRASS CHOIR                           H06
   2TPT, 2HN, TRB(TU), (OPT SDR, TIMP)
BACH, J.S.  2 PRAELUDII.  2TPT, HN, TRB, TU                            D94
BACH, J.S.  PRAELUDIUM XXII (WELL TEMPERED CLAVICHORD)                 B44
   2TPT, HN, TRB, TU
BACH, J.S.-ROSENTHAL.  PRELUDE & FUGUE, G MINOR                        G21
   2TPT, HN, TRB, TU
BACH, J.S.-ANDERSON.  PRELUDE AND FUGUE IN E MINOR                     G21
   2TPT, HN, TRB, TU
BACH, J.S.-TAYLOR.  PRELUDE AND FUGUE NO. 11.  2TPT, HN, 2TRB          M79
BACH, J.S.  PRELUDE AND FUGUE NO. 4 IN C-SHARP MINOR                   G83
   2TPT, HN, TRB, TU (TRB)
BACH, J.S.-ANDERSON.  PRELUDE AND FUGUE XVI                            G21
   2TPT, HN, TRB, TU
BACH, J.S.-MC GREGOR.  SARABANDE AND COURANTE                         G83
   2TPT, HN, TRB, TU (TU)
BACH, J.S.-ROSENTHAL.  TRUMPET FUGUE.  2TPT, HN, TRB, TU               G21
BACH, J.S.-ROSENTHAL.  WIR GLAUBEN ALL' AN EINEN GOTT                  G21
   2TPT, HN, TRB, TU
BACH, JAN.  LAUDES.  2TPT, HN, TRB, TU                                 D73
BAKER, D.  PASSIONS FOR BRASS QUINTET.  2TPT, HN, TRB, TU              D94
BALADA.  MOSAICO.  2TPT, HN, 2TRB                                      C40
BALDWIN.  CONSORT MUSIC.  2TPT, HN, TRB, TU                            G83
BALDWIN.  NOTES.  2TPT, HN, TRB, TU                                    N42
BANCHIERI & SCHUTZ.  2 SINFONIAS.  2TPT, HN, TRB, TU                   D94
BANCHIERI, A.-EDWARDS.  SINFONIA.  2TPT, HN, TRB, TU                   G83
BARBOTEU, G.  ASTRAL.  2TPT, HN, TRB, TU                               B24
BARON, S.  IMPRESSIONS OF A PARADE.  2TPT, HN, TRB, TU                 F23
BARTOK, B.-GORDON.  3 FOLK DANCES.  2TPT, HN(TRB), TRB, TU             F60
BARTOK, B.-BROWN.  LITTLE BARTOK SUITE, A                              E80
   2TPT, HN, TRB, TU (EU)
BARTSCH, C.  SUITE.  2TPT, HN, TRB, TU                                 D67
BASTIEN.  EXIGENCE.  2TPT, HN, TRB, TU                                 P47
BASTIEN, G.  EXIGENCE POUR QUINTETTE DE CUIVRES                        D94
   2TPT, HN, TRB, TU
BAZELON.  BRASS QUINTET.  2TPT, HN, 2TRB                               G68
BEACH, B.C.  MUSIC FOR BRASS QUINTET.  2TPT, HN, TRB, TU               F80
BEETHOVEN, L.V.-SEAR.  OPUS 130, FINALE.  2TPT, HN, TRB, BTRB          B44
BEETHOVEN, L.V.-SEAR.  OPUS 130, 2ND MVT.  2TPT, HN, TRB, TU           B44
BEETHOVEN, L.V.-ROSS.  PRAYER, OP.48/1.  2TPT, HN, TRB(EU), TU         D14
BEETHOVEN, L.V.  2 STUCKE.  2TPT, HN, TRB, TU                          D94
BENNETT, R.R.  COMMEDIA IV.  2TPT, HN, TRB, TU                         E41
BENOIST, A.-TALLMADGE.  FANTAISIE L'AMERIQUE.  2TPT, HN, 2TRB          C11
BERGENFELD.  FESTA BAROCCA.  2TPT, HN, TRB, EU                         F79
BERLIN, D.  QUADROPHONICS.  2TPT, HN, TRB, BTRB                        P48
BERLIOZ, H.  FUGUE A 3 SUJETS.  2TPT, HN, TRB, TU                      D94
BERLIOZ, H.-HOMZY.  FUGUE.  2TPT, HN, TRB, TU                          G83
BERMAN, M.  QUINTET FOR BRASS.  2TPT, HN, TRB, TU                      D94
```

```
BERTALI, A.-HILL & BLOCK.  6 SONATAS.  2TPT, HN(TRB), 2TRB          E14
BIGGS, J.  3 EARLY PIECES.  2TPT, HN, TRB, TU                       G21
BLANK, A.  4 PIECES.  2TPT, 3TRB                                    E68
BLANK, A.  4 PIECES.  2TPT, 3TRB                                    G66
BOHM.  PRESTO.  2TPT, HN, TRB, TU                                   N61
BOHM, G.-DISHINGER.  PRESTO.  2TPT, HN, TRB, TU                     N61
BORNEFELD.  SONATINE.  2TPT, 2TRB, TU                               N04
BOTTJE, W.G.  VARIATIONS.  2TPT, HN, TRB, TU                        A13
BOUTRY, R.  PRELUDE, CHORALE ET FUGUE                               D36
   2TPT, HN(TRB), TRB(HN), TU(TRB)
BOZZA, E.  BIS.  2TPT, HN, TRB, TU                                  D36
BOZZA, E.  GIRATION.  2TPT, HN, TRB, TU                             D36
BOZZA, E.  SONATINE.  2TPT, HN, TRB, TU                             D36
BOZZA, E.  SUITE FRANCAISE.  2TPT, HN, TRB, TU                      D36
BOZZA, E.  SUITE NO.2.  2TPT, HN, TRB, TU                           D94
BOZZA, E.  TRILOGIE.  2TPT, HN, TRB, TU                             D36
BRACALI.  SEXTOUR SUR UN THEME DE MONTEVERDI                        D36
   3TPT, PERC, TIMP
BRADE, W.  4 DANCES.  2TPT, HN, TRB, TU                             D94
BRADE, W.-KING.  2 PIECES.  2TPT, 2TRB(2HN), TRB-TU                 D16
BRADE, W.  52 SHORT PIECES.  3TRB, 2CTT(2TPT)                       E14
BRAHMS, J.-LOCKWOOD.  CHORALE AND FUGUE.  2TPT, HN, TRB, TU         N42
BRAHMS, J.-WALDECK.  CHORALE AND FUGUE.  2TPT, HN, TRB, TU          B44
BRAHMS, J.-FOTE.  CHORALE PRELUDE NO. 8                             D14
   2TPT, HN, TRB, TRB(TU)
BRAHMS, J.-ROSENTHAL.  3 CHORALE PRELUDES.  2TPT, HN, TRB, TU       G21
BRAHMS, J.  ES IST EIN ROS' ENTSPRUNGEN                             D16
   TPT, HN(TRB), TRB, TRB-TU, TPT(HN)
BRAHMS, J.-JOLLEY.  3 MOTETS.  2TPT, HN, 2TRB                       M79
BRAHMS, J.-LOCKWOOD.  2 SONGS.  2TPT, HN, TRB, TU                   G83
BRANA.  A LA CALYPSO.  2TPT, HN, TRB, TU                            C40
BRANA.  A LA FUGA.  2TPT, HN, TRB, TU                               C40
BRANA.  A LA MODE.  2TPT, HN, TRB, TU                               C40
BRANA.  A LA ROCK.  2TPT, HN, TRB, TU                               C40
BRANA.  BASSO OSTINATO.  2TPT, HN, TRB, TU                          C40
BRANA.  ROCKING METRONOME.  2TPT, HN, TRB, TU                       C40
BRANCH.  3 SYMPHONIC SONGS.  2TPT, HN, TRB, TU                      N07
BRANDON, S.  MOVEMENTS FOR BRASS QUINTET.  2TPT, HN, TRB, TU        P48
BREHM, A.  QUINTET FOR BRASS.  2TPT, HN, 2TRB                       D63
BRIEGEL, G.F.(ARR).  TAPS & ECHO TAPS.  TPT, 4TRB                   A91
BROTT, A.  MUTUAL SALVATION ORGY.  2TPT, HN, TRB, TU               D94
BROWER, J.  BELLE FRANCE, LA.  2TPT, HN, TRB, TU                   B44
BROWER, J.-SEAR.  SUSSEX MUMMER'S CAROL & ANGELS...REALMS          B44
   2TPT, HN, TRB, TU
BROWN, R.  BRASS QUINTET NO.2.  2TPT, HN, TRB, TU                   G21
BROWN, R.E.  DELINEATIONS.  2TPT, HN, TRB, TU                       M80
BRUHNS-KLEIN.  FUGUE.  2TPT, HN, TRB, TU                            G78
BUBALO, R.  3 PIECES FOR BRASS QUINTET.  2TPT, HN, TRB, TU          C33
BUFFINGTON.  TYING THE KNOT.  2TPT, HN, TRB, TU                     C25
BUONAMENTE, G.B.  CANZON A 5.  3TRB, 2CTT(2TPT)                     E14
BUONAMENTE, G.B.-SHOEMAKER.  SONATA A 5 NO. 20                      N47
   2TPT, HN(TRB), TRB, TU(TRB)
BURGMULLER-ZUSKIN.  4 KINDERSTUCKE.  2TPT, HN, TRB, TU              D94
BURRELL.  FESTIVE OCCASION.  2TPT, HN, TRB, TU                      B23
BURY, P.  DOWN IN THE DEEP CELLAR (TUBA DEMO PIECE)                 B04
   2TPT, HN, TRB, TU
BUSCH, C.  DIALOGUE.  2TPT, HN, TRB, EU                             A62
BUSCH, C.  IN A HAPPY MOOD.  2TPT, HN, TRB, EU                      B53
BUSCH, C.  QUINTETTE.  2TPT, HN, TRB, EU                            A62
BUXTEHUDE, D.  ORGAN PRELUDE--CHRIST UNSER HERR...                  D14
   2TPT, HN, TRB, TU
BYRD-WISE.  ALLELUIA, ALLELUIA.  2TPT, HN, TRB, TU(TRB)             M79
```

```
CABUS, P.N.   ELEGIA.   2TPT, HN, 2TRB                              D67
CALABRO, L.   CEREMONIAL MARCH FOR BRASS & PERC.                    B92
   2TPT, 2TRB, PERC
CALDARA-DOCKSTADER.   GRAVE.   2TPT, HN, TRB, TU                    G78
CALVERT, M.   OCCASIONAL SUITE FOR BRASS QUINTET, AN               D94
   2TPT, HN, TRB, TU
CALVERT, M.   SUITE FROM THE MONTEREGIAN HILLS                      D94
   2TPT, HN, TRB, TU
CAMBRELING.   DIVERTISSEMENT.   2TPT, HN, TRB, TU                   A71
CAMESI.   2 PIECES.   2TPT, HN, TRB, TU                             M79
CAMPO.   MADRIGALS.   2TPT, HN, TRB, TU                             G21
CANNING, T.S.   4 CHRISTMAS PIECES.   2TPT, HN, TRB, TU             A13
CARTER.   BRASS QUINTET.   2TPT, HN, 2TRB                           A38
CASANOVA.   3 MOMENTI.   2TPT, HN, TRB, TU                          A71
CHAGRIN, F.   DIVERTIMENTO.   2TPT, HN, TRB, TU                     C35
CHARLES, V.   QUINTET.   2TPT, HN, TRB, TU                          B04
CHEETHAM, J.   SCHERZO.   2TPT, HN, TRB, TU                         G21
CHERUBINI, L.-HAAS.   8 MARCHES.   TPT, 3HN, TRB                    D84
CHILDS, B.   BRASS QUINTET.   2TPT, HN, TRB, TU                     E68
CHILDS, B.   2ND BRASS QUINTET.   2TPT, HN, TRB, TU                 E68
CHILDS, B.   3RD BRASS QUINTET.   2TPT, HN, TRB, TU                 E68
CHILDS, B.   QUINTET NO. 2.   2TPT, HN, TRB, TU                     A13
CHILDS, B.   QUINTET NO. 3.   2TPT, HN, TRB, TU                     A13
CHILDS, B.   QUINTET.   2TPT, HN, 2TRB                              A13
CHILDS, B.   VARIATIONS SUR UNE CHANSON DE CANOTIER                 B98
   2TPT, HN, TRB, TU
CHILESE, B.   CANZONA 22.   2TPT, TRB(HN), 2TRB                     E14
CHOPIN, F.-SHVEDOFF.   MILITARY POLONAISE, OP.40/1                  G31
   2TPT, 2HN, EU
CHRISTENSEN, J. (ARR).   3 BACH CHORALES.   2TPT, HN, TRB, EU-TU    D14
CLARK.   BELGIAN MARCH.   2TPT, HN, TRB, TU                         F60
CLARK.   PIOUS SELINDA.   TPT, TPT(HN), HN(TRB), TRB, SOLO EU       B85
CLARK, S.-WILLIAMS.   BELGIAN MARCH.   5INST ?                      F60
CLARKE.   GOD REST YE MERRY GENTLEMEN.   2TPT,HN, TRB, TU           D14
COBINE, A.   TRILOGY FOR BRASS.   2TPT, HN, TRB, TU                 B98
COBINE, A.   WABASH VALLEY SUITE.   2TPT, HN, TRB, TU               D94
COLEMAN, C.-BAINES.   4 PIECES FOR SACKBUTS & CORNETTS             E51
   2TPT, 3TRB
CONGREVE-CLARK.   PIOUS SELINDA                                     B85
   TPT, TRB, EU, TPT(HN), TRB(HN)
CONNOLLY.   CINQUEPACES.   2TPT, HN, TRB, TU                        E51
CONVERSE, F.S.   2 LYRIC PIECES, OP.106/1 & 2                       F07
   2TPT, HN(EU), TRB, TU
CORBETT.   ALLEMANDE.   2TPT, HN, TRB, TU                           N42
CORELLI, A.-WELSHMAN.   ADAGIO AND ALLEMANDE                        G78
   2TPT, HN, TRB, TU
CORELLI, A.-SCHAEFFER.   ADAGIO.   2TPT, HN, TRB, TU(TRB)           E80
CORELLI, A.   GAVOTTE & GIGA (HN DEMO PIECE)                        B04
   2TPT, HN, TRB, TU
CORELLI, A.-POWELL.   PRELUDE & SARABANDE.   2TPT, HN, TRB          F60
CORELLI, A.-TAYLOR.   SERENATA.   2TPT, HN, EU, TU                  D84
CORELLI, A.-SUDMEIER.   SUITE.   2TPT, HN, 2TRB                     B04
COSCIA.   MADRIGAL AND FUGUE.   2TPT, HN, TRB, TU                   N95
COSCIA.   SUITE IN 3 MOODS.   2TPT, HN, TRB, TU                     N95
COURNOYER.   BRASS QUINTET.   2TPT, HN, TRB, TU                     B04
COWELL.   ACTION IN BRASS.   2TPT, HN, 2TRB                         B85
CROLEY, R.   CONCERT MUSIC.   2TPT, HN, TRB, TU                     G83
CROLEY, R.   DISQUISITION, CYCLIC CHORALE.   2TPT, HN, TRB, TU      F88
CROLEY, R.   SINFONIETTA.   2TPT, HN, TRB, TU                       G83
CRUFT, A.F. (ARR).   3 ENGLISH KEYBOARD PIECES                     G26
   2TPT, 2TRB, BTRB
CUNNINGHAM, M.G.   CONCERTANT.   2TPT, HN, TRB, TU                  G66
```

CUSTER, A.R. CONCERTO. 2TPT, HN, TRB, TU (TRB)   C40
CZERNOHORSKY-DISHINGER. FUGUE. INST ?   N61
DAETWYLER, J. CONCERTO POUR 4 CORS ET PERC. 4HN, PERC   H03
DAHL, I. MUSIC FOR BRASS INSTRUMENTS   H06
     2TPT, HN, 2TRB, (OPT TU)
DAUM. SUITE FOR YOUNG LISTENERS. 2TPT, HN, TRB, TU   B32
DAVIS. SONATA. 2TPT, HN, TRB, TU   F60
DE JONG, C. ESSAY FOR BRASS QUINTET. 2TPT, HN, TRB, TU   G83
DE JONG, M. HUMORISTISCHE SUITE, OP.128. 2TPT, HN, TRB, TU   B12
DE JONG, M. SUITE, OP.100B. 3TPT, HN, TRB   B12
DE KRUYF. AUBADE. 2TPT, HN, TRB, TU   B74
DE WERT, G.-AMEND. CANZONA. 2TPT, HN, TRB, TU   M80
DELA, M. DIVERTISSEMENT POUR QUINTETTE DE CUIVRES   D94
     2TPT, HN, TRB, TU
DELAMONT. MODERATO AND BLUES. 2TPT, HN, TRB, TU   M65
DELP, R. HYPOSTASIS. 2TPT, TRB, TU, FLG   N37
DERING-COOL. FANTASIA. 2TPT, HN, TRB, TU   G83
DES PREZ, J. FAULTE D'ARGENT. 2TPT, HN, TRB, TU   D94
DESPREZ, F. THEME ET VARIATIONS SUR "LA FOLIA"   D67
     4TPT, TRB, (OPT TIMP)
DESPREZ, J.-LEE. FAULTE D'ARGENT. 2TPT, HN, TRB, TU(BTRB)   G78
DI LASSO, O.-LEE. TRISTIS EST ANIMA MEA   G78
     2TPT, HN, TRB, TU(BTRB)
DIETERICH, M. HORIZONS. 2TPT, HN, TRB, TU   F07
DILLON, R.M. SUITE FOR BRASS QUINTET   A02
     2TPT, HN(FLG, TRB), TRB(HN), TU(BTRB)
DONDERER, G. SUITE. 4 NATURAL TPT, TIMP   A90
DOWLAND. 2 DANCES. 2TPT, HN, TRB, TU   F59
DRAKEFORD. TOWER MUSIC. 2TPT, HN, TRB, TU   E41
DUKAS, P.-BARRINGTON. FANFARE (LA PERI). 2TPT, HN, TRB, TU   B92
DVORAK, A. SONGS OF NATURE. 2TPT, HN, TRB, TU   N42
EAST-FROMME. DESPERAVI. 2TPT, HN, 2TRB   A38
EHMANN, W. (CMPL). ALTE SPIELMUSIK FUR BLASER. 5INST ?   A51
EHMANN, W. (CMPL). CLASER-INTRADEN ZUM WOCHENLIED.... 5INST ?   A51
EMMETT, D.D.-ROBERTS. DIXIE. 2TPT, HN, TRB, TU   B44
END, J. 3 SALUTATIONS. 2TPT, HN, TRB, TU   E87
ETLER, A.D. QUINTET FOR BRASS INSTRUMENTS. 2TPT, HN, TRB, TU   A38
ETLER, A.D. SONIC SEQUENCE. 2TPT, HN, 2TRB   A38
EWALD, V.-VOXMAN. QUINTET IN B MINOR (3RD MVT)   F07
     2TPT, HN, TRB, TU
EWALD, V. QUINTET, OP.5. 2TPT, HN, TRB, TU   B98
EWALD, V.-KING. SYMPHONY FOR BRASS CHOIR, OP.5   D16
     2TPT, HN, TRB, TRB-TU
FANTINI, G. 2 IMPERIALES. 2TPT, HN(TRB), 2TRB   M80
FARBERMAN, H. 5 IMAGES. 2TPT, HN, TRB, TU   C40
FARNABY, G. FANCIES, TOYES & DREAMES   D58
     TPT, HN(TRB), TRB, TU, TPT(HN)
FEGERS. FRISCH AUF INS WEITE FELD. 3TPT, 2TRB   D98
FEGERS. 2 WEIHNACHTLICHE LIEDKANTEN. 3TPT, 2TRB   D98
FELD, J. QUINTETTE. 2TPT, HN, TRB, TU(TRB)   D36
FENNELLY, B. COMPOSITION FOR 5 BRASSES. 2TPT, HN, TRB, TU   A13
FENNELLY, B. PRELUDE & ELEGY. 2TPT, HN, TRB, TU   A13
FENNELLY, B. PRELUDE. 2TPT, HN, TRB, TU   A13
FERRABOSCO-JAMESON. FOUR NOTE PAVAN, THE   G78
     2TPT, HN, TRB, TU(BTRB)
FERRABOSCO-BALDWIN. HEXACHORD, THE. 2TPT, HN, TRB, TU   N42
FILLMORE, H. LASSUS TROMBONE (TRB DEMO PIECE)   B04
     2TPT, HN, TRB, TU
FINCK-SIRINEK. GREINER ZANNER. 2TPT, HN, TRB, TU   M79
FISCHER, J.-WALDECK. BOURREE & MINUET. 2TPT, HN, TRB, TU   B44
FISCHER, J.-WALDECK. ENTREE & RONDO. 2TPT, HN, TRB, TU   B44
FISCHER, J.-WALDECK. JOURNAL DU PRINTEMPS, LE, OP.1   B44
     2TPT, HN, TRB, TU

```
FLAGELLO.  PHILOS.  2TPT, HN, TRB, TU(BTRB)                        C40
FLEMING, R.  3 MINIATURES ("3-4-5").  2TPT, HN, TRB, TU           D94
FLEMING, R.  QUINTET FOR BRASS.  2TPT, HN, TRB, TU               D94
FRACKENPOHL, A.R.  BRASS QUINTET NO. 2                            M98
   2TPT, HN, TRB, TU(TRB)
FRACKENPOHL, A.R.  BRASS QUINTET.  2TPT, HN, TRB, TU             B92
FRACKENPOHL, A.R.  GLAD RAGS SUITE.  2TPT, HN, TRB, TU           D63
FRACKENPOHL, A.R.  POP SUITE.  2TPT, HN, TRB, TU                 D14
FRACKENPOHL, A.R.  RAGTIME SUITE.  2TPT, HN, TRB, TU             D63
FRANCK.  LYRIC POEM.  2EU, 3TU                                    C25
FRANCK, M.-LEE.  2 GALLIARDS.  2TPT, HN, TRB, TU(BTRB)           G78
FRANCK, M.  2 PAVANS.  2TPT, HN(TRB), TRB(HN), TRB-TU            D16
FRANCO, J.  CHORALE & CONTEMPLATION.  3TPT, HN, TRB             A13
FREDRICKSON.  BRASS QUINTET.  2TPT, HN, TRB, TU                 B30
FRESCOBALDI, G.-BLOCK.  CANZONA 21.  2TPT, TRB(HN), 2TRB        E14
FRESCOBALDI, G.-LEE.  FUGA.  2TPT, HN, TRB, TU(BTRB)            G78
FRESCOBALDI, G.-SABATINI.  FUGUE & CAPRICCIO                     B04
   2TPT, HN, TRB, TU
FROMME.  3 SHORT STUDIES.  2TPT, HN, 2TRB                        D40
GABRIELI, A.-LENHERT.  CANZONA.  2TPT, HN, TRB, TU              D14
GABRIELI, A.  RICERCAR ARIOSO I.  INST ?                         P19
GABRIELI, A.-WALDECK.  3 RICERCARI.  2TPT, HN, TRB, TU          B44
GABRIELI, G.-THOMAS.  CANZON NO. 1.  2TPT, HN(TRB), 2TRB        E14
GABRIELI, G.-THOMAS.  CANZON NO. 2.  3TPT, HN(TRB), TRB         E14
GABRIELI, G.-THOMAS.  CANZON NO. 3.  2TPT, HN(TRB), 3TRB        E14
GABRIELI, G.-THOMAS.  CANZON NO. 4.  4TPT, 2TRB                  E14
GABRIELI, G.-FROMME.  CANZONA PRIMA A 5.  2TPT, HN, 2TRB        C25
GABRIELI, G.-FROMME.  CANZONA PRIMA A 5                          D73
   2TPT, TRB(HN), TRB, TRB(TU)
GABRIELI, G.-WALDECK.  CANZONA.  2TPT, HN, TRB, TU              B44
GABRIELI, G.  SACRO TEMPIO D'HONOR.  2TPT, HN, TRB, TU          D94
GARLICK, A.  4 EPISODES.  2TPT, HN, TRB, TU                     G66
GAULT, G.C.  CALEDONIA.  2TPT, HN, TRB, TU                      H06
GENZMER, H.  QUINTETT.  2TPT, HN, TRB, TU                       E65
GERVAISE, C.  3 DANCES.  TPT, HN(TPT), TRB(HN), TRB, PERC       B23
GERVAISE, C.  3 DANCES.  TPT, HN(TRB), TRB(TU), PERC, TPT(HN)   D58
GESUALDO, D.C.  4 MADRIGALS FOR BRASS QUINTET.  5INST ?         D71
GESUALDO, D.C.-UPCHURCH.  3 MADRIGALS.  2TPT, HN, 2TRB          F60
GESUALDO, D.C.  4 MADRIGALS.  2TPT, HN(TRB), TRB-TU             G85
GHENT.  DITHRAMBOS.  2TPT, HN, 2TRB                             E51
GIBBONS.  SILVER SWAN, THE.  2TPT, HN, 2TRB                     N61
GIBBONS, O.-DISHINGER.  PIECE FROM THE SILVER SWAN             N61
   2TPT, HN, 2TRB
GIBBONS, O.  SILVER SWAN, THE.  2TPT, HN, TRB, TU              B04
GILLIAM, R.  VARIATIONS ON 8 NOTES.  2TPT, HN, TRB, TU         G66
GIRON.  DISPARITIES AND DIFFERENCES.  2TPT, HN, TRB, TU        C11
GLASEL, J. (ARR).  16TH CENTURY CARMINA.  2TPT, HN, TRB, TU    D73
GLASEL, J.  SAINTS ALIVE.  2TPT, HN, TRB, TU, OPT PERC         B15
GLICKMAN, E.  DIVERTIMENTO.  2TPT, HN, TRB, TU                 D94
GLUCK, C.W.-ZUSKIN.  IPHIGENIA IN AULIS OVERTURE               D94
   2TPT, HN, TRB, TU
GOFF, B.  VIDIMUS STELLUM.  2TPT, HN, TRB, TU                  M80
GOLDSTEIN, A.E.  BRASS FANFARES & EXCERPTS FR...ORCH LIT       B44
   2TPT, HN, TRB, TU
GORDON.  FOUR CENTURIES FOR BRASS.  2TPT, HN, 2TRB             C11
GRANT, P.  LENTO & ALLEGRO, OP.49.  2TPT, HN, TRB, TU          E68
GREEBE, B.  PADUANA.  2TPT, HN(TPT), TRB(HN), TRB-TU           D16
GREGSON, E.  QUINTET FOR BRASS.  2TPT, HN, TRB, TU             E41
GREP-KING.  PADUANA.  2TPT, HN(TPT), TRB(HN), EU(TRB), TU      D16
GUAMI, G.-BLOCK.  CANZON 19.  2TPT, TRB(HN), 2TRB              E14
GUARNI, G.  17 CANZONAS.  2TPT, TRB(HN), 2TRB                  E14
GUBBY.  GREAT PANATHENAEA, THE.  2TPT, HN, 2TRB                A78
```

```
GUENTZEL, G.  AUTUMN VOICES.  2TPT, HN, TRB, EU                        A62
GUENTZEL, G.  AUTUMN VOICES.  2TPT, HN, TRB, EU                        A78
GUIDE, P.D.  FANFARES, OP.34.  2TPT, HN, TRB, TU                       B12
HAAS, E.(ED).  2 16TH C. FLEMISH SONGS                                 F43
     2TPT, HN(TRB), TRB, TRB-TU
HADDAD, D.  JAZZ ETUDE.  2TPT, HN, TRB, TU                             F60
HAINES.  SONATA.  2TPT, HN, TRB, TU                                    M98
HAMILTON, I.  QUINTET.  2TPT, HN, TRB, TU                              F31
HANDEL, G.F.-KNIGHT.  HANDEL FOR BRASS.  2TPT, HN, 2TRB                C25
HANDEL, G.F.  LARGO (TRB DEMO PIECE).  2TPT, HN, TRB, TU               B04
HANDEL, G.F.  OVERTURE TO BERENICE.  2TPT, HN, TRB, TRB-TU             D16
HANDEL, G.F.-LOCKWOOD.  OVERTURE TO SOLOMON                            N42
     2TPT, HN, TRB, TU
HANDEL, G.F.-LOCKWOOD.  SECOND SUITE.  2TPT, HN, TRB, TU               G83
HANSEN, T.  COLORATION IN BRASS.  2TPT, HN, 2TRB                       B35
HARRIS, A.  4 MOODS FOR BRASS QUINTET.  2TPT, HN, TRB, TU              D73
HARRIS, R.W.  QUINTET NO.2 FOR BRASS.  2TPT, TRB, TU, EU               B35
HARTLEY, W.S.  DIVERTISSEMENT FOR BRASS.  2TPT, HN, TRB, TU            B98
HARTLEY, W.S.  ORPHEUS.  2TPT, HN, 2TRB                                G70
HARTLEY, W.S.  QUINTET.  2TPT, HN, TRB, TU                             F80
HARTMAN, G.P.-MOLENAAR.  RETURN, THE.  TPT, HN, TRB, EU, TU            D92
HASSLER, L.  ACH SCHATZ.  2TPT, HN, TRB, TU                            D14
HAUFRECHT, H.  CONVERSATIONS FOR BRASS QUINTET                        E68
     2TPT, HN, TRB, TU
HAUFRECHT, H.  KLEINE TRAUERMUSIK, EINE.  2TPT, HN, 2TRB               A13
HAUFRECHT, H.  SUITE.  2TPT, HN, TRB, TU                               A38
HAUSSMANN, V.-LEE.  PADUAN & GALLIARD                                  G78
     2TPT, HN, TRB, TU (BTPB)
HAUSSMANN, V.  PADUANE MIT GALLIARDE.  2TPT, HN, TRB, TU               D94
HAUSSMANN, V.-REIN.  3 TANZE FUR 2 TPT & 3 POSAUNEN                    A89
     2TPT, 3TRB
HAYDN, J.-SABATINI.  DIVERTIMENTO IN A-FLAT                            B04
     2TPT, HN, TRB, TU
HEIDEN, B.  4 DANCES.  2TPT, HN, TRB, TU                               P38
HELLERMANN, W.  RESONATA.  2TPT, HN, TRB, TU                           A13
HENKEMANS, H.  AERE FESTIVO.  3TPT, 2TRB                               B74
HESSEN, M.G.L.V.  PADUANA.  INST ?                                     P19
HEUSSENSTAMM, G.  REISE, DIE.  2TPT, HN, TRB, TU                       G66
HLOUSCHEK.  3 BLASERSTUCKE.  2TPT, HN, 2TRB                            C75
HOFFMANN, E.A.  ALTE BLASERMUSIKEN AUS D.16.-18.JAHRHUNDERT            D78
     5INST ?
HOGG, M.E.  INVENTION FOR BRASS QUINTET.  2TPT, HN, TRB, TU            G83
HOLBORNE, A.  5-PART BRASS MUSIC.  2TPT, 3TRB                          E14
HOLBORNE, A.  FRUIT OF LOVE, THE.  5INST ?                             D74
HOLBORNE, A.  HEIGH-HO HOLIDAY.  5INST ?                               D74
HOLBORNE, A.-KING.  2 PIECES                                           D16
     TPT(COR), HN(TRB), TRB, EU-TU, TPT(COR, HN)
HOLBORNE, A.-GIASEL.  3 PIECES.  2TPT, HN(TRB), TRB, TU                D73
HOLBORNE, A.-KING.  5 PIECES.  2TPT, HN, TRB, EU-TU                    D16
HOLBORNE, A.-DART.  SUITE FOR BRASS                                    E51
     2TPT, TRB, TRB(HN), TRB(EU)
HOLMBOE.  QUINTET, OP. 79.  2TPT, HN, TRB, TU                          H30
HOLMES, P.  BRASS QUINTET.  2TPT, HN, TRB, TU                          F43
HOMZY.  SONATINA.  2TPT, HN, TRB, TU                                   N42
HOPKINS.  BRASS QUINTET I.  2TPT, HN, TRB, TU                          M92
HOROVITZ.  MUSIC HALL SUITE.  2TPT, HN, TRB, TU                        E41
HOVHANESS, A.S.  6 DANCES.  2TPT, HN, TRB, TU                          E65
HOWE-SCHAEFFER.  BATTLE HYMN OF THE REPUBLIC                           E80
     BRASS & PERC QUINTET
HUBSCHMANN, W.  MUSIK FUR 2 TPT & 3 POSAUNEN.  2TPT, 3TRB              C75
HUFFNAGLE, H.J.  DEEP RIVER.  2TPT, HN, 2TRB                           C25
HUGGLER, J.  QUINTET FOR BRASS INSTRUMENTS                             C25
     2TPT, HN, TU, BTRB
```

HUMPHREYS. SHOWCASE 5. 2TPT, HN, TRB, TU   G21
HUSA, K. DIVERTIMENTO. 2TPT, HN, TRB, TU   A38
ISAAC, H. CANZONA & LIED. 2TPT, HN, TRB, TU   D94
IVESON. FRERE JACQUES. 2TPT, HN, TRB, TU   B23
JANEQUIN. CHANT DES OYSEAUX, LE. 2TPT, HN, TRB, TU   N42
JANEQUIN. CHANT DES OYSEAUX, LE. INST ?   P19
JENKINS-BALDWIN. NEWARK SIEGE. 2TPT, HN, TRB, TU   N42
JOHNSON, C.W. MOOD MILITANT. 2TPT, HN, TRB, TU   F07
JOHNSON, W.S. SCHERZO. 2TPT, HN, TRB, EU   A62
JONES, C. 4 MOVEMENTS FOR 5 BRASS. 2TPT, HN, TRB, TU   D73
JOPLIN, S.-FRACKENPOHL. 3 SCOTT JOPLIN RAGS   E67
      2TPT, HN, TRB, TU
JOPLIN, S. SUNFLOWER & CHRYSANTHEMUM. 2TPT, HN, TRB, TU   P55
JOSQUIN. FAULTE D'ARGENT. 2TPT, HN, TRB, TU   D94
KAPLAN, D. FUGUE ON FUGUE. 2TPT, HN, TRB, TU   B20
KAPLAN, D. PRELUDE AND FUGUE. 2TPT, HN, TRB, TU   B44
KERSTERS. 3 RONDOS. 2TPT, HN, TRB, TU   B12
KESSEL, J.-KING. SONATA. 2TPT, HN(TRB), TRB(HN), TRB-TU   D16
KEYES. HARDINSBURG JOYS. 2TPT, HN, TRB, TU   G21
KING, R.D.(ARR). SONATA FOR DIE BANKELSANGERLIEDER   D16
      2TPT, HN(TRB), TRB, BTRB(EU, TU)
KLERK, J.D. PREAMBULE. 2TPT, 3TRB   D92
KNIGHT, M. BRASS QUINTET #1. INST ?   N61
KNIGHT, M. BRASS QUINTET #2. INST ?   N61
KNIGHT, M. BRASS QUINTET #3. INST?   N61
KOCH, J.H.E. NACH DEM WINTER DA KOMMT DER SOMMER. 3TPT, 2TRB   A51
KODALY. ELEGIA. INST ?   P19
KOETSIER, J. BAMBERGER PROMENADE. 2TPT, 3TRB   B74
KOETSIER, J. BRASS QUINTET. 2TPT, HN, TRB, TU   B74
KOMIVES. EPILOGUES. 2TPT, HN, 2TRB   G60
KORN. PRELUDE AND SCHERZO. 2TPT, HN, TRB, TU(TRB)   A78
KORTE, K. INTRODUCTIONS FOR BRASS QUINTET. 2TPT, HN, TRB, TU   B92
KREISLER, A.V. PRELUDE. 2TPT, HN, TRB, TU   F60
KROEGER, K. PARTITA. 2TPT, HN, TRB, TU   E68
KUBIK, G. CELEBRATIONS FOR BRASS QUINTET. 2TPT, HN, TRB, TU   B32
KUPFERMAN. BRASS QUINTET. 2TPT, HN, TRB, TU(TRB)   C40
LAMB, J.D. PRAIRIE SUITE. 2TPT, HN, TRB, TU   F43
LANCHBERY. 3 GIRLS FOR FIVE BRASS. 2TPT, HN, TRB, TU   E41
LANIER-OSBORNE. ALMAND AND SARABAND   B05
      2TPT, HN(TPT), TRB, TRB-TU
LANTZ. QUINTET IN FOUR MOVEMENTS. 2TPT, HN, TRB, TU   F43
LASSUS, R.D. TRISTIS EST ANIMA MEA. 2TPT, HN, TRB, TU   D94
LAWRENCE, F.L. 5 SHORT PIECES. 3TPT, EU(TRB), TU   G31
LE GRADY, T. DIVERTIMENTO FOR BRASS QUINTET   D94
      2TPT, HN, TRB, TU
LE GRADY, T. SUITE FOR BRASS QUINTET. 2TPT, HN, TRB, TU   D94
LE JEUNE, C. DEBA CONTRE MES DEBATEURS. 5INST ?   D94
LEBOW, L.S. POPULAR SUITE. 2TPT, HN, TRB, TU, (OPT PERC)   D34
LECLERC, M. PAR MONTS ET PAR VAUX. 2TPT, HN, TRB, TU   D67
LEE, W. MOSAICS. 2TPT, HN, TRB, TU   H30
LEE, W. REGIMENTATION. 2TPT, HN, TRB, TU   C25
LEICHTLING, A. BAGATELLES. 2TPT, HN, TRB, TU   G66
LEICHTLING, A. BRASS QUINTET. 2TPT, HN, TRB, TU   G66
LEVY, F. BRASS QUINTET. 2TPT, HN, TRB, TU   G88
LEVY, F. BRASS QUINTET, 1966. INST ?   G66
LEVY, F. FANFARE. 2TPT, HN, TRB, TU   B44
LEVY, F. QUINTET. 2TPT, HN, TRB, TU   B44
LEWIS & ODE. HYMNS, DESCANTS & FANTASIAS. 2TPT, HN, TRB, TU   L74
LIEB. FEATURE SUITE. 2TPT, HN, TRB, TU   M65
LOCHEL, A. WEIHNACHTICHE TURMMUSIK FUR 5-9 BLASER   F31
      2TPT, 2TRB, TU
LOCKE, M.-BAINES. MUSIC FOR HIS MAJESTY'S SACKBUTS & CORNETTS   E51
      2TPT, 3TRB

```
LOEILLET, J.B.-CROWN.  ALLEGRO.  2TPT, HN, TRB, TU                      M92
LONDON, E.  BRASS QUINTET.  2TPT, HN, TRB, TU                           E35
LOUVIER.  5 PIECES.  2TPT, HN, TRB, TU                                  D36
LOVELOCK, W.  3 PIECES FOR BRASS.  5INST ?                              B20
LULLY, J.B.-KING.  OVERTURE TO CADMUS ET HERMIONE                       D16
   2TPT, HN, TRB, EU-TU
LUPO-BALDWIN.  FANTASIA.  2TPT, HN, TRB, TU                             N42
MAES, J.  PRELUDE ET ALLEGRO.  2TPT, HN, TRB, TU                        B12
MAGANINI, Q.E.  FLOURISH FOR A HERO, A.  2TPT, 2TRB, TU                 B85
MAI.  SCHERZO FOR BRASS QUINTET.  INST ?                                P19
MANCINI, A.(ARR).  CONCERT HIGHLIGHTS.  4TPT, TRB                       B31
MARENZIO, L.  BELLA, LA.  2TPT, HN, TRB, TU                             D94
MARENZIO, L.  SOLO E PENSOSO.  2TPT, HN, TRB, TU                        D94
MARENZIO, L.-DISHINGER.  THIS PARTING KILLS ME                         N61
   2TPT, HN, TRB, TU
MASCHERA, F.-EDWARDS.  CANZONA LA MARLINENGA                            G83
   2TPT, HN, TRB, TU
MASCHERA, F.  CANZONA.  2TPT, HN, TRB, TU                               D94
MATTERN, J.  SONATA BREVE.  2TPT, HN, TRB, TU                           M92
MAURER, L.-GAY.  12 LITTLE PIECES.  2TPT, HN, TRB, TU                   E41
MAURER, L.  4 SONGS FOR BRASS.  2TPT, HN, TU(TRB), HN(TRB)              D73
MAURER, L.W.-NAGEL.  3 PIECES.  2TPT, HN, TRB(TU), HN(TRB)              D73
MAURER, L.W.-NAGEL.  SCHERZO & LIED                                     D73
   2TPT, HN(TRB), TRB(HN), TRB-TU
MAYER.  BRASS QUINTET.  2TPT, HN, TRB, TU                               B92
MAZUREK.  CHRISTMAS MEDLEY.  2TPT, HN(EU), TRB, TU                      E80
MC BETH, F.  4 FRESCOES.  2TPT, HN, TRB, TRB(TU)                        F60
MC CABE, J.  ROUNDS FOR BRASS QUINTET.  2TPT, HN, TRB, TU               E41
MC GREGOR.  CHRISTMAS MUSIC.  2TPT, HN, TRB, TU                         G83
MC GREGOR.  CHRISTMAS SERVICE.  2TPT, HN, TRB, TU                       G83
MC KAY, G.F.  SONATINA EXPRESSIVA.  TPT, TPT(HN), HN, TRB, TU           F60
MC KENNA & SWINBURNE.  BRASS FOR BEGINNERS                              E51
   TPT, HN, TRB, TU, EU
MC KIE, J.G.  ANDANTE.  2TPT, HN, TRB, TU                               B98
MC KIE, J.G.  THEME FOR A CAROUSEL.  2TPT, HN, TRB, TU                  B98
MC KIE, J.G.  WALTZ.  2TPT, HN, TRB, TU                                 B98
MENDELSSOHN, F.-MOORE.  ANDANTE TRANQUILLO.  2TPT, HN, TRB, TU          M71
MENDELSSOHN, F.-AGOUNOFF.  HUNTER'S FAREWELL, THE                       B85
   2TPT(2HN), 3TRB
MENDELSSOHN, F.-WALDECK.  WEDDING MARCH.  2TPT, HN, TRB, TU             B44
MERULA, T.  CANZONA LA STRADA.  2TPT, HN, TRB, TU                       D94
MERULO, C.-BLOCK.  CANZONI 18, 23, 36.  2TPT, TRB(HN), 2TRB             E14
MICHALSKY, D.R.  FANTASIA ALLA MARCIA.  2TPT, HN, TRB, TU               F43
MICHEELSEN, H.F.  EI, DU FEINER REITER.  2TPT, 3TRB                     A51
MILLER, E.  FOLLY STONE, THE.  2TPT, HN, TRB, TU                        A13
MILLS, C.  BRASS QUINTET IN 3 MVTS.  5INST ?                            E68
MILLS, C.  QUINTET IN 3 MOVEMENTS.  2TPT, HN, 2TRB                      A13
MOLINEUX.  ENCOUNTER.  2TPT, HN, TRB, TU                                F43
MONTEVERDI, C.-LEE.  MADRIGAL.  2TPT, HN, TRB, TU(BTRB)                 G78
MONTEVERDI, C.-TOWNSEND.  SINFONIA FROM 7TH MADRIGAL BOOK               B32
   2TPT, HN, 2TRB
MOORE, C.  BRASS QUINTET.  2TPT, HN, TRB, TU                            B35
MOREL, F.  QUINTETTE POUR CUIVRES.  2TPT, HN, TRB, TU                   D94
MOROSS.  SONATINA.  2TPT, HN, TRB, TU                                   B20
MOSS, L.  MUSIC FOR 5.  2TPT, HN, TRB, TU                               D76
MOURET-KING.  RONDEAU.  2TPT, HN(TRB), TRB(HN), TRB                     D16
MOYZES, A.  BRASS QUINTET IN B MAJOR.  5INST ?                          A33
MOZART, W.A.-LOCKWOOD.  CHURCH SONATA NO. 6                             G83
   2TPT, HN, TRB, TU
MOZART, W.A.-HOMZY.  DIVERTIMENTO.  2TPT, HN, TRB, TU                   G83
MOZART, W.A.-LOCKWOOD.  QUINTET NO. 8, K. 614 (4TH MVMT)                G83
   2TPT, HN, TRB, TU
```

```
MOZART, W.A.-LOCKWOOD.  SALZBURG SINFONIE, K. 136 (1ST MVMT)      G83
     2TPT, HN, TRB, TU
MUSSORGSKY & SAINT-SAENS.  BYDLO(PICTURES)&ELEPHANT(CARNIVAL)     M79
     2TPT, HN, TRB, TUBA SOLO
NAGEL, R.  SINFONIA FOR BRASS QUINTET.  2TPT, HN, TRB, TU         E68
NAGEL, R.  THIS OLD MAN.  2TPT, HN, TRB, TU                       D73
NASH.  FORTE DE ROSA.  4HN, TU                                    M96
NASH.  VARIATIONS FOR TUBA.  2TPT, HN, TRB, TU                    M96
NELHYBEL, V.  BRASS QUINTET NO. 1.  2TPT, HN, TRB, TU             C40
NELHYBEL, V.  BRASS QUINTET NO. 2.  2TPT, HN, TRB, TU             C40
NENNA-EICHMAN.  APRI IL SEN ALLE FIAMME.  2TPT, HN, 2TRB          F60
NENNA-EICHMAN.  DOLCE MIO FOCO ARDENTE.  2TPT, HN, 2TRB           F60
NENNA-EICHMAN.  ECCO O MIA DOLCE PENA.  2TPT, HN, 2TRB            F60
NENNA-EICHMAN.  ITENE O MIEI SOSPIR.  2TPT, HN, 2TRB              F60
NENNA-EICHMAN.  OCCHI MIEI CHE VEDESTE.  2TPT, HN, 2TRB           F60
NERIJNEN, J.V.  3 INVENTIONE VOOR KOPERKWINTET.  3TPT, TRB, EU    D92
O'REILLY.  METROPOLITAN QUINTET.  2TPT, HN, 2TRB, TRB(TU)         D14
ODE & LEWIS.  HYMNS, DESCANTS & FANTASIAS.  2TPT, HN, TRB, TU     L74
OROLOGIO, A.  INTRADA NO.3.  2TPT, HN, TRB, TU                    D94
OROLOGIO, A.  INTRADAS, PART 1.  2TPT, HN, TRB, TU                D94
OROLOGIO, A.  INTRADAS, PART 2.  2TPT, HN, TRB, TU                D94
OROLOGIO, A.  INTRADAS, PART 4.  2TPT, HN, TRB, TU                D94
ORR, R.  DIVERTIMENTO.  2TPT, TRB, TRB(HN), TRB(TU)               E41
ORR, R.  SONATA.  2TPT, HN(TRB), 2TRB                             D16
OSTRANSKY, L.  CHARACTER VARIATIONS ON A MODAL THEME             F07
     2TPT, HN(TRB), TRB(EU), TU
OTT, J.  TOCCATA FOR BRASS QUINTET.  INST ?                       A65
OTT, J.  TOCCATA.  2TPT, HN, TRB, TU                              B53
PACHELBEL, J.  3 FUGUES ON THE MAGNIFICAT.  2TPT, HN, TRB, TU     F59
PALESTRINA, G.P.-WALDECK.  AGNUS DEI.  2TPT, HN, TRB, TU          B44
PALESTRINA, G.P.-VOLKMANN.  ALLELUIA TULERUNT                     B40
     2TPT, HN, TRB, EU
PALESTRINA, G.P.-VOLKMANN.  LAUDATE DOMINUM.  2TPT, HN, 2TRB      B40
PALESTRINA, G.P.-LEMARC.  SURGE PROPERA.  2TPT, HN, TRB, EU       F81
PALESTRINA, G.P.-COURNOYER.  SYMPHONIC CANON                      B04
     2TPT, HN, TRB, TU
PARRIS, R.  SINFONIA.  2TPT, HN, 2TRB                             A13
PASSEREAU.  CHANSON "IL EST BEL ET BON".  INST ?                  P19
PAYNE, F.L.  BRASS QUINTET.  2TPT, HN, TRB, TU                    B35
PEARCE.  ADAGIO & ALLEGRO.  3TPT, 2TRB                            N98
PEASLEE.  DEVEL'S HERALD.  SOLO TU, 4HN, PERC                     G68
PERSICHETTI, V.  PARABLE.  2TPT, HN, TRB, TU                      B92
PERUTI, C.  BRASS QUINTET.  2TPT, HN, TRB, TRB(TU)                P48
PEUERL, P.-LEE.  CANZON XIII.  2TPT, HN, TRB, TU(BTRB)            G78
PEYSSIES, M.  PLEIN SOLEIL.  3TPT, TPT(TRB), PERC                 B66
PEZEL, J.C.-SEAR.  ALLEMANDE & COURANTE.  2TPT, HN, TRB, TU       B44
PEZEL, J.C.-SEAR.  BAL & SARABANDE.  2TPT, HN, TRB, TU            B44
PEZEL, J.C.-LUMSDEN.  5-PART BRASS MUSIC(3 VOL)                   E14
     2TPT, TRB(HN), 2TRB
PEZEL, J.C.  16 DANCES.  2TPT, HN(TRB), TRB, BTRB                 B98
PEZEL, J.C.  HORA DECIMA (2 VOL).  2TPT, TRB(HN), 2TRB            E14
PEZEL, J.C.  HORA DECIMA MUSICORUM LIPSIENSIUM.  TPT, 2TRB        D78
PEZEL, J.C.-SEAR.  INTRADE & BAL.  2TPT, HN, TRB, TU              B44
PEZEL, J.C.-KING.  3 PIECES                                       D16
     2TPT, HN(TPT, TRB), TRB(HN), TRB-TU
PEZEL, J.C.  6 PIECES.  2TPT, HN(TPT, TRB), TRB(HN), TRB-TU       D16
PEZEL, J.C.-KING.  SONATA NO. 1                                   D16
     2TPT(2COR), TRB(HN), EU, TU(BTRB)
PEZEL, J.C.-KING.  SONATA NO. 2                                   D16
     2TPT, HN(TPT, TRB), TRB(HN), TRB-TU
PEZEL, J.C.-KING.  SONATA NO. 3                                   D16
     2TPT, HN(TRB), TRB, BTRB(EU, TU)
```

PEZEL, J.C.-MENKEN & BARON. SONATA NO. 5   A78
   2TPT, HN, TRB, TU(BTRB)
PEZEL, J.C.-GREENBERG. SONATA NO.12 IN F   D84
   2TPT, HN, TRB, BTRB(TU)
PEZEL, J.C.-WALDECK. SONATA NO.14 (HORA DECIMA)   B44
   2TPT, HN, TRB, TU
PEZEL, J.C.-KING. SONATA NO.22   D16
   2TPT, HN(TRB), TRB(HN), EU-TU
PEZEL, J.C.-KING. SONATA NO.25   D16
   2TPT, HN(TRB), TRB(HN), TRB-TU
PEZEL, J.C.-BROWN. SONATA NO.27. 2TPT, HN(TRB), TRB, TU   F07
PEZEL, J.C.-GREENBERG. SONATA NO.28 IN E-FLAT   D84
   2TPT, HN, TRB, BTRB(TU)
PEZEL, J.C. SONATA NO.39. 2TPT, HN, 2TRB   D67
PEZEL, J.C.-BROWN. 12 SONATAS (3 VOL). 2TPT, 3TRB   C91
PEZEL, J.C. 12 SONATAS. 2TPT, TRB(HN), 2TRB   B98
PEZEL, J.C.-SCHLEGEL. 5- STIMMIGTE BLASENDE MUSIK   D78
   2CTT, 3TRB
PEZEL, J.C. SUITE DE DANSES. 2TPT, HN, 2TRB   D67
PEZEL, J.C.-ROMM. SUITE OF DANCES. 2TPT, HN, 2TRB   M79
PEZEL, J.C.-BROWN. SUITE OF 16 PIECES (2 VOL). 2TPT, 3TRB   C91
PEZEL, J.C.-SCHERING. 2 SUITEN. 2TPT, 3TRB   A90
PEZEL, J.C.-REIN. TURM-SONATE NR.27. 2TPT, 3TRB   A89
PEZEL, J.C.-MEYER. TURMMUSIK. 2TPT, 3TRB   A89
PFANNENSTIEL, E. ENTRADA NR.1. 3TPT, 2TRB   F31
PILSS, K. SCHERZO. 2TPT, TRB, TPT(HN), TRB(HN, BTPT)   D26
PINKHAM, D. PRELUDE, ADAGIO & CHORALE. 2TPT, HN, TRB, TU   E65
PLOG. MINI-SUITE. 2TPT, HN, TRB, TU   M79
PLONER, J. KLEINE BLECHBLASER-MUSIK (3 SATZE)   C54
   2TPT, HN, EU, TU
POGLIETTI-HILFIGER. RICERCARE. 2TPT, HN, TRB, TU   D14
POLIN, C. CADER IDRIS. 2TPT, HN, TRB, TU   F23
POLIN, C. MAKIMONO II. 2TPT, HN, TRB, TU   G66
POSCH, I.-LEE. PADUANA & GAGLIARDA. 2TPT, HN, TRB, TU(BTRB)   G78
POWELL. MUSIC FOR BRASS QUINTET #2. 2TPT, HN, TRB, TU   N91
PRESSER, W. FOLK SONG FANTASY. BRASS QUINTET   G66
PRESSER, W.H. BRASS QUINTET # 3. 2TPT, HN, TRB, TU   M80
PRESSER, W.H. BRASS QUINTET NO. 2. 2TPT, HN, TRB, TU   F80
PRESSER, W.H. BRASS QUINTET. 2TPT, HN, TRB, TU   G83
PRESSER, W.H. BRASS QUINTET. 2TPT, HN, TRB, TU   G93
PRESSER, W.H. FOLK SONG FANTASY. 2TPT, TRB, EU, TU   B38
PREVIN, A. 4 OUTINGS FOR BRASS. 2TPT, HN, TRB, TU   D58
PREVOST, A. MOUVEMENT POUR QUINTETTE DE CUIVRES   D94
   2TPT, HN, TRB, TU
PURCELL, H.-SEAR. 4 PART FANTASY NO.5. 2TPT, HN, TRB, TU   B44
PURCELL, H.-SEAR. 4 PART FANTASY NO.8. 2TPT, HN, TRB, TU   B44
PURCELL, H.-BENOY. PURCELL SUITE, A. 2TPT, 2TRB, TRB(HN)   E51
PURCELL, H.-LOCKWOOD. PURCELL SUITE, A. 2TPT, HN, TRB, TU   G83
PURCELL, H.-MASSO. SUITE FROM BONDUCA. 2TPT, HN, TRB, TU   E83
PURCELL, H.-SEAR. TRUMPET OVERTURE(ACT 3, INDIAN QUEEN)   B44
   2TPT, HN, TRB, TU
PURCELL, H.-CORLEY. TRUMPET VOLUNTARY   D16
   2TPT, HN(TPT), TRB(HN), EU-TU
PURCELL, H.-CORLEY. VOLUNTARY ON OLD 100TH   D16
   2TPT, HN(TRB), TRB(HN), EU-TU
PURDY, W. MUSIC FOR BRASS. 2TPT, HN, TRB, TU   D94
RAKSIN, D. OJAI FESTIVAL FANFARES. 2TPT, HN, TRB, TU   G21
RAPH, A. CALL AND RESPONSE. 2TPT, HN, TRB, TU   B85
RAPH, A. 9 CHRISTMAS CAROLS. 2TPT, HN, TRB, TU   M70
RATHAUS, K. TOWER MUSIC. 2TPT, TRB(HN), 2TRB   A38
REBNER, E.W. VARIATIONEN FUR 5 BLECHBLASER   D88
   2TPT, HN, TRB, BTRB

```
REDDING.  QUINTET.  2TPT, HN, TRB, TU                                    B44
REED.  VARIATIONS ON LONDON BRIDGE IS FALLING DOWN                       N98
  2TPT, HN, TRB, TU
REICHE, G.-FROMME.  BAROQUE SUITE.  2TPT, HN, TRB, TU                    A38
REICHE, G.-SUDMEIER.  SONATA NO. 13.  2TPT, HN, TRB, TU                  B04
REICHE, G.  SONATA NO.15.  2TPT, HN, TRB, TU                            B04
REICHE, G.-HOMZY.  SONATINA 1.  2TPT, HN, TRB, TU                        G83
REIF, P.  BRASS QUINTET.  2TPT, HN, 2TRB                                 G88
REIF, P.  BRASS QUINTET, 1967.  INST ?                                   G66
RENWICK.  DANCE.  2TPT, HN, TRB, TU                                      N66
REYNOLDS, V.  SUITE FOR BRASS QUINTET.  2TPT, HN, TRB, TU                D71
REYNOLDS, V. (ARR).  CENTONE NO. 1.  2TPT, HN, TRB, TU                   F60
REYNOLDS, V. (ARR).  CENTONE NO. 2.  2TPT, HN, TRB, TU                   F60
REYNOLDS, V. (ARR).  CENTONE NO. 3.  2TPT, HN, TRB, TU                   F60
REYNOLDS, V. (ARR).  CENTONE NO. 4.  2TPT, HN, TRB, TU                   F60
REYNOLDS, V. (ARR).  CENTONE NO. 5.  2TPT, HN, TRB, TU                   F60
REYNOLDS, V. (ARR).  CENTONE NO. 6.  2TPT, HN, TRB, TU                   F60
REYNOLDS, V. (ARR).  CENTONE NO. 7.  2TPT, HN, TRB, TU                   F60
REYNOLDS, V. (ARR).  CENTONE NO. 8.  2TPT, HN, TRB, TU                   F60
RICE, T.  BRASS QUINTET.  2TPT, HN, TRB, TU                              G66
RICHTER, A.-SEAR.  HUNT, THE.  2TPT, HN, TRB, TU                         B44
RIDDLE.  MUSEUM PIECE.  2TPT, HN, TRB, TU                                M96
RIDDLE.  5 PIECES FOR BASS TROMBONE.  2TPT, HN, TRB, TU                  M96
RIDDLE, N.  THREE-QUARTER SUITE FOR BRASS QUINTET                        D71
  2TPT, HN, TRB, TU
RIETI, V.  INCISIONI (ENGRAVINGS).  2TPT, HN, 2TRB                       C40
RILEY, J.  4 ESSAYS.  2TPT, HN, TRB, TU                                  F43
RIVERS (ED).  12 CHRISTMAS HYMNS AND CAROLS                              E41
  TPT, TPT(HN), HN(TRB), TRB,TRB-TU
ROBBINS.  FANFARE AND EXPANSIONS.  2TPT, HN(TRB), TRB, TU                N32
ROBERTS.  DIXIE.  2TPT, HN, TRB, TRB(TU)                                 B44
ROBERTS.  GOD REST YE MERRY GENTLEMEN.  COR, FLG, HN, EU, TU             B44
ROBERTS.  VARIATIONS ON AN ENGLISH THEME.  2TPT, HN, TRB, TU             B44
ROBERTS, W.  3 HEADLINES.  2TPT, HN, TRB, TU                             B44
ROE.  MUSIC FOR BRASS QUINTET.  2TPT, HN, TRB, TRB(TU)                   D14
ROIKJER.  SCHERZO.  2TPT, HN, TRB, TU                                    H30
ROOLE, E.-VOXMAN.  QUINTET NO.1.  2TPT, HN, TRB, TU                      F07
ROOLE, E.-VOXMAN.  QUINTET NO.6.  2TPT, HN, TRB, TU                      F07
ROSENMULLER, J.-WALDECK.  COURANTE, SARABANDE & BAL                      B44
  2TPT, HN, TRB, TU
ROSENMULLER, J.-WALDECK.  INTRADA.  2TPT, HN, TRB, TU                    B44
ROSENMULLER, J.-WALDECK.  SINFONIA PRIMA.  2TPT, HN, TRB, TU             B44
ROSENTHAL, C.A.  3 RENAISSANCE MADRIGALS.  2TPT, HN, TRB, TU             G21
ROSENTHAL, I. (ARR).  LITTLE BROWN JUG.  2TPT, HN, TRB, TU               G21
ROSSI-LOCKWOOD.  3 PIECES.  2TPT, HN, TRB, TU                            G83
RUBANK FESTIVAL REPERTOIRE.  2TPT, HN(TRB), TRB, TU                      F07
RUGGIERI-PEROWSKI.  ADAGIO.  2TPT, HN, TRB, TU                           G78
RUGGIERI-PEROWSKI.  ALLEGRO.  2TPT, HN, TRB, TU                          G78
SABATINI, G.  EPIGRAM.  2TPT, HN, TRB, TU                                B04
SABATINI, G.  FUGUE IN THE ANCIENT MANNER.  2TPT, HN, TRB, TU            B04
SABATINI, G.  3 HEADLINES.  2TPT, HN, TRB, TU                            B04
SABATINI, G.  MUSIC FOR CURLY(HN DEMO PIECE)                             B04
  2TPT, HN, TRB, TU
SABATINI, G.  PUPPET WALTZ.  2TPT, HN, TRB, TU                           B44
SAGUET.  GOLDEN SUITE.  2TPT, HN, TRB, TU                                F87
SAINT¬SAENS, C.-SEAR.  MARCH MILITAIRE FRANCAISE                         B44
  2TPT, HN, TRB, TU
SALTHOUSE, G.  STATEMENTS.  2TPT, HN, TRB, TU                            G66
SANDERS, R.L.  QUINTET IN B-FLAT.  2TPT, HN, 2TRB                        D74
SATIE.  SARABANDE I.  2TPT, HN, TRB, TU                                  F16
SCARLATTI, A.-JOHNSON.  ARIA & MINUET.  2TPT, HN(TRB), TRB, TU           F07
SCHAEFFER, D.  5 BRASS QUINTETS.  2TPT, HN(TRB), TRB, TU                 E80
```

```
SCHEIDT, S.  BATTLE SUITE.  2TPT, HN(TRB), TRB(EU), TU(BTRB)       D58
SCHEIDT, S.  CANZON SUPER INTRADAM AECHIOPICAM                     D94
    2TPT, HN, TRB, TU
SCHEIDT, S.-DE JONG.  CANZONA BERGAMASCA.  2TPT, HN, TRB, TU       B98
SCHEIDT, S.-FROMME.  CANZONA BERGAMASCA.  2TPT, HN, 2TRB           A38
SCHEIDT, S.-GREEN.  SUITE FOR BRASS QUINTET                        E77
    2TPT, HN, TRB, EU(TU)
SCHEIN, J.H.-HESSLER.  ALLEMANDE & TRIPLA NO.1 & 2                 B44
    2TPT, HN(TRB), TRB, TU
SCHEIN, J.H.-HESSLER.  ALLEMANDE & TRIPLA NO.15 & 19               B44
    2TPT, HN(TRB), TRB, TU
SCHEIN, J.H.-HESSLER.  ALLEMANDE & TRIPLA NO.6 & 9                 B44
    2TPT, HN(TRB), TRB, TU
SCHEIN, J.H.-HESSLER.  ALLEMANDE & TRIPLA NO.8                     B44
    2TPT, HN(TRB), TRB, TU
SCHEIN, J.H.-SEAR.  INTRADA.  2TPT, HN, TRB, TU                    B44
SCHEIN, J.H.  2 PIECES.  2TPT, HN(TPT, TRB), TRB(HN), TRB-TU       D16
SCHEIN, J.H.-MAGANINI.  SUITE FROM A MUSICAL BANQUET               B85
    2TPT, 3TRB
SCHILLING.  TRIPARTITA.  2TPT, HN(TPT), TRB, TRB/TU, OPT PERC      D36
SCHMELZER, J.H.-STINE.  SONATA XII.  2TPT, HN, TRB, TU             M92
SCHMIDT.  7 VARIATIONS ON A HEXACHORD.  2TPT, HN, TRB, TU          A43
SCHMIDT, W.  VARIATIONS ON A NEGRO FOLK SONG                       G21
    2TPT, HN, TRB, TU
SCHMIDT, W.J.  SUITE NO. 1.  2TPT, HN, TRB, TU                     G21
SCHMIDT, W.J.  SUITE NO. 2.  2TPT, HN, TRB, TU                     A43
SCHMIDT, W.J.  SUITE NO. 3.  2TPT, HN, TRB, TU                     A43
SCHMITT, H.(CMPL).  ALTE BLASERSATZE (HEFT I)                      F31
    2TPT, TRB(HN), 2TRB
SCHMUTZ, A.D.  PRELUDE & GAVOTTE.  2TPT, HN, TRB, TU(EU)           C13
SCHORGE.  3 THREES FOR FIVE BRASS.  2TPT, HN, TRB, TU              D14
SCHUBERT, F.P.-HAUPRECHT.  KLEINE TRAUERMUSIK, EINE.  5 INST ?     E68
SCHULLER, G.  MUSIC FOR BRASS QUINTET.  2TPT, HN, TRB, TU          A38
SCHUMANN, G.  BLASERMUSIK II.  2TPT, HN, TRB, TU                   F53
SCHUMANN, R.-WILLIAMS.  2 KINDERSCENEN, OP.15/8 & 9.  5INST ?      F60
SCHUMANN, R.  MARCH, CHORALE & NORTHERN SONG                       D73
    2TPT, HN, TRB, TU
SCHUTZ & BANCHIERI.  2 SINFONIAS.  2TPT, HN, TRB, TU               D94
SEAR, W.E. (ARR).  3 CHRISTMAS CAROLS.  2TPT, HN, TRB, TU          B44
SEAR, W.E.  2 INVENTIONS.  2TPT, HN, TRB, TU                       B44
SEAR, W.E.  QUINTET FOR BRASS.  2TPT, HN, TRB, TU                  B44
SEEGER, P.  KLEINE JAGDGESCHICHTE.  3TPT, HN, TRB                  C54
SEYFRIT, M.  BRASS RINGS.  2TPT, HN, TRB, TU                       A13
SHERARD-DOCKSTADER.  ADAGIO & ALLEGRO                              G78
    2TPT, HN, TRB, TU(BTRB)
SHINER, M.  MEXICAN CARNIVAL.  4TRB, TU                            D14
SHINN, R.  SERENADE.  2TPT, HN, TRB, TU(TRB)                       D16
SHORT.  BRASS QUINTET.  2TPT, HN, TRB, TU                          A71
SHOSTAKOVITCH, D.D.  SATIRICAL DANCE.  2TPT, HN, TRB, TU           B85
SIEGNER, E.  INVENTION IN BRASS.  2TPT, HN, TRB, TU                D94
SIMMES, W.  FANTASIA.  2TPT, HN, TRB, TU                           D94
SIMON-WILSON.  FIRST QUINTET, OP.26/2.  2TPT, HN, TRB, TU          H06
SIMON.  4 PIECES, OP. 26.  2TPT, HN, TRB, HN(TRB)                  F07
SIMON, A.Y.-WILSON.  FIRST QUINTET, OP.26/2                        E11
    2TPT, HN, TRB, EU
SIMON, A.Y.-SEAR.  QUINTET IN 3 MOVEMENTS, OP.26                   B44
    2TPT, HN, TRB, TU
SIMPSON, T.  OPUS NEWER PAUDUANEN... (2 VOL)                       E14
    3TRE, 2CTT(2TPT)
SIMPSON, T.-WALDECK.  THEME & VARIATIONS.  2TPT, HN, TRB, TU       B44
SLYCK, V.  PASSAMEZZO ANTICO.  2TPT, HN, TRB, TU                   F60
SMITH (ARR).  STAR SPANGLED BANNER, THE.  2TPT, HN, TRB, TU        B44
```

```
SNYDER.  VARIATIONS ON A FOLK THEME.  2TPT, HN, TRB, TU           B15
SODERINI, A.-LEE.  2 CANZONI.  2TPT, HN, TRB, TU (BTRB)           G78
SOLOMON.  QUINTET NO. 1.  2TPT, 2TRB, TU                          F60
SOLOMON.  SOMBRERO.  2TPT, HN(TRB), 2TRB                          F59
SOMMER, J.-HARDING.  2 DANCES ON THE SAME THEME                   D16
   2TPT, HN, TRB, TRB-TU
SONATA FROM DIE BANDELSANGERLIEDER.  2TPT, HN, TRB, TU            B44
SOUSA, J.P.-MENKEN.  SEMPER FIDELIS.  2TPT, HN, TRB, TU           A78
SPEARS.  4 MINIATURES.  2TPT, HN, TRB, TU                         F80
SPEER, D.  2 SONATAS.  2TPT, 3TRB, (OPT *PF OR *ORG)              C91
SPEER, D.-MILLER.  2 SONATAS.  2TPT, TRB(HN), TRB, BTRB           B98
SPIREA, A.  MUSIC FOR BRASS.  2TPT, HN, TRB, TU                   G85
STANLEY, J.-LIGOTTI.  TRUMPET VOLUNTARY.  2TPT, HN, TRB, TU       B44
STARER, R.  5 MINIATURES FOR BRASS QUINTET.  2TPT, 2HN, TRB       F59
STEINER, G.  BRASS QUINTET.  2TPT, HN, TRB, TU                    G66
STEVENS, H.  2 IMPROVISATIONS ON FOLK SONGS.  2TPT, 2TRB, BTRB    G26
STEWART, F.  CHARACTERISTICS.  2TPT, HN, TRB, TU                  G66
STEWART, R.  CANZONA & RICERCAR.  2TPT, HN, 2TRB                  A13
STEWART, R.  3 PIECES FOR THE AMERICAN BRASS QUINTET              E68
   2TPT, HN, TRB, BTRB
STEWART, R.  3 PIECES.  2TPT, HN, 2TRB                            A13
STEWART, R.  QUINTET NO. 2.  2TPT, HN, TRB, TU                    A13
STOLTZ, W.  BRASS SYMPHONY.  2TPT, HN, TRB, TU                    B44
STOLTZER, T.A.-KING.  FANTASIA.  2TRB(2HN), 2TRB, BTRB(TU)        D16
STRADELLA, A.-SABATINI.  CONCERTO IN C(TPT DEMO PIECE)            B04
   2TPT, HN, TRB, TU
STRATTON, D.  VARIATIONS ON A THEME BY HENRY VIII                 B44
   2TPT, HN, TRB, TU
STRAUSS, J.-LIGOTTI.  TRITSCH TRATSCH POLKA                       B44
   2TPT, HN, TRB, TU
STREET, A.  VARIATIONS ON A MOZART ANDANTE.  2TPT, HN, TRB, TU    N58
SUDMEIER, W.  FANFARES FOR BRASS.  2TPT, HN, TRB, TU              B04
SUDMEIER, W.  GOIN HOME (JAZZ DEMO PIECE).  2TPT, HN, TRB, TU     B34
SVOBODA.  CHORALE AND DANCE.  TPT, TRB, TU, TPT(HN), TRB(HN)      B32
SWANSON, H.  SOUNDPIECE.  2TPT, HN, TRB, TU                       G17
SWEELINCK, J.P.-VOLKMANN.  HODIE CHRISTUS NATUS EST               B40
   2TPT, HN, TRB, EU-TU
SWINBURNE & MCKENNA.  BRASS FOR BEGINNERS                         E51
   TPT, HN, TRB, TU, EU
SYDEMAN, W.  BRASS QUINTET.  2TPT, HN, TRB, TU                    G88
SYDEMAN, W.  TOWER MUSIC.  2TPT, HN, TRB, TU                      G66
TANENBAUM, E.  STRUCTURES.  2TPT, HN, TRB, TU(TRB)                A13
TCHAIKOVSKY, P.I.-SHINER.  DANCE OF THE REED PIPES.  4TRB, TU     D14
TCHAIKOVSKY, P.I.-SHINER.  DANCE OF THE SUGAR PLUM FAIRY          D14
   4TRB, TU
TCHAIKOVSKY, P.I.-WALDECK.  NEOPOLITAN DANCE                      B44
   2TPT, HN, TRB, TU
TCHEREPNIN, A.N.  QUINTET, OP. 105.  2TPT, HN, TRB, TU            E65
THATCHER, H.R.  SUITE OF DANCES.  5INST ?                         B04
TICE, D.  4 PIECES FOR BRASS QUARTET & TIMP.                     G01
   2TPT, 2TRB, TIMP
TISNE, A.  STANCES MINOENNES.  2TPT, HN, TRB, TU                  D36
TOMKINS.  COME SHEPHERDS.  2TPT, HN, TRB, TU                      N42
TOMKINS.  MADRIGAL "COME, SHEPHERDS, SING WITH ME".  INST?        P19
TORELLI, G.-WELSHMAN.  ALLEGRO.  2TPT, HN, TRB, TU                G78
TOWNSEND.  TOWER MUSIC, OP. 7.  2TPT, HN, TRB, TU                 N18
TREVARTHEN, R.  SONATA FOR BRASS QUARTET.  2TPT, HN, TRB          G83
TUFILLI.  PRAYER, A.  2TPT, HN, TRB, TU                           E80
TULL, F.  COUP DE BRASS.  2TPT, HN, TRB, TU                       M96
TULL, F.  EXHIBITION (DEMO PIECE).  2TPT, HN, TRB, TU             G21
TULL, F.  LAMENT, OP. 32.  4HN, TU                                M96
TULL, F.  SKETCHES.  TPT, 2HN, TRB, TU                            M96
```

```
TURNER.  4 FRAGMENTS.  2TPT, HN, TRB, TU(TRB)                          E61
UBER, D.A.  ADVENTURES OF A TIN HORN.  2TPT, HN(EU), TRB, TU          B85
UBER, D.A.  BATTLE HYMN OF THE REPUBLIC                                A94
   2TPT, HN(TRB), TRB, TU
UBER, D.A.  BUILD-A-BAND MARCH.  2TPT, HN, TRB, TU, NAR               B85
UBER, D.A.  DAY AT THE CAMPTOWN RACES, A                              B85
   2TPT, HN(EU), TRB, TU
UBER, D.A.  GREENSLEEVES.  2TPT, HN(EU), TRB, TU                      B85
UBER, D.A.  LO, HOW A ROSE E'ER BLOOMING                              A94
   2TPT, HN(TRB), TRB, TU
UBER, D.A.  QUINTET FOR BRASS.  2TPT, HN, TRB, TU                     A03
UBER, D.A.  5 SHORT SKETCHES.  2TPT, HN, TRB, TU                      A94
UBER, D.A.  STREETS OF LAREDO.  2TPT, HN, TRB, TU                     B98
ULF, O.  AUGSBURGER TAFELMUSIK.  2TPT, HN, 2TRB                       D98
VALCOURT, J.  PENTAPHONIE POUR QUINTETTE DE CUIVRES                   D94
   2TPT, HN, TRB, TU
VAN DE VATE, N.  QUINTET FOR BRASS.  2TPT, HN, TRB, TU                P48
VECCHI, D.-UPCHURCH.  SALTARELLO.  2TPT, HN, TRB, TU                  D14
VERDI, G.-ZUSKIN.  MOMENTS FROM LA TRAVIATA                           D94
   2TPT, HN, TRB, TU
VERDI, G.-BROWER.  TRIUMPHAL MARCH.  2TPT, HN, TRB, TU                B44
VETESSY.  PARTITA.  2TPT, HN, TRB, TU                                 B32
VIVALDI, A.-BALDWIN.  FUGUE.  2TPT, HN, TRB, TU                       G83
VIVALDI, A.-WEISHMAN.  GAVOTTA.  2TPT, HN, TRB, TU                    G78
VIVALDI, A.  SUITE IN E-FLAT.  2TPT, HN, TRB, TU                      B04
WAGNER, E. (ED).  FANFARES FOR A FESTIVAL BANQUET.  INST ?            N47
WAGNER, R.  HYMN MEISTERSINGER.  2TPT, HN, TRB, TU                    B04
WAIGNEIN, A.  IMPRESSIONS HARMONIQUES.  2TPT, TRB, TU                 D67
WALDECK(ARR).  CHRIST IST ERSTANDEN.  2TPT, HN, TRB, TU              B44
WALTON, W.T.-DE JONGH.  6 PIECES, SET 2.  2TPT, HN(TRB), 2TRB         E51
WARD-STEINMAN, D.  QUINTET FOR BRASS.  5INST ?                        E68
WARD, W.R.-BALDWIN.  FANTASIA.  2TPT, HN, TRB, TU                     G83
WASHBURN, G.  QUINTET.  2TPT, HN, TRB, TU                             E51
WAUGHAN-WILLIAMS.  REST.  INST ?                                      P19
WEILLE, B.  SUITE FOR BRASS QUINTET.  2TPT, HN, TRB, TU               B44
WEILLE, B.  SUITE.  2TPT, HN, TRB, TU                                 E77
WEINER.  SUITE, OP. 40.  2TPT, HN, TRB, TU                           A71
WERDIN, E.  KLEINE SUITE.  3TPT, 2TRB                                 F31
WERT.  CANZONA.  2TPT, HN, 2TRB                                       M80
WHEAR, P.W.  INVOCATION & STUDY.  2TPT, HN, TRB, EU(TRB)             D16
WHITTENBERG, C.  TRIPTYCH.  2TPT, HN, 2TRB                           C40
WIGGLESWORTH, F.  QUINTET.  2TPT, HN, TRB, TU                        A13
WILBYE-BALDWIN.  2 MADRIGALS.  2TPT, HN, TRB, TU                      G83
WILDER, A.  BRASS QUINTET NO. 2.  2TPT, HN, TRB, TU                  H09
WILDER, A.  BRASS QUINTET NO. 3.  2TPT, HN, TRB, TU                  H09
WILDER, A.  BRASSININITY.  2TPT, HN, TRB, TU                          D14
WILDER, A.  EFFIE JOINS THE CARNIVAL.  2TPT, HN, TRB, TU             B04
WILSON.  TARANTELLA.  2TPT, HN, TRB, TU                               N42
WILSON, G.  QUINTET FOR BRASS.  2TPT, 2TRB, TU                        B35
WINKLER, P.P.  FESTRUF.  3TPT, 2TRB                                   C54
WURZ, R.  TURMMUSIK NR.1.  2TPT IN F, 3TRB                            A90
WURZ, R.  TURMMUSIK NR.2.  2TPT IN F, 3 TRB                           A90
WURZ, R.  TURMMUSIK NR.4.  2TPT, 3TRB                                 A89
YANNATOS, J.  7 EPISODES.  2TPT, HN, TRB, TU(TRB)                    A13
YOUNG, P.  MUSIC FOR BRASS.  2TPT, HN, TRB, TU                        D94
YOUNG, P.  TRIPTYCH.  2TPT, HN, TRB, TU                               D94
ZANINELLI, L.  DESIGNS FOR BRASS QUINTET                              F78
   2TPT, TRB(HN), TRB, BTRB(TU)
ZELENKA, J.D.-JANETZKY.  6 REITERFANFAREN.  4TPT, TIMP               C75
ZINDARS.  QUINTET NO. 2.  2TPT, HN, TRB, TU                           B04
ZINDARS.  4 THOUGHTS.  2TPT, HN, TRB, TU                              B04
ZINDARS, E.  QUINTET.  2TPT, HN, TRB, TU                              D16
```

```
ZINDARS, F.  TONE POEM.  2TPT, HN, TRB, TU                    B04
ZVEREV, V.I.  SUITE.  2TPT, HN, 2TRB                          D81
ZVEREV, V.I.-BOSWELL.  SUITE.  2TPT, HN, 2TRB                 N42
```


5 PARTS: HORN-WOODWIND


```
ABSIL, J.  DANSES BULGARES, OP.103.  HN, FL, OB, CL, BSN      D41
ABSIL, J.  QUINTETTE, OP.16.  HN, FL, OB, CL, BSN            B12
AESCHBACHER, W.  THEMA, VAR. & FUGUE...WEIHNACHTSLIED         H03
   HN, FL, OB, CL, BSN
AGAY, D.  5 EASY DANCES.  HN, FL, OB, CL, BSN               E77
AHNELL, E.  WIND QUINTET #1.  'N,FL, OB, CL, BSN            P48
AITKEN, H.  8 STUDIES FOR WIND QUINTET.  HN, FL, OB, CL, BSN B92
AMES, W.  MOVEMENT.  HN, FL, OB, CL, BSN                    A13
AMES, W.  WOODWIND QUINTET.  HN, FL, OB, CL, BSN            A13
AMRAM, D.W.  QUINTET.  HN, FL, OB, CL, BSN                  E65
ANDERSEN, J.  KVINTET.  HN, FL, OB, CL, BSN                 C17
ANDERSON, T.J.  5 ETUDES & A FANCY.  HN, FL, OB, CL, BSN    A13
ANDRAUD, A.J.(CMPL).  22 WOODWIND QUINTETS                  F60
   HN, FL, OB, CL, BSN
ANDRIESSEN, H.  QUINTET.  HN, FL, OB, CL, BSN               B74
ANDRIESSEN, J.  SCIARADA SPAGNUOLA.  HN, FL, OB, CL, BSN    B74
ANGERER, P.  QUINTETT.  HN, FL, OB, CL, BSN                 B73
ARNELL-GOOSSENS.  CASSATION, OP. 45.  HN, FL, OB, CL, BSN   C71
ARNOLD, M.  3 SHANTIES.  HN, FL, OB, CL, BSN                E58
ARRIEU, C.  QUINTETTE, C.  HN, FL, OB, CL, BSN              A71
ASPLMAYR, F.-PULKERT.  PARTITA IN D.  2HN, 2OB, BSN         D44
ASPLMAYR, F.  PARTITA IN F.  2HN, 2OB, BSN                  D44
AVNI.  WIND QUINTET.  HN, FL, OB, CL, BSN                   D84
BAAREN, K.V.  QUINTETTO A FIATI.  HN, FL, CB, CL, BSN       B74
BACEWICZ, G.  QUINTET.  HN, FL, OB, CL, BSN                 A31
BACH, J.C.-STEIN.  BLASER-SINFONIEN.  2HN, 2CL, BSN         C75
BACH, J.C.-WOJCIECHOWSKI.  3 MARCHES IN ES MAJOR            F50
   2HN, 2OB(2FL), BSN
BACH, J.S.-OREM.  BOURREE FR. OVERTURE NO.3 IN D MAJOR      E77
   HN, FL, OB, CL, BSN
BACH, J.S.-BREARLEY.  3 CHORALE PRELUDES.  HN, FL, OB, CL, BSN E41
BACH, J.S.  FUGUE IN C MINOR.  HN, FL, OB, CL, BSN          E77
BACH, J.S.-KESSLER.  FUGUE XXII, VOL.1.  HN, FL, OB, CL, BSN F07
BACH, J.S.  2 FUGUES.  HN, FL(OB), OB, CL, BSN              C71
BACH, J.S.-ROSENTHAL.  PRELUDE & FUGUE IN E MINOR           G21
   HN, FL, OB, CL, BSN
BACH, J.S.-ROSENTHAL.  PRELUDE & FUGUE IN G MINOR           G21
   HN, FL, CB, CL, BSN
BACH, J.S.-VON KREISLER.  PRELUDE & FUGUE                   F60
   HN, FL, OB, CL, BSN
BACH, J.S.-KESSLER.  PRELUDE XXII, VOL 1.  HN, FL, OB, CL, BSN F07
BACH, J.S.-SADIE.  QUINTETS NOS. 1 & 2.  2HN, 2CL, BSN      A78
BACH, J.S.-SADIE.  QUINTETS NOS. 3 & 4.  2HN, 2CL, BSN      A78
BACH, J.S.-GORDON.  SARABANDE & GAVOTTE.  HN, FL, OB, CL, BSN B53
BADINGS, H.  QUINTET NO.2.  HN, FL, OB, CL, BSN             B74
BADINGS, H.  QUINTETT II.  HN, FL, OB, CL, BSN              B99
BADINGS, H.  QUINTETT IV.  HN, FL, OB, CL, BSN              B99
BAEYENS, A.I.  QUINTETTE A VENT.  HN, FL, OB, CL, BSN       B12
BALAY, G.  MINIATURE SUITE IN THE 18TH CENTURY STYLE        D36
   HN, FL, OB, CL, BSN
BALFE, M.  KVINTETT, OP.2.  HN, FL, OB, CL, BSN             B90
BALMER, L.  LANDSHUTER FROSCHSERENADE, DIE                  H03
   HN, FL, OB, CL, BSN
```

BALMER, L. FAUVRE JACQUES. HN, FL, OB, CL, BSN		H03
BARBER, S. SUMMER MUSIC, OP.31. HN, FL, CB, CL, BSN		F23
BARGIEL, W.-HARRIS. MEDITATION. HN, FL, CB, CL, BSN		B53
BARNES, C.P. ROBBINS COLLECTION OF ENSEMBLES		F01
HN(CL), FL, OB, CL, BSN		
BARROW, R.G. SUITE FOR WOODWIND QUINTET. HN, FL, OB, CL, BSN		B35
BARROWS, J.R. MARCH. HN, FL, OB, CL, BSN		F23
BARTHE, A.-ANDRAUD. PASSACAILLE. HN, FL, OB, CL, BSN		F60
BARTHE, A. PASSACAILLE. HN, FL, OB, CL, BSN		F07
BARTOS, F. BOURGEOIS GENTILHOMME, LE. HN, FL, OB, CL, BSN		A33
BARTOS, F. BURGER ALS EDELMANN. HN, FL, CB, CL, BSN		A51
BASSETT, L.R. WOODWIND QUINTET. HN, FL, OB, CL, BSN		A13
BAUER, M. QUINTET, OP. 48. HN, FL, OB, CL, BSN		A13
BAUM, A. DIVERTIMENTO. HN, FL, OB, CL, BSN		H03
BAUMANN, M. KLEINE KAMMERMUSIK. HN, FL, OB, CL, BSN		F53
BAUR, J. QUINTETTO SERENO. HN, FL, OB, CI, BSN		A90
BAYER-VETESSY, G. SERENADE FUR BLASERQUINTETT		D88
HN, FL, OB, CL, BSN		
BEACH, H.H.A. PASTORALE. HN, FL, OB, CL, BSN		B38
BECKLER, S.R. FIVE. HN, FL, OB, CL, BSN		B35
BEEKHUIS, H. ELEGIE EN HUMORESKE. HN, FL, OB, CL, BSN		B74
BEETHOVEN, L.V.-BREARLEY. BAGATELLE, OP.199/1		E41
HN, FL, CB, CL, BSN		
BEETHOVEN, L.V.-DE BUERIS. COUNTRY DANCE NO.3		A91
HN, FL, OB, CL, BSN		
BEETHOVEN, L.V.-SCOTT. PIANO SONATA, OP.49/1		G13
HN, FL, OB, CL, BSN		
BEETHOVEN, L.V. QUINTET IN E-FLAT, OP.71		E77
HN, FL, OB, CL, BSN		
BEETHOVEN, L.V.-HESS-ZELLNER. QUINTET. 3HN, OB, BSN		A38
BEETHOVEN, L.V.-HESS-ZELLNER. QUINTET. 3HN, OB, BSN		F31
BEETHOVEN, L.V. QUINTETT. 3HN, OB, BSN		F31
BEETHOVEN, L.V.-TAYLOR. RONDO IN F FROM "FA.SONATA, OP.10/2"		B53
HN, FL, CB, CL, BSN		
BEETHOVEN, L.V.-BELLISON. VARIATIONS ON A THEME		B32
HN, FL, CB, CL, BSN		
BENSON, W.F. MARCHE. HN, FL, OB, CL, BSN		F43
BEREZOWSKY, N. SUITE NO.2, OP.22. HN, FL, OB, CL, BSN		D84
BERGER, J. 6 KLEINE STUCKE. HN, FL, OB, CL, BSN		G43
BERGMANN, W. MUSIK FUR BLASERQUINTETT. HN, FL, OB, CL, BSN		B73
BERGSMA, W.I. CONCERTO FOR WIND QUINTET. HN, FL, OB, CL, BSN		C33
BEZANSON, P. WOODWIND QUINTET (HOMAGE TO GREAT AMERICANS)		A13
HN, FL, OB, CL, BSN		
BIRTWISTLE, H. REFRAINS & CHORUSES. HN, FL, OB, CL, BSN		F97
BLUM, R. CONCERTO 1961. HN, FL, OB, CL, BSN		H03
BLUM, R. STATIONEM. HN, FL, OB, CL, BSN		H03
BLUMER, T. SCHWEIZER QUINTETT. HN, FL, OB, CL, BSN		F50
BOCCHERINI, L.-HARRIS. MENUET-AIR. HN, FL, OB, CL, BSN		B53
BOEDIJN, G.H. KWINTET CONCERTANTE, OP.150		B74
HN, FL, OB, CL, BSN		
BOELLMAN, L. MENUET GOTHIQUE. HN, OB, CL, BSN, EH		B81
BOELY, A.P.F.-TAYLOR. ANDANTE. HN, FL, OB, CL, BSN		A91
BOIS, F.D. CHANTS ET CONTREPOINTS. HN, FL, OB, CL, BSN		B74
BONSEL, A. KWINTET NO.1. HN, FL, OB, CL, BSN		B74
BONSEL, A. KWINTET NO.2. HN, FL, OB, CL, BSN		B74
BORRIS, S. BLASERQUINTETT, OP.25/2. HN, FL, OB, CL, BSN		F53
BOURGUIGNON, F.D. 2 PIECES, OP.71. HN, FL, OB, CL, BSN		B12
BOWDER, J. QUINTET. HN, FL, OB, CL, BSN		E87
BOZAY, A. QUINTETTO PER FIATI, OP.6. HN, FL, OB, CL, BSN		B84
BOZZA, E. PENTAPHONICS. HN, FL, OB, CL, BSN		D36
BRANDON, S. RONDO. HN, FL, OB, CL, BSN		P(8
BREHM, A. DIVERTIMENTO FOR WOODWIND QUINTET		D63
HN, FL, OB, CL, BSN		

```
BRENTA, G.  SOLDAT FANFARON, LE.   HN, FL, OB, CL, BSN          D80
BRICKMAN, J.  SUITE FOR WOODWIND QUINTET.  HN, FL, OB, CL, BSN  N59
BRIGHT, H.  3 SHORT DANCES.  HN, FL, OB, CL, BSN                F43
BROD, H.-SCHULLER.  QUINTET OP.2/1 IN E-FLAT MAJOR             D55
   HN, FL, OB, CL, BSN
BRONS, C.  BALLETTO.  HN, FL, OB, CL, BSN                      B74
BRONS, C.  MUTAZIONE.  HN, FL, OB, CL, BSN                     B74
BROWN.  QUINTETTE.  HN, FL, OB, CL, BSN                        B24
BRUGK, H.M.  SERENADE, OP.22.  HN, FL, OB, CL, BSN             F50
BRUNS, V.  BLASERQUINTETT, OP. 16.  HN, FL, OB, CL, BSN        C75
BURIAN, E.F.  QUINTET FOR WIND INSTR..  HN, FL, OB, CL, BSN    A33
BURIAN, E.F.  QUINTET.  HN, FL, OB, CL, BSN                    A51
BUTT, J.B.  WINSOME'S FOLLY.  HN, FL, OB, CL, BSN              E41
CABEZON A.D.  CANCION RELIGIOSO.  HN, FL, CB, CL, BSN          B04
CALABRO, L.  DIVERTIMENTO.  HN, FL, OB, CL, BSN                B92
CAMBINI, G.G.-MARX.  WOODWIND QUINTET NO.1                     D55
   HN, FL, OB, CL, BSN
CAMBINI, G.G.-MARX.  WOODWIND QUINTET NO.3                     D55
   HN, FL, OB, CL, BSN
CARABELLA, E.  SUITE.  HN, FL, OB, CL, BSN                     E98
CARLSTEDT, J.  KVINTETT.  HN, FL, OB, CL, BSN                  B90
CARLSTEDT, J.  SINFONIETTA.  HN, FL, OB, CL, BSN               B90
CARTER, E.C.  QUINTET.  HN, FL, OB, CL, BSN                    A38
CAVADINI, C.  SUITE II PER QUINTETTO DI FIATTI                 H03
   HN, FL, OB, CL, BSN
CAZDEN, N.  3 CONSTRUCTIONS, OP.38.  HN, FL, OB, CL, BSN       F62
CELLIER, A.  IMAGE MEDIEVALES.  HN, FL, OB, CL, BSN            F87
CHAGRIN, F.  DIVERTIMENTO.  HN, FL, OB, CL, BSN                A42
CHAVEZ, C.  SOLI NO.2.  HN, FL, OB, CL, BSN                    D84
CHAYNES, C.  SERENADE.  HN, FL, OB, CL, BSN                    D36
CHEMIN-PETIT, H.  QUINTET.  HN, FL, OB, CL, BSN                D46
CHENAUX, A.  QUINTETTE POUR INSTR. A VENT                      H03
   HN, FL, OB, CL, BSN
CHEVREUILLE, R.  DIVERTISSEMENT, OP.21.  HN, FL, OB, CL, BSN   B12
CHEVREUILLE, R.  SERENADE, OP.65.  HN, FL, OB, CL, BSN         B12
CHILDS, B.  FIFTH WIND QUINTET.  HN, FL, OB, CL, BSN           N29
CHILDS, B.  QUINTET I.  HN, FL, OB, CL, BSN                    A13
CHILDS, B.  QUINTET II.  HN, FL, OB, CL, BSN                   A13
CHILDS, B.  QUINTET III.  HN, FL, OB, CL, BSN                  A13
CHILDS, B.  QUINTET IV.  HN, FL, OB, CL, BSN                   A13
CLARKE, H.L.  CONCATENATA; QUODLIBET.  HN, FL, OB, CL, BSN     A13
COCKER, M.  WOODWIND QUINTET IN 3 MVTS.  HN, FL, OB, CL, BSN   F56
COLACO OSORIO-SWAAB, R.  SUITE.  HN, FL, OB, CL, BSN           B74
COLOMER, B.M.  BOUREE.  HN, FL, OB, CL, BSN                    B53
COLOMER, B.M.  MENUET.  HN, FL, OB, CL, BSN                    B53
CONE, E.T.  STANZAS FOR WIND QUINTET.  HN, FL, CL, BSN, EH     D63
COWELL, H.  BALLAD.  HN, FL, OB, CL, BSN                       A38
COWELL, H.  SUITE.  HN, FL, OB, CL, BSN                        D74
CRUFT, A.F.  2 ENGLISH KEYBOARD PIECES.  HN, FL, OB, CL, BSN   G26
DAHL, I.  ALLEGRO & ARIOSO.  HN, FL, OB, CL, BSN              D55
DANZI, F.-WEIGELT.  BLASERQUINTETT B-DUR, OP. 56/1            D44
   HN, FL, OB, CL, BSN
DANZI, F.-WEIGELT.  BLASERQUINTETT G-MOLL, OP. 56/2           D44
   HN, FL, OB, CL, BSN
DANZI, F.-KNEUSSLIN.  BLASERQUINTETT, OP.56/3 IN F MAJOR      D44
   HN, FL, OB, CL, BSN
DANZI, F.-ROTTLER.  BLASERQUINTETT, OP.67/1 IN G MAJOR        D44
   HN, FL, OB, CL, BSN
DANZI, F.  QUINTET IN D MINOR, OP.41.  HN, FL, OB, CL, BSN    F23
DANZI, F.-RAMPAL.  QUINTET IN E MINOR, OP.67/2               C91
   HN, FL, OB, CL, BSN
DANZI, F.  QUINTET, D MINOR,OP.68/3.  HN, FL, OB, CL, BSN     E14
```

```
DANZI, F.   QUINTETTE, OP.67/2,E MINOR.   HN, FL, OB, CL, BSN        D21
DANZI, F.   QUINTETTE, OP.68/1,A MAJOR.   HN, FL, OB, CL, BSN        D21
DANZI, F.   QUINTETTE, OP.68/2,F MAJOR.   HN, FL, OB, CL, BSN        D21
DAVID, G.   QUINTET FOR WIND INSTRS.   HN, FL, OB, CL, BSN           B84
DAVID, G.   QUINTET NO.3.   HN, FL, OB, CL, BSN                      B84
DAVID, K.H.   KLEINE SUITE.   HN, FL, OB, CL, BSN                    H03
DAVID, T.C.   QUINTETT.   HN, FL, OB, CL, BSN                        B73
DE COURSEY, R.   FUGUE A LA RUMBA.   HN, FL, OB, CL, BSN             A93
DE JONG, M.   APORISTISCH TRIPTICK, OP.82B                          B12
   HN, FL, OB, CL, BSN
DEBUSSY, C.-ROSENTHAL.   ARABESQUE NO.1.   HN, FL, OB, CL, BSN       G21
DELANEY, C.   SUITE FOR WOODWIND QUINTET.   HN, FL, OB, CL, BSN      F60
DENZA, L.-HARRIS.   FUNICULI-FUNICULA.   HN, FL, OB, CL, BSN         B53
DESPORTES, Y.   PRELUDE, VARIATIONS & FINALE...GREGORIAN CHANT       F60
   HN, FL, OB, CL, BSN
DIAMOND, D.   QUINTET.   HN, FL, OB, CL, BSN                         F59
DIETHELM, C.   BLASERQUINTETT NO.2.   HN, FL, OB, CL, BSN            H03
DIETHELM, C.   BLASERQUINTETT.   HN, FL, OB, CL, BSN                 H03
DIETHELM, C.   SERENADE.   HN, FL, OB, CL, BSN                       H03
DITTERSDORF, K.D.V.   PARTHIA IN D.   2HN, 2OB, BSN                  E14
DITTERSDORF, K.D.V.-RHAU.   PARTITA NR. F, A MAJOR                   A90
   2HN, 2OB, BSN
DITTERSDORF, K.D.V.-RHAU.   PARTITA NR. 4, A MAJOR                   A90
   2HN, 2OB, BSN
DITTERSDORF, K.D.V.-RHAU.   PARTITA NR.20, D MAJOR                   A90
   2HN, 2OB, BSN
DOBIAS, V.   PASTORAL QUINTET.   HN, FL, OB, CL, BSN                 A33
DOMENICO, D.DI.   QUINTETTO.   HN, FL, OB, CL, BSN                   D36
DOUGLAS, R.R.   DANCE CARICATURES.   HN, FL, OB, CL, BSN             C71
DUBOIS, T.   FIRST SUITE.   HN, FL, OB, CL, BSN                      C65
DUPONT.   3 PIECES BREVES QUINTETTE A VENT                           A71
   HN, FL, OB, CL, BSN
DVORAK, A.   HUMORESKE.   HN, FL, OB, CL, BSN                        B53
EBEN, P.   QUINTETTO.   HN, FL, OB, CL, BSN                          C17
EBERHARD, D.   PARAPHRASES.   HN, FL, OB, CL, BSN                    N29
EDER, H.   QUINTETT, OP.25.   HN, FL, OB, CL, BSN                    B73
EKLUND, H.   IMPROVISATA.   HN, FL, OB, CL, BSN                      B90
ENGLERT, G.G.   RIME SERIE OP.5.   HN, FL, OE, CL, BSN               H03
ERDLEN, H.   KLEINE VARIATIONEN UBER EIN FRUHLINGSLIED, OP.27/1      G43
   HN, FL, OB, CL, BSN
ESSEX, K.   QUINTET.   HN, FL, OB, CL, BSN                           C71
ETLER, A.D.   QUINTET NO.1.   HN, FL, OB, CL, BSN                    A38
ETLER, A.D.   QUINTET NO.2.   HN, FL, OB, CL, BSN                    A38
FARKAS, F.   ANTICHE DANZE UNGHERESI DAL SECOLO XVII                 D29
   HN, FL, OB, CL, BSN
FARKAS, F.   OLD HUNGARIAN DANCES FROM THE 17TH C.                   B84
   HN, FL, OB, CL, BSN
FARKAS, F.   SERENADE.   HN, FL, OB, CL, BSN                         B84
FAURE, G.U.-WILLIAMS.   BERCEUSE, FR. "DOLLY",OP.51/1                F60
   HN, FL, OB, CL, BSN
FERGUSON, S.   OVERTURE FOR WINDS.   HN, FL, OB, CL, BSN             B35
FERNANDEZ, O.L.   SUITE, OP.37.   HN, FL, OB, CL, BSN                A38
FERNSTROM, J.   KVINTETT, OP.59.   HN, FL, OB, CL, BSN               B90
FERRARI, D.   PASTORALE.   HN, FL, OB, CL, BSN                       B44
FINK.   4 MOODS FOR WINDS.   HN, FL, OB, CL, BSN                     F72
FINKE, F.F.   QUINTETT.   HN, FL, OB, CL, BSN                        A89
FORTNER, W.   5 BAGATELLES.   HN, FL, OB, CL, BSN                    A38
FORTNER, W.   5 BAGATELLES.   HN, FL, OB, CL, BSN                    F31
FRAGALE, F.   QUINTET.   HN, FL, OB, CL, BSN                         A38
FRANCAIX, J.   QUINTET.   HN, FL, OB, CL, BSN                        F31
FRANGKISER, C.   EPISODES.   HN, FL, OB, CL, BSN                     A62
FREY, E.   VARIATIONEN, A, OP.47.   HN, FL, CB, CL, BSN              H03
```

```
FRICKER, P.R.  QUINTET, OP.5.  HN, FL, OB, CL, BSN               F31
FRID, G.  SERENADE, OP.4.  HN, FL, 2CL, BSN                      B74
FURER, A.  QUINTETT, OP.21.  HN, FL, OB, CL, BSN                 K19
FURST, P.W.  BLASERQUINTETT, OP.29/3.  HN, FL, OB, CL, BSN       B73
FURST, P.W.  KONZERTANTE MUSIK, OP.25.  HN, FL, OB, CL, BSN      B73
FUTTERER, C.  ELASERQUINTETT, B MAJOR.  HN, FL, OB, CL, BSN      D21
GAMBINI, G.G.-MARX.  WOODWIND QUINTET NO.3                       D55
     HN, FL, OB, CL, BSN
GARRIDO¬LECCA, C.  DIVERTIMENTO.  HN, FL, OB, CL, BSN            E53
GASSMANN, F.-HOCKNER.  PARTITA.  2HN, 2CL, BSN                   B73
GEISSLER, F.  HEITERE SUITE.  HN, FL, OB, CL, BSN                A89
GENZMER, H.  QUINTET.  HN, FL, OB, CL, BSN                       D48
GERAEDTS, J.  KLEINE WATERMUZIEK.  HN, FL, OB, CL, BSN           B74
GERHARD, R.  WIND QUINTET.  HN, FL, OB, CL, BSN                  D84
GILLIS, D.  AND MR. TORTOISE WINS THE RACE                       D84
     HN, FL, OB, CL, BSN
GILLIS, D.  BR'ER RABBIT DREAMS.  HN, FL, CB, CL, BSN            D84
GILLIS, D.  FROLIC IN B-BOP MAJOR, A.  HN, FL, OB, CL, BSN       D84
GILLIS, D.  GONE WITH THE WOODWINDS, SUITE NO.3                  D84
     HN, FL, OB, CL, BSN
GILLIS, D.  3 SKETCHES;SUITE NO.2.  HN, FL, OB, CL, BSN          D84
GILLIS, D.  TAKE FIVE BLUES.  HN, FL, OB, CL, BSN               D84
GILLIS, D.  THEY'RE OFF!(FABLE OF TORTOISE & HARE)               D84
     HN, FL, CB, CL, BSN
GOEB, R.J.  PRAIRIE SONGS.  HN, FL, OB, CL, BSN                  E61
GOLABEK, J.-OCHLEWSKI.  PARTITA FOR WIND ENSEMBLE                A31
     2HN, 2CL, BSN
GONZALEZ¬ZULETA, F.  QUINTETO.  HN, FL, OB, CL, BSN              F59
GORDON, P.  ELKAN-VOGEL WOODWIND ENSEMBLE FOLIO                  B92
     HN, FL, OB, CL, BSN
GOTTLIEB, J.-YUZURU.  TWILIGHT CRANE.  HN, FL, OB, CL, BSN       F23
GOULD, M.-TAYLOR.  PAVANNE.  HN, FL, OB, CI, BSN                 D84
GRETRY, A.E.M.  TAMBOURINE.  HN, FL, OB, CI, BSN                 B44
GRIEG, E.H.  MORNING MOOD FROM PEER GYNT SUITE, OP.46/1          G31
     HN, FL, OB, CL, BSN
GRIEG, E.H.-TRINKAUS.  MORNING MOOD.  HN, FL, OB, CL, BSN        H06
GROOT, H.D.  VARIATIONS ON DUTCH MELODIES                       A95
     HN, FL, OE, CL, BSN
GUENTHER, R.  RONDO.  HN, FL, OB, CL, BSN                        B53
GUILMANT, A.-TAYLOR.  CANZONETTA.  HN, FL, OB, CL, BSN           H06
GYRING, E.  QUINTET.  HN, FL, OB, CL, BSN                        A13
GYROWETZ, A.-HUBER.  SERENATA I.  2HN, 2CL, BSN                  C60
GYROWETZ, A.-HUBER.  SERENATA II.  2HN, 2CI, BSN                 C60
GYULA, D.  THIRD WIND QUINTET.  HN, FL, OB, CL, BSN              C40
HAAS, P.  WOODWIND QUINTET, OP.10.  HN, FL, OB, CL, BSN          D55
HADDAD, D.  BLUES AU VENT.  HN, FL, OB, CL, BSN                  F43
HADDAD, D.  ENCORE "1812".  HN, FL, OB, CL, BSN                  F43
HALL, P.  WIND QUINTET.  HN, FL, OB, CL, BSN                     D54
HAMERIK, E.  KVINTET.  HN, FL, OB, CL, BSN                       N53
HANDEL, G.F.-HAAS.  2 ARIAS.  2HN, 2OB, BSN                      E14
HANDEL, G.F.-BAUER.  6 LITTLE FUGUES.  HN, FL, OB, CL, BSN       A38
HARTLEY, G.  DIVERTISSEMENT.  HN, FL, OB, CL, BSN                A38
HARTLEY, W.S.  2 PIECES FOR WW QUINTET.  HN, FL, OB, CL, BSN     B52
HARTLEY, W.S.  2 PIECES.  HN, FL, OB, CL, ESN                    G70
HAUBIEL, C.  5 PIECES FOR 5 WINDS.  HN, FL, OB, CL, BSN          B38
HAUFRECHT, H.  AIRS POUR JOUES A LA TROUPE MARCHANT              A13
     HN, FL, OB, CL, BSN
HAUFRECHT, H.  DIVERTIMENTO IN C.  HN, FL, OB, CL, BSN           A13
HAUFRECHT, H.  FROM THE HILLS.  HN, FL, OB, CL, BSN              A13
HAUFRECHT, H.  SERENADE, OP. 44.  HN, FL, OB, CL, BSN            A13
HAUFRECHT, H.  WOODLAND SERENADE, A.  HN, FL, OB, CL, BSN        F03
HAYDN, J.-LONG.  DIVERTIMENTO IN C(MAN & WIFE)                   F23
     HN, FL, OB, CL, BSN
```

```
HAYDN, J.  DIVERTIMENTO NO.1 IN B-FLAT.  HN, FL, OB, CL, BSN      E77
HAYDN, J.-PERRY.  DIVERTIMENTO.  HN, FL, OB, CL, BSN             A78
HAYDN, J.-MEEK.  LARGO (STR QUARTET OP.76/5                      B72
    HN, FL, OB, CL, BSN
HAYDN, J.-VON KREISLER.  MENUETTO & SCHERZO                     F60
    HN, FL, OB, CL, BSN
HAYDN, J.-JANETZKY.  PARTHIA IN F, H.II:F.12.  2HN, 2OB, BSN     E14
HAYDN, J.  QUINTET FOR WINDS.  HN, FL, OB, CL, BSN              B44
HAYDN, J.-LONG.  QUINTET NO.1 FROM HAYDN TRIO                   F60
    HN, FL, OB, CL, BSN
HAYDN, J.-LONG.  QUINTET NO.4 FROM HAYDN TRIO                   F60
    HN, FL, OB, CL, BSN
HAYDN, J.-KESZLER.  QUINTET.  HN, FL, OB, CL, BSN              B84
HAYDN, J.-ANDRAUD.  2 SHORT QUINTETS.  HN, FL, OB, CL, BSN      F60
HEIDEN, B.  SINFONIA.  HN, FL, OB, CL, BSN                      A38
HENKEMANS, H.  QUINTET NO.2.  HN, FL, OB, CL, BSN              B74
HENZE, H.W.  QUINTETT.  HN, FL, OB, CL, BSN                    F31
HESS, W.  DIVERTIMENTO, OP.51 IN B-FLAT MAJOR                   C71
    HN, FL, OB, CL, BSN
HEWITT¬JONES, T.  THEME & VARIATIONS.  HN, FL, OB, CL, BSN(VC)   E41
HINDEMITH, P.  KLEINE KAMMERMUSIK, OP.24/2                      F31
    HN, FL, OB, CL, BSN
HIRSH, H.S.  NOCTURNE.  HN, FL, OB, CL, BSN                     A91
HIRSH, H.S.(ARR).  TURTLE DOVE, THE.  HN, FL, OB, CL, BSN       D71
HOFFER, P.  QUINTET.  HN, FL, OB, CL, BSN                       E65
HOFMANN, W.  SERENADE.  HN, FL, OB, CL, BSN                     B53
HOHENSEE, W.  BLASERQUINTETT IN D.  HN, FL, OB, CL, BSN         A89
HOLLER, K.  SERENADE, OP. 42A.  HN, FL, OB, CL, BSN             E02
HOLLIGER, H.  "H" FUR BLASERQUINTETT.  HN, FL, OB, CL, BSN      H03
HOSMER, J.B.  FUGUE IN C.  HN, FL, OB, CL, BSN                  E11
HOVHANESS, A.S.  QUINTET, OP.159.  HN, FL, OB, CL, BSN          E65
HUBER, K.  BLASERQUINTETT.  HN, FL, OB, CL, BSN                 A51
HUBER, K.  3 SATZE IN 2 TEILEN.  HN, FL/PIC, OB/EH, CL, BSN     A51
HUBER, P.  BLASERQUINTETT.  HN, FL, OB, CL, BSN                 H03
HUBER, P.  KLEINE BALLETTMUSIK.  HN, FL, OB, CL, BSN            H03
HUFFER, F.K.  SAILOR'S HORNPIPE, THE.  HN, FL, OB, CL, BSN      G31
HUYBRECHTS, A.  QUINTETTE.  HN, FL, OB, CL, BSN                 B12
INGENHOVEN, J.  QUINTET.  HN, FL, OB, CL, BSN                   F82
JACOBY, H.  QUINTET.  HN, FL, OB, CL, BSN                       D71
JARDANYI, P.  FANTASY & VARIATIONS ON A HUNGARIAN FOLKSONG      B84
    HN, FL, OB, CL, BSN
JERSILD, J.  SERENADE; MUSIC-MAKING IN THE FOREST              H30
    HN, FL, OB, CL, BSN
JONGEN, J.  CONCERTO, OP.124.  HN, FL, OB, CL, BSN              F60
JUNGK, K.  CHACONNE.  HN, FL, OB, CL, BSN                       F50
KADOSA, P.  QUINTET, OP.49/A.  HN, FL, OB, CL, BSN             B84
KALLSTENIUS, E.  DIVERTIMENTO, OP.29.  HN, FL, OB, CL, BSN      B90
KAPP, V.  SUITE.  HN, FL, OB, CL, BSN                           D81
KARKOFF, M.  KVINTETT, OP.24.  HN, FL, OB, CL, BSN             B90
KARKOFF, M.  SERENATA PICCOLA, OP.34C.  HN, FL, OB, CL, BSN     B90
KARLINS, W.  QUINTET.  HN, FL, OB, CL, BSN                      A13
KAUFMANN, W.  PARTITA FOR WIND QUINTET.  HN, FL, OB, CL, BSN    F43
KELLY, R.  PASSACAGLIA & FUGUE.  HN, FL, OB, CL, BSN            A13
KELTERBORN, R.  7 BAGATELLEN.  HN, FL, OB, CL, BSN             D88
KING, H.C.  KWINTET.  HN, FL, OB, CL, BSN                       B74
KINGMAN, D.  QUINTET FOR WINDS.  HN, FL, OB, CL, BSN            G21
KLAUSS, N.  JAKARTA.  HN, 4INST ?                               B35
KLIMKO, R.J.  QUINTET FOR WOODWINDS.  HN, FL, OB, CL, BSN       B35
KLUGHARDT, A.F.M.  QUINTET, OP.79.  HN, FL, OB, CL, BSN         C75
KLUGHARDT, A.F.M.  QUINTETT, OP.79.  HN, FL, OB, CL, BSN        G43
KOETSIER, J.  DIVERTIMENTO, OP.16/1.  HN, FL, OB, CL, BSN       B74
KOETSIER, J.  2E DIVERTIMENTO, OP.35/1.  HN, FL, OB, CL, BSN    B74
```

```
KOHOUT, J.  MINIATUREN.  HN, FL, OB, CL, BSN                              C75
KOHS, E.B.  QUINTET (STUDIES IN VARIATIONS-PART 1)                        A13
     HN, FL, OB, CL, BSN
KOMMA, K.M.  DIVERTIMENTO.  HN, FL, OB, CL, BSN                           C82
KONT, P.  QUINTETT IN MEMORIAM FR.DANZI.  HN, FL, OB, CL, BSN             B73
KORDA, V.  DIVERTIMENTO.  HN, FL, OB, CL, ESN                             B73
KORN, P.J.  QUINTET.  HN, FL, OB, CL, BSN                                 E65
KOTONSKI, W.  QUINTET FOR WIND INSTRUMENTS                                E72
     HN, FL, OB, CL, BSN
KRAUSE¬GRAUMNITZ, H.  BLASERQUINTETT NR.1                                 A89
     HN, FL, OB, CL, BSN
KREISLER, A.V.  CHORALE, PRELUDE & FUGUE.  HN, FL, OB, CL, BSN            F60
KREISLER, A.V.  FABLE (NO.2 FROM QUINTET)                                 F60
     HN, FL, OB, CL, BSN
KREISLER, A.V.  HUMOROUS MARCH (NO.4 FROM QUINTET)                        F60
     HN, FL, OB, CL, BSN
KREISLER, A.V.  PASTORALE.  HN, FL, OB, CL, BSN                           F60
KREISLER, A.V.  POSSUM TROT (NO.3 FROM QUINTET)                           F60
     HN, FL, OB, CL, BSN
KREISLER, A.V.  TRIPTYCH.  HN, FL, OB, CL, BSN                            F60
KRENEK, E.  PENTAGRAMM.  HN, FL, OB, CL, BSN                              A51
KUBIZEK, A.  KAMMERQUINTETT FUR BLASER.  HN, FL, OB, CL, BSN              B73
KUHN, M.  SERENADE/NOTTURNO.  HN, FL, OB, CL, BSN                         H03
KUNERT, K.  DIVERTIMENTO NR.2, OP.18.  HN, FL, OB, CL, BSN                C75
KUNERT, K.  ZWEITES BLASERQUINTETT, OP.17                                 C75
     HN, FL, OB, CL, BSN
KURI¬ALDANA, M.  WOODWIND QUINTET "CANDELARIA"                            E14
     HN, FL, OB, CL, BSN
KURTAG, G.  QUINTETTO PER FIATI, OP.2.  HN, FL, OB, CL, BSN               B84
LACERDA, O.  VARIACOES E FUGA PARA QUINTETO DE SOPRO                      E53
     HN, FL, OB, CL, BSN
LACHNER, F.  QUINTET.  HN, FL, OB, CL, BSN                                E14
LANDRE, G.  KWINTET (1960).  HN, FL, OB, CL, BSN                          B74
LANDRE, G.  QUINTETTO (1930).  HN, FL, CL, BSN                            B74
LANG, I.  QUINTET.  HN, FL, OB, CL, BSN                                   B84
LANG, M.  3 SATZE FUR BLASERQUINTETT.  HN, FL, OB, CL, BSN                H03
LAUBER, J.  QUINTETTE.  HN, FL, OB, CL, BSN                               H03
LAUDENSLAGER, H.  QUINTET.  HN, FL, OB, CL, BSN                           B44
LEEUW, T.D.  ANTIPHONIE VOOR BLASSKWINTET EN 4 KLANKSPOREN                B74
     HN, FL, OB, CL, BSN
LEFEBVRE, C.  SUITE, OP. 50/2.  HN, FL, OB, CL, BSN                       C55
LEFEBVRE, C.  SUITE, OP.57.  HN, FL, OB, CL, BSN                          B53
LEFEBVRE, C.  SUITE, OP.57.  HN, FL, OB, CL, BSN                          C55
LEGLEY, V.  QUINTETTE, OP.58.  HN, FL, OB, CL, BSN                        B12
LEHMANN, H.U.  EPISODEN.  HN, FL, OB, CL, BSN                             H03
LEUKAUF, R.  BLASERQUINTETT, OP.25.  HN, FL, OB, CL, BSN                  B73
LEVY, S.P.-REIBOLD.  LOVELETTE.  HN, FL, OB, CL, BSN                      A62
LEWIS, P.T.  CONTRASTS.  HN, FL, OB, CL, BSN                              A13
LEWIS, P.T.  5 MOVEMENTS.  HN, FL, OB, CL, BSN                            A13
LIADOV, A.  8 RUSSIAN FOLK SONGS, OP.58.  HN, FL, OB, CL, BSN             D81
LICKL, J.G.  BLASERQUINTETT, F MAJOR.  HN, FL, OB, CL, BSN                D21
LIEDBECK, S.  IMPROMPTU.  HN, FL, OB, CL, BSN                             B90
LILIEN, I.  QUINTETTO NO.2.  HN, FL, OB, CL, BSN                          B74
LILIEN, I.  VOYAGE AU PRINTEMPS.  HN, FL, CB, CL, BSN                     B74
LINN, R.  QUINTET.  HN, FL, OB, CL, BSN                                   G21
LISZT, F.-SEAY.  WEIHNACHTSLIED.  HN, FL, CB, CL, BSN                     F62
LOCKWOOD, N.  FUN PIECE.  HN, FL, OB, CL, BSN                             A13
LONDON, E.  QUINTET.  HN, FL, OB, CL, BSN                                 D86
LORA, A.  6 DANCES, OLD & NEW.  HN, FL, OB, CL, BSN                       A13
LOUEL, J.  QUINTETTE.  HN, FL, OB, CL, BSN                                B12
LUCKY, S.  QUINTET FOR WIND INSTRS, OP.11                                 A33
     HN, FL, CB, CL, BSN
```

LUNDEN, L.   VARIATIONS ON "BYSSAN LULL".   HN, FL, OB, CL, BSN   E39
MACDOWELL, E.A.-TRINKAUS.   IDYL, OP.28/2.   HN, FL, OB, CL, BSN   H06
MAGANINI, Q.E.-HARRIS.   REVERIE.   HN, FL, OB, CL, BSN   B53
MAGI, E.   OSTINATO (SCORE ONLY).   HN, FL, CB, CL, BSN   D81
MALIPIERO, G.F.   DIALOGHI IV.   HN, FL, OB, CL, BSN   E98
MALIPIERO, R.   MUSICA DA CAMERA.   HN, FL, OB, CL, BSN   G41
MAMLOK, U.   QUINTET.   HN, FL, OB, CL, BSN   A13
MARECHAL, H.C.   AIR DU GUET.   HN, FL, OB, CL, BSN   C65
MAREZ OYENS, T.D.   2 SKETCHES.   HN, FL, OB, CL, BSN   B74
MARIE, G.-HARRIS.   BERCEUSE.   HN, FL, OB, CL, BSN   B53
MAROS, R.   MUSICA LEGGIERA PER FIATI.   HN, FL, OB, CL, BSN   B84
MARTINO, D.   CONCERTO FOR WIND QUINTET-36   D55
     HN, FL, OB, CL, BSN
MASSIS.   THEME ET VARIATIONS.   HN, FL, OB, CL, BSN   A71
MATTHES, R.   SCHERZI E NOTTURNI.   HN, FL, OB, CL, BSN   H03
MAXWELL, C.   FAIRY TALE.   HN, FL, OB, CL, BSN   P49
MC BRIDE, R.   FANFARE FOR YOUNG PEOPLE.   HN, FL, OB, CL, BSN   A13
MC BRIDE, R.   HOME ON THE RANGE.   HN, FL, OB, CL, BSN   A13
MC BRIDE, P.   JAM-SESSION.   HN, FL, OB, CL, BSN   B38
MC BRIDE, R.   MEXICAN DANCE.   HN, FL, OB, CL, BSN   A13
MC BRIDE, R.   PAJARILLO BARRANQUENO.   HN, FL, OB, CL, BSN   A13
MC BRIDE, R.   ROCK 'EM COWBOY.   HN, FL, OB, CL, BSN   A13
MC BRIDE, R.   SERENADE TO COUNTRY MUSIC.   HN, FL, OB, CL, BSN   A13
MC CALL, H.E.   2 TUNES FROM MOTHER GOOSE.   HN, FL, OB, CL, BSN   F60
MC KAY, G.F.   JOYFUL DANCE.   HN, FL, OB, CL, BSN   D74
MEDERACKE, K.   BOHMISCHE SUITE, OP.43.   HN, FL, OB, CL, BSN   C75
MEESTER, L.D.   DIVERTIMENTO.   HN, FL, OB, CL, BSN   B12
MEIER, J.   BLASERQUINTETT.   HN, FL, OB, CL, BSN   H03
MENDELSSOHN, F.   KRAKOWIAK.   HN, FL, OB, CL, BSN   A91
MENDELSSOHN, F.-SEAY.   SCHERZETTO, OP.102/3   F62
     HN, FL, CB, CL, BSN
MENDELSSOHN, F.-CAFARELLA.   SONG WITHOUT WORDS, OP.62/4   G10
     HN, FL, OE, CL, BSN
MERSSON, B.   MUSIK FUR BLASERQUINTETT.   HN, FL, OB, CL, BSN   H03
MEULEMANS, A.   1ER QUINTET.   HN, FL, OB, CL, BSN   B12
MEULEMANS, A.   2E QUINTETTE.   HN, FL, OB, CL, BSN   B12
MEULEMANS, A.   3E QUINTETTE.   HN, FL, OB, CL, BSN   B12
MEYER-TORMIN, W.   KLEINES QUINTETT FUR BLASER   A83
     HN, FL, OB, CL, BSN
MEYER-TORMIN, W.   QUINTET.   HN, FL, OB, CL, BSN   F31
MILHAUD, D.   CHEMINEE DU ROI RENE, LA.   HN, FL, OB, CL, BSN   F60
MILHAUD, D.   DIVERTISSEMENT IN 3 PARTS.   HN, FL, OB, CL, BSN   C65
MILLS, C.   SONATA FANTASIA.   HN, FL, OB, CL, BSN   A13
MOESCHINGER, A.   QUINTETT, OP.53.   HN, FL, OB, CL, BSN   H03
MOORE, D.S.   WOODWIND QUINTET.   HN, FL, OB, CL, BSN   D84
MORITZ, E.   QUINTETT, OP.41.   HN, FL, OB, CL, BSN   G43
MORTENSEN, F.   QUINTET, OP.4.   HN, FL, OB, CL, BSN   H30
MOYSE, I.   QUINTET FOR WOODWINDS.   HN, FL, OB, CL, BSN   D55
MOZART, W.A.   ADAGIO.   HN, FL, OB, CL, BSN   B53
MOZART, W.A.-WEIGELT.   ADAGIO, B MAJOR,K.411   D44
     HN, FL, OB, CL, BSN
MOZART, W.A.-VESTER.   ANDANTE FUR EINE ORGELWALZE   D84
     HN, FL, OB, CL, BSN
MOZART, W.A.-MEYER.   ANDANTE, F MAJOR,K.616   F50
     HN, FL, OB, CL, BSN
MOZART, W.A.-WEIGELT.   DIVERTIMENTO # 8, F MAJOR,K.213   D44
     HN, FL, OB, CL, BSN
MOZART, W.A.-WEIGELT.   DIVERTIMENTO # 9, B MAJOR,K.240   D44
     HN, FL, OB, CL, BSN
MOZART, W.A.-BRYANT.   DIVERTIMENTO #12.   HN, FL, OB, CL, BSN   G26
MOZART, W.A.-WEIGELT.   DIVERTIMENTO #13, F MAJOR,K.253   D44
     HN, FL, OB, CL, BSN

```
MOZART, W.A.-WEIGELT.  DIVERTIMENTO #14, B MAJOR,K.270        D44
   HN, FL, OB, CL, BSN
MOZART, W.A.  DIVERTISSEMENT # 9 FOR WIND QUINTET            F36
   HN, FL, OB, CL, BSN
MOZART, W.A.-MEYER.  FANTASIE IN F MINOR, K.594              F50
   HN, FL, OB, CL, BSN
MOZART, W.A.-MEYER.  FANTASIE IN F MINOR, K.608              F50
   HN, FL, OB, CL, BSN
MOZART, W.A.-CAPUTO.  MINUET.  HN, OB, 2CL, BSN              G10
MOZART, W.A.-SNIECKOWSKI.  QUINTET IN D MINOR               E72
   HN, FL, OB, CL, BSN
MOZART, W.A.-CAILLIET.  QUINTET IN F MAJOR                  B92
   HN, FL, OB, CL, BSN
MOZART, W.A.-ANDRAUD.  2 SHORT QUINTETS.  HN, FL, OB, CL, BSN  F60
MUELLER.  (SEE ALSO "MULLER")
MUELLER, F.  5 PIECES.  HN, FL, OB, CL, BSN                 B44
MUELLER, F.  3 TRANSCRIPTIONS FOR WW5.  HN, FL, OB, CL, BSN  B44
MUELLER, P.  QUINTET NO.1 IN E-FLAT.  HN, FL, OB, CL, BSN   E14
MUELLER, P.  3 QUINTETS.  HN, FL, OB, CL, BSN               E14
MULDER, H.  KWINTET, OP.119.  HN, FL, OB, CL, BSN           B74
MULLER VON KULM, W.  TRIPTYCHON, OP.85.  HN, FL, OB, CL, BSN  H03
MULLER, P.  QUINTET NO. 2 IN E-FLAT.  HN, FL, OB, CL, BSN   E14
MULLER, P.  QUINTET NO. 3 IN A.  HN, FL, OE, CL, BSN        E14
MUSSORGSKY, M.P.-KESSLER.  BALLET OF CHICKENS IN THEIR SHELLS  F07
   HN, FL,OB, CL, BSN
NEVIN, F.W.-GORDON.  GONDOLIERI.  HN, FL, CB, CL, BSN       E77
NIELSEN, C.  QUINTET, OP.43.  HN, FL, CB-EH, CL, BSN        H30
NOCKE-TAYLOR.  MILL OF SANS-SOUCI, THE.  HN, FL, CL, OB, BSN  D84
ONSLOW, G.-REDEL.  BLASERQUINTETT F MAJOR, OP.81/3          D44
   HN, FL, OB, CL, BSN
ONSLOW, G.  WOODWIND QUINTET.  HN, FL, OB, CL, BSN          D55
OTTEN, L.  BLAASKWINTET NO.2.  HN, FL, OB, CL, BSN          B74
OTTOSON, D.  SUITE.  HN, FL, OB, CL, BSN                    B90
PACIORKIEWICZ, T.  QUINTET FOR WIND INSTRS..               A31
   HN, FL, OB, CL, BSN
PAUER, J.  BLASQUINTETT.  HN, FL, OB, CL, ESN              A51
PAUER, J.  QUINTET FOR WIND INSTRS..  HN, FL, OB, CL, BSN   A33
PERSICHETTI, V.  PASTORAL, OP. 21.  HN, FL, OB, CL, BSN     F23
PESSARD, E.L.F.  AUBADE.  HN, FL, OB, CL, ESN              B53
PETERSON, H.  SCHERZO & TRIO.  HN, FL, OB, CL, BSN         P31
PETROVICS, E.  QUINTET.  HN, FL, OB, CL, BSN               B84
PFISTER, H.  QUINTETT "OTTOBEUREN".  HN, FL, OB, CL, BSN    H03
PHILLIPS, D.V.  LULLABIC DIGRESSIONS.  HN, FL, OB, CL, BSN  B35
PHILLIPS, P.  LITTLE PRELUDE & BLUES.  HN, FL, OB, CL, BSN  D86
PIERCE, E.H.  ALLEGRO PIACEVOLE & SCHERZO                  H06
   HN, FL, OB, CL, BSN
PIERCE, E.H.  IN MERRY MOOD.  HN, FL, OB, CL, BSN          E11
PIERCE, E.H.  SHORT QUINTET IN B-FLAT.  HN, FL, OB, CL, BSN  F11
PIERNE.  MARCH OF THE LITTLE TIN SOLDIERS, OP. 14, NO. 6    D36
   HN, FL, OB, CL, BSN, PF, SDR
PIERNE, G.  PASTORALE, OP.14/1.  HN, FL, OE, CL, BSN        B53
PIERNE, P.  SUITE PITTORESQUE.  HN, FL, OB, CL, BSN         D36
PIJPER, W.  QUINTET.  HN, FL, OB, CL, BSN                  B74
PILSS, K.  SERENADE.  HN, FL, OB, CL, BSN                  B73
PISTON, W.  QUINTET.  HN, FL, OB, CL, BSN                  A38
PLACHETA, H.  DIVERTIMENTO, OP.8.  HN, FL, OB, CL, BSN      B73
PLEYEL, I.J.-HARRIS.  RONDO, OP.48.  HN, FL, OB, CL, BSN    B53
POLDOWSKI-BARRERE.  SUITE MINIATURE.  HN, FL, OB, CL, BSN   C33
PONSE, L.  KWINTET, OP.32.  HN, FL, OB, CL, BSN            B74
PONSE, L.  2 PIECES.  HN, FL, OB, CL, BSN                  B74
POOT, M.  CONCERTINO.  HN, FL, OB, CL, BSN                 D36
PORSCH, G.  SUITE MODIQUE.  HN, FL, OB, CL, BSN            H06
```

PORTER, Q. DIVERTIMENTO FOR WW5. HN, FL, OB, CL, BSN   E65
PRAAG, H.C.V. KWINTET. HN, FL, OB, CL, BSN   B74
PRAAG, H.C.V. QUINTET. HN, FL, OB, CL, BSN   B99
QUINET, M. 8 PETITES PIECES. HN, FL, OB, CL, BSN   B12
QUINET, M. QUINTETTE. HN, FL, OB, CL, BSN   B12
RACKLEY, L. 2 MADRIGALS & A JIG. HN, FL, OB, CL, BSN   B35
RAINER, P. 6 PIECES. HN, FL, OB, CL, BSN   F31
RAMEAU, J.P.-LOCKHART. TAMBOURIN. HN, FL, OB, CL, BSN   F31
RANKI, G. PENTAEROPHONIA. HN, FL, OB, CL, BSN   B84
RAPOPORT, E. INDIAN LEGEND. HN, FL, OB, CL, BSN   A38
READ, G. SCHERZINO. HN, FL, OB, CL, BSN   F59
REICHA, A.-ERIHRLY. BLASERQUINTETT ES MAJOR, OP.88/2   D44
     HN, FL, OB, CL, BSN
REICHA, A.-SEYDEL. BLASERQUINTETT, OP.88,B MAJOR   D44
     HN, FL, OB, CL, BSN
REICHA, A. QUINTET OP.99/2. HN, FL, OB, CL, BSN   E14
REICHA, A.-KNEUSSLIN. QUINTETT, OP.100/4   D21
     HN, FL, OB, CL, BSN
REICHA, A.-KNEUSLIN. QUINTETT, OP.91/1,C MAJOR   D21
     HN, FL, OB, CL, BSN
REICHA, A.-KNEUSSLIN. QUINTETT, OP.91/3,D MAJOR   D21
     HN, FL, OB, CL, BSN
REICHA, A.-KNEUSSLIN. QUINTETT, OP.91/5,A MAJOR   D21
     HN, FL, OB, CL, BSN
REICHA, A. QUINTETTE A VENT, OP.91/4. HN, FL, OB, CL, BSN   A71
REICHA, A.-HERTL & SMETACEK. 3 QUINTETTI   A33
     HN, FL, OB, CL, BSN
REICHA, A.-WISE. WOODWIND QUINTET #2, OP. 88/2   M79
     HN, FL, OB8 CL, BSN
REICHEL, B. PRELUDE, PASSACAILLE,POSTLUDE   H03
     HN, FL, OB, CL, BSN
REINHOLD, C. QUINTET. HN, FL, OB, CL, BSN   E65
REITER, A. MUSIK FUR 5 BLASER. HN, FL, OB, CL, BSN   B73
REVUELTAS, S. FIRST LITTLE SERIOUS PIECE FOR WW5   F59
     HN, FL, OB, CL, BSN
REVUELTAS, S. SECOND LITTLE SERIOUS PIECE FOR WW5   F59
     HN, FL, OB, CL, BSN
RHODES, P. ENSEMBLE ETUDES. HN, FL, OB, CL, BSN   A13
RHODES, P. SUITE. HN, FL, OB, CL, BSN   A13
RIEGGER, W. WIND QUINTET. HN, FL, OB, CL, BSN   F31
RIETI, V. QUINTET. HN, FL, OB, CL, BSN   A38
RINCK, J. WOODWIND QUINTET. HN, FL, OB, CL, BSN   B44
ROETSCHER, K. QUINTETT, OP.41. HN, FL, OB, CL, BSN   A83
ROGERS, J.E. ROTATIONAL ARRAYS. HN, FL, OB, CL, BSN   P37
ROPARTZ, J.G.M. 2 PIECES. HN, FL, OB, CL, BSN   B81
RORICH, C. QUINTET, OP.58. HN, FL, OB, CL, BSN   G43
ROSENBERG, H. KVINTETT. HN, FL, OB, CL, BSN   B90
ROSETTI, F.A.-KNEUSSLIN. QUINTETT, ES-DUR   D21
     HN(EH), FL, OB, CL, BSN
ROSSEAU, N. QUINTETTE, OP.54. HN, FL, OB, CL, BSN   B12
RUGOLO, P. BOSSA-WALTZ. HN, FL, OB, CL, BSN   G21
RUYNEMAN, D. NIGHTINGALE QUINTET. HN, FL, OB, CL, BSN   B74
RUYNEMAN, D. REFLEXIONS NO.4. HN, FL, OB, CL, BSN   B74
SANTOLIQUIDO, F. NOCTURNE & PASTORALE FOR WW5   B44
     HN, FL, OB, CL, BSN
SCARLATTI, D. SUITE IN F FOR WW5. HN, FL, OB, CL, BSN   B44
SCHAEFER, T. QUINTET FOR WIND INST.,OP.5   A33
     HN, FL, OB, CL, BSN
SCHAT, P. IMPROVISATIONS & SYMPHONIES. HN, FL, OB, CL, BSN   B74
SCHIBLER, A. KALEIDOSKOP, OP.41. HN, FL, OB, CL, BSN   A08
SCHIERBECK, P. CAPRICCIO, OP.53. HN, FL, OB, CL, BSN   H30
SCHISKE, K. QUINTETT, OP.24. HN, FL, OB, CL, BSN   B73

```
SCHLEMM, G.A.  BLASER-QUINTET.  HN, FL, OB, CL, BSN              C54
SCHMID, H.K.  QUINTET, OP.28.  HN, FL, OB, CL, BSN              F31
SCHMIDEK, K.  SONATINE FUR 5 BLASER, OP.31                      B73
    HN, FL, OB, CL, BSN
SCHMIDT, E.  QUINTETT.  HN, FL, CL, BSN, EH                     H03
SCHMITT, F.  CHANTS ALIZES, OP.125.  HN, FL, OB, CL, BSN        B81
SCHMUTZ, A.D.  SCHERZO POETIQUE.  HN, FL, OB, CL, BSN           B53
SCHOENEERG, A.  QUINTET, OP.26.  HN, FL, OE, CL, BSN            F97
SCHOUWMAN, H.  NEDERLANDSE SUITE..., OP.40B                     B74
    HN, FL, OB, CL, BSN
SCHUBERT, F.P.-TAYLOR.  MARCHE HONGROISE.  HN, FL, OB, CL, BSN  D84
SCHUBERT, F.P.  ROSAMUNDE.  HN, FL, OB, CL, BSN                 B53
SCHUBERT, F.P.-SCHOENBACH.  SHEPHERD MELODY #6 (ROSAMUNDE)      E77
    HN, FL, OB, CL, BSN
SCHULLER, G.  SUITE.  HN, FL, OB, CL, BSN                       D55
SCOTT, S.  WOODWIND QUINTET.  HN, FL, OB, CL, BSN               B35
SEHLBACH, O.E.  KORTUM-SERENADE, OP.30.  HN, FL, OB, CL, BSN    D98
SEIBER, M.  PERMUTAZIONI A CINQUE.  HN, FL, OB, CL, BSN         F31
SENAILLE, J.B.-TAYLOR.  RONDO SERIOSO.  HN, FL, OB, CL, BSN     D84
SEREBRIER, J.  PEQUENA MUSICA.  HN, FL, OB, CL, BSN             F59
SETER, M.  DIPTYQUE.  HN, FL, CL, BSN, EH                       C93
SKORZENY, F.  NACHTMUSIK, EINE.  HN, FL, OB, CL, BSN            B73
SLOWINSKI, W.  QUINTET FOR WIND INSTRS.  HN, FL, OB, CL, BSN    A31
SMITH, L.  QUINTET.  HN, FL, OB, CL, BSN                        A13
SODERO, C.  MORNING PRAYER.  HN(TSAX), FL, OB, CL, BSN          A38
SODERO, C.  VALSE SCHERZO.  HN(TSAX), FL, OB, BSN               A38
SORRENTINO.  BENEATH THE COVERED BRIDGE.  HN, FL, OB, CL, BSN   D84
SOWERBY, L.  POP GOES THE WEASEL.  HN, FL, OB, CL, BSN          C13
SPENCER, J.  PLAYTIME.  HN, FL, OB, CL, BSN                     A91
SPISAK, M.  QUINTET.  HN, FL, OB, CL, BSN                       A31
SPRONGL, N.  BLASERQUINTETT, OP.90.  HN, FL, OB, CL, BSN        B73
STAEMPFLI, E.  QUINTETTE.  HN, FL, OB, CL, BSN                  H03
STAMITZ, K.-LEBERMANN.  12 SERENADES, OP.28.  2HN, 2FL, BSN     F50
STEARNS, P.P.  QUINTET.  HN, FL, OB, CL, BSN                    A13
STEEL, C.  DIVERTIMENTO.  HN, FL, OB, CL, BSN                   E41
STEIN, L.  SUITE.  HN, FL, OB, CL, BSN                          A13
STEWART, R.  2 MOVEMENTS.  HN, FL, OB, CL, BSN                  A13
STEWART, R.  3 PIECES.  HN, FL, OB, CL, BSN                     A13
STEWART, R.  5 VISIONS.  HN, FL, OB, CL, BSN                    A13
STONE, D.  PRELUDE & SCHERZETTO.  HN(CL), FL, CL(OB), CL, BSN   E41
STRADELLA, A.  SONATA IN G.  HN, FL, OB, CL, BSN                B44
SUTER, R.  4 ETUDES.  HN, FL, OB, CL, BSN                       C61
SYDEMAN, W.  WOODWIND QUINTET NO.2.  HN, FL, OB, CL, BSN        D55
SZEKELY, E.  QUINTET NO.2.  HN, FL, OB, CL, BSN                 B84
SZEKELY, E.  WIND QUINTET.  HN, FL, OB, CL, BSN                 D84
SZELIGOWSKI, T.  QUINTET.  HN, FL, OB, CL, BSN                  E72
SZERVANSKY, E.  QUINTET NO.1.  HN, FL, OB, CL, BSN              B84
SZERVANSKY, E.  QUINTET NO.2.  HN, FL, OB, CL, BSN              B84
TAKACS, J.  KLEINE TAFELMUSIK, EINE, OP.74                      B73
    HN, FL, OB, CL, BSN
TANENBAUM, E.  QUINTET NO. 2.  HN, FL, OB, CL, BSN              A13
TARTINI, G.-TRINKAUS.  LARGO (VIOLIN SONATA, G MINOR)           H06
    HN, FL, OB, CL, BSN
TARTINI, G.-TRINKAUS.  LARGO.  HN, FL, OB, CL, BSN              G31
TAYLOR, C.  QUINTET NO. 2.  HN, FL, OB, CL, BSN                 A13
TAYLOR, C.  QUINTET, OP. 7.  HN, FL, OB, CL, BSN                A13
TAYLOR, L.D.(ARR).  PETITE SUITE FR. THE 18TH C.               D84
    HN, FL, OB, CL, BSN
TAYLOR, L.D.  ROMANZA.  HN, FL, OB, CL, BSN                     D84
TAYLOR, L.D.  SUITE MINIATURE IN F.  HN, FL, OB, CL, BSN        E11
TAYLOR, R.  3 TRANSCRIPTIONS.  HN, FL, OB, CL, BSN              G21
TAYLOR, R.  WOODWIND QUINTETS.  HN, FL, OB, CL, BSN             F60
```

```
TCHAIKOVSKY, P.I.-SEAY.   CHANT SANS PAROLES, OP.40/6              F62
   HN, FL, OB, CL, BSN
TCHAIKOVSKY, P.I.-TAYLOR.   MUSIC FOR THE YOUNG (3 VOL)            G21
   HN, GL, OB, CL, BSN
TELEMANN, G.P.-WEIGELT.   OUVERTUREN-SUITE                        D44
   HN, FL, OB, CL, BSN
TELEMANN, G.P.-HINNENTHAL.   OUVERTUREN-SUITEN.   2HN, 2OB, BSN   D44
TISNE.   DISPARATES POUR QUINTETTE A VENT.   HN, FL, OB, CL, BSN  A71
TOEBOSCH, L.   SARABANDE EN ALLEGRO, OP.71                        B74
   HN, FL, OB, CL, BSN
TOEWS, T.   MUSIC FOR WW5.   HN, FL, OB, CL, BSN                  B35
TOMASI, H.   QUINTETTE.   HN, FL, OB, CL, BSN                     D41
TROJAN, V.   QUINTETT.   HN, FL, OB, CL, BSN                      A51
TURECEK, E.   INTRODUCTION & SCHERZO.   HN, FL, OB, CL, BSN       G31
UBER, D.A.   SUITE FOR WOODWIND QUINTET, NO.1                     B35
   HN, FL, OB, CL, BSN
URAY, E.L.   MUSIK FUR BLASERQUINTETT IN 2 SÀTZEN                 B73
   HN, FL, OB, CL, BSN
URAY, E.L.   SCHLADMINGER TANZE.   HN, FL, OB, CL, BSN            B73
URBANNER, E.   ETUDE FUR BLASER.   HN, FL, OB, CL, BSN            B73
VALEN, F.   SERENADE FOR 5 WIND INSTRS., OP.42                    B34
   HN, FL, OB, CL, BSN
VAN HULSE, C.   QUINTET, OP.111.   HN, FL, OB, CL, BSN            E43
VAN VACTOR, D.   MUSIC FOR WOODWINDS.   HN, FL, OB, CL, BSN       P44
VAN VACTOR, D.   SUITE.   HN, FL, OB, CL, BSN                     P44
VEERHOFF, C.H.   BLASERQUINTETT.   HN, FL, OB, CL, BSN            A83
VERRALL, J.   SERENADE NO.2.   HN, FL, OB, CL, BSN                B36
VERRALL, J.   SERENADE.   HN, FL, OB, CL, BSN                     E77
VILLA-LOBOS, H.   QUINTETO.   HN(EH), FL, OB, CL, BSN             C01
VINCZE, I.   DIVERTIMENTO.   HN, FL, OB, CL, BSN                  B84
VLIJMEN, J.V.   QUINTETTO.   HN, FL, OB, CL, BSN                  B74
VOSS, F.   CAPRICCIOSO FUR SOLO-FLOTE & BLASER-QUARTET            A90
   HN, FL, OB, CL, BSN
VREDENBURG, M.   AU PAYS DES VENDANGES;SUITE BREVE                B74
   HN, FL, OB, CL, BSN
VREDENBURG, M.   AUS DEN NIEDERLANDEN, KURZE SUITE                B99
   HN, FL, OB, CL, BSN
VUATAZ, R.   MUSIQUE POUR 5 INSTRS..   HN, FL, OB, CL, BSN        H03
WALZEL, L.M.   QUINTETTO IMPETUOSO, OP.42.   HN, FL, OB, CL, BSN  B73
WARD, W.R.   LITTLE DANCE SUITE.   HN, FL, OB, CL, BSN            D84
WASHBURN, R.   SUITE FOR WW5.   HN, FL, OB, CL, BSN               B92
WEBER, B.   CONSORT OF WINDS, OP. 66.   HN, FL, OB, CL, BSN       A13
WEBER, C.M.V.   MINUET FROM "QUINTETTE, OP.34"                    B53
   HN, FL, OB, CL, BSN
WEBER, C.M.V.-KESNAR.   RONDO.   HN, FL, OB, CL, BSN              E11
WEBER, L.   WIND QUINTET.   HN, FL, OB, CL, BSN                   D98
WEIGL, V.   4 BAGATELLES.   HN, FL, OB, CL, BSN                   A13
WEIS, F.   SERENADE.   HN, FL, OB, CL, BSN                        H30
WELLEJUS, H.   KVINTET, OP. 36.   HN, FL, OB, CL, BSN             C17
WELLESZ, E.   SUITE, OP.73.   HN, FL, OB, CL, BSN                 F50
WENDEL, M.   QUINTETT FUR BLASER.   HN, FL, CB, CL, BSN           H03
WHEAR, P.W.   QUINTET FOR WOODWINDS.   HN, FL, OB, CL, BSN        D34
WHITE, D.   3 FOR 5.   HN, FL, OB, CL, BSN                        F43
WHITTENBERG, C.   FANTASY.   HN, FL, OB, CL, BSN                  A13
WIDMER, E.   QUINTETT.   HN, FL, OB, CL, BSN                      H03
WIJDEVELD, W.   QUINTET.   HN, FL, OB, CL, BSN                    B74
WILDER, A.   WOODWIND QUINTET NO.3.   HN, FL, OB, CL, BSN         F23
WILLIAMS.   CONCERT SUITE.   HN, FL, OB, CL, BSN                  F60
WIRTH, H.   KLEINE CLEMENTIADE, SCHERZO.   HN, FL, OB, CL, BSN    F50
WISSE, J.   LIMITAZIONI NO.2.   HN, FL, OB, CL, BSN               B74
WISSMER, P.   QUINTETTE.   HN, FL, OB, CL, BSN                    E98
WOOLLEN, R.   QUINTET.   HN, FL, OB, CL, BSN                      A13
```

```
WUORINEN, C.   MOVEMENT FOR WIND QUINTET.   HN, FL, OB, CL, BSN      E77
YORK, W.W.   NEO GOTHICS.   HN, FL, OB, CL, BSN                      E87
ZAGWIJN, H.   QUINTETTO.   HN, FL, OB, CL, BSN                       B74
ZANINELLI, L.   DANCE VARIATIONS.   HN, FL, OB, CL, BSN              F43
ZELENKA, I.   CHRONOLOGIE.   HN, FL, OB, BSN, BCL                    B73
ZENDER, H.   QUINTET, OP.3.   HN, FL, OB, CL, BSN                    A83
ZILCHER, H.   QUINTETT, OP. 91.   HN, FL, OB, CL, BSN                E02
ZILLIG, W.   LUSTSPIELSUITE.   HN, FL, OB, CL, BSN                   A51
ZIPP, F.   SERENADE FOR WIND QUINTET.   HN, FL, OB, CL, BSN          D98
```

5 PARTS: BRASS-WOODWIND

```
BLANK, A.   4 PIECES.   2TPT, 3BSN                                   A13
BROWN, N.K.   PASTORALE & DANCE.   TPT, TRB, FL, CL, SAX             B35
BUTTS, C.M.   GERMAN BAND ENCORES.   TPT, TRB, TU, 2CL               D14
CAMBINI, G.G.   3 QUINTETS, OP. 4.   HN, FL, OB(CL), CL, BSN         E14
DIJK, J.V.   CHORALES.   TPT, HN, FL, CL, BSN                        B74
HARTLEY, W.S.   SONATA DA CAMERA.   TRB, OB, 2CL, BSN                C89
HARTLEY, W.S.   SUITE FOR FIVE WINDS.   TRB, FL, OB, CL, ASAX        C89
HENNEMAN.   AMERICAN FIVE.   TPT, TRB, TU, 2CL                       G85
HENNEMAN.   HEINE'S HAPPY FIVE IN GERMANY.   TPT, TRB, TU, 2CL       C11
HENNEMAN.   SCHNICKLEFRITZ BAND, THE.   TPT, TRB, TU, 2CL            E80
HERTEL, J.W.-SALLAGAR.   CONCERTO A 5, D MAJOR.   TPT, 2OB, 2BSN     E37
MACERO, T.A.J.   CANZONA NO. 1.   TPT, 2ASAX, BARSAX                 E30
MULLER VON KULM, W.   KLEINE SERENADE FUR 5 BLASER, OP.35            H03
   TPT, TRB, OB, CL, BSN
NOON.   INTRODUCTION, DIRGE & FRLOIC.   TPT, TRB, FL, CL, BSN        C11
PREMRU, R.E.   CONCERTINO FOR TRB SOLO.   TRB, FL, OB, CL, BSN       E14
URAY, E.L.   SCHLADMINGER TANZE.   TPT, HN, FL, CL, BSN              B73
WECKMANN.   NUN FREUT EUCH.   2TRB, OB, BSN, EH                      A38
```

5 PARTS: WINDS-KEYBOARD

```
BALISSAT, J.   SONATE.   TPT, HN, TRB, PERC, PA                      H03
BEETHOVEN, L.V.   OP.16.   HN, OB, CL, BSN, PA                       D08
BEETHOVEN, L.V.   PIANO QUINTET, OP. 16.   HN, OB, CL, BSN, PF       P43
BEETHOVEN, L.V.   QUINTET ES-DUR, OP.16.   HN, OB, CL, BSN, PA       A90
BEETHOVEN, L.V.   QUINTET IN E-FLAT, OP.16                           C91
   HN, OB, CL, BSN, PA
BEETHOVEN, L.V.   QUINTET OP. 16.   HN, OB, CL, BSN, PF              G85
BEETHOVEN, L.V.   QUINTET, OP.16.   HN, OB, CL, BSN, PA              D48
BEETHOVEN, L.V.   QUINTET, OP.16.   HN, OB, CL, BSN, PA              E14
BEETHOVEN, L.V.   QUINTET, OP.16.   HN, OB, CL, BSN, PF              E19
BENNETT, D.   FRENCH HORN FRAPPE.   4HN, *PF                         C11
BENNETT, D.   TOURNAMENT OF TPTS.   4TPT, *PF                        C11
BENNETT, D.   TROMBONE TROUBADOURS.   4TRB, *PF                      C11
BORRESEN, H.   RAADHUS-INTRADA FOR LURER.   4HN, *PF                 N53
CACAVAS, J.   SERENADE IN GOLD.   4TRB, *PF                          F60
CASTEREDE, J.   PRELUDE ET DANSE.   3TRB, TU, PERC, PF               D36
CHILDS, B.   QUINTET FOR BRASS & PA.   TPT, HN, TRB, TU, PF          E68
CONSTANT, M.   4 ETUDES DE CONCERT.   TPT, 2HN, TRB, PERC, PF        D36
COVINGTON-KENNY.   TOY TROMBONE.   4TRB, *PF                         G85
DANZI, F.   QUINTET IN D MINOR, OP.41.   HN, OB, CL, BSN, PF         A95
DANZI, F.   QUINTET IN D MINOR, OP.41.   HN, OB, CL, BSN, PF         E14
```

```
DANZI, F.  QUINTET, OP. 53.  HN, FL, CL, BSN, PF                    E14
DANZI, F.  QUINTET, OP. 54.  HN, FL, CL, BSN, PF                    E14
DANZI, F.  SINFONIA CONCERTANTE.  HN, FL, CB, BSN, PF               E14
DELANNOY, M.  RAPSODIE.  TPT, VN, VC, XYL, PA                       C65
ENESCO, G.-STONE.  ROUMANIAN INTERMEZZO.  2TPT, 2TRB, *PF           C45
FLOTHUIS, M.  KLEINE SUITE, OP. 47.  TPT, OB, CL, PF, SSAX          B99
FRESCOBALDI, G.  CANSONAS 1-6                                       E14
  TRB, CTT(TPT), TRB(BTRB), ATRB, BC(ORG)
FRESCOBALDI, G.  CANZONA 3.  2TRB, 2CTT(2TPT), BC(ORG)              E14
FRESCOBALDI, G.  CANZONAS 30-34.  2TRB, 2CTT, BC(ORG)               E14
FRESCOBALDI, G.  CANZONAS 35-37.  2TRB, CTT(TPT), ATRB, BC          F14
GOLOS (ARR).  CANZON IN D.  2TPT, TRB, TIMP, HPCD(ORG)              E72
GYROWETZ, A.  SINFONIA CONCERTANTE                                  E14
  HN, OB, CL, BSN, *PF, *ORCH
HANUS, J.  IMPROMPTUS, OP.45.  TPT, FL, OB, CL, PF                  A33
HAVLICEK, I.C.  TRUMPETERS' POLKA.  4TPT, *PF                       F79
HERZOGENBERG, H.V.  QUINTET, OP.43.  HN, OB, CL, BSN, PF            E14
HOLEWA, H.  KVINTETT.  TRB, CL, VC, PERC, PA                        B90
HOWE-SCHAEFFER.  BATTLE HYMN OF THE REPUBLIC.  2TPT, 2TRB, PF       E80
HUBLER, H.  CONCERTO FOR 4 HNS.  4HN, *ORCH, *PF                    D11
HUBLER, H.  CONCERTO FOR 4 HORNS.  4HN, PF                          D11
IVES, C.E.  FROM THE STEEPLES & THE MOUNTAINS                       F59
  TPT, TRB, 2PF, BELLS(CHIMES)
JONGEN, L.  QUINTUOR.  HN, FL, CL, BSN, PF                          B12
KILPATRICK, J.  WAITING FOR GODOT.  HN, FL, CL, VN, PA              B36
LANOY, F.  QUINTET, OP.2.  HN, OB, CL, BSN, PF                      E14
LETHBRIDGE, L.  BRASS QUARTET, THE, BK 4.  2TPT, HN(TRB), TRB       E51
LLEWELLYN, E.  MY REGARDS.  4TRB, *PF                               C11
LLEWELLYN, E.  PREMIER POLKA.  4TRB, *PF                            C11
MAW, N.  CHAMBER MUSIC.  HN, OB, CL, BSN, PF                        B23
MOZART, W.A.  KONZERTANTES QUARTETTE, K.297B                        B53
  HN, OB, CL, BSN, PF
MOZART, W.A.  QUINTET IN E FLAT, K 452.  HN, OB, CL, BSN, PF        C91
MOZART, W.A.  QUINTET IN E FLAT, K. 452.  HN, OB, CL, BSN, PF       E14
MOZART, W.A.-FEDERHOFER.  QUINTET IN E FLAT, K. 452                 A51
  HN, OB, CL, BSN, PF
MOZART, W.A.  QUINTET, K. 452.  HN, OB, CL, BSN, PF                 F60
MOZART, W.A.  QUINTETT ES-DUR, K. 452.  HN, OB, CL, BSN, PF         A90
MOZART, W.A.-STARK.  SINFONIA CONCERTANTE ES-DUR, K. 297B           A89
  HN, OB, CL, BSN, PF
MOZART, W.A.  SINFONIA CONCERTANTE IN E FLAT, K. 297B               E14
  HN, OB, CL, BSN, PF
MOZART, W.A.  SINFONIA CONCERTANTE, K. 297B                         C91
  HN, OB, CL, BSN, PF
NAGEL, R.  SUITE.  TPT, HN, TRB, TU, PF                             D73
NELHYBEL, V.  QUINTETTO CONCERTANTE.  TPT, TRB, PF, VN, XYL         C40
OETIT (ARR).  SONATE (DIE BANKELSANGERLIEDER)                       A71
  2TPT, HN(TRB), TRB, PF
PLEYEL, I.J.  QUINTET.  HN, OB, CL, BSN, PF                         E14
PLEYEL, I.J.  SINFONIA CONCERTANTE.  HN, FL, OB, BSN, PF            E14
PLEYEL, I.J.  FIFTH SYMPHONIC CONCERTANTE                           F87
  HN, FL, OB(CL), BSN, PF
PURCELL, H.-OSTRANDER.  SOUND THE TRUMPETS.  4TPT, *PF              B85
RIMSKY-KORSAKOV, N.A.  QUINTET IN B FLAT MAJOR                      C91
  HN, FL, CL, BSN, PF
ROSSINI, G.-LELOIR.  RENDEZVOUS DE CHASSE, LE.  4HN, *PF            A71
SCHUMANN, R.  CONCERT PIECE, OP. 86.  4 HN, PF                      D11
SCHUMANN, R.  CONCERTPIECE, OP. 86.  4HN, PF                        C91
SPEER, D.-BROWN.  SONATA.  4TRB, *PF                                C91
SPOHR, L.  QUINTET, OP. 52.  HN, FL, CL, BSN, PF                    E14
SPOHR, L.-SCHMITZ.  QUINTETT C MINOR, OP.52                         A51
  HN, FL, CL, BSN, PF
```

```
STONE, G.  KONZERTSTUECK.  4TPT, *PF                              C45
STRAVINSKY, I.-STONE.  FIRE-BIRD & PETRUSHKA EXCERPTS             C45
   2TPT, 2TRB, PF
TCHAIKOVSKY, P.I.-STONE.  THEME FR CONCERTO #1, OP.23             G10
   2TPT, 2TRB, PF
TELEMANN, G.P.-BLOCK.  CONCERTO #3 IN D.  TPT, 2OB, PF            E14
TORELLI, G.-CIPOLLA.  SINFONIA IN B-FLAT.  4TPT, *PF             F43
TORELLI, G.-CIPOLLA.  SINFONIA IN D.  4TPT, *PF                  F43
VERHEY, T.H.  QUINTET ES-DUR, OP. 20.  HN, OB, CL, BSN, PF        A90
VOLBACH, F.  QUINTETT ES-DUR, OP. 24.  HN, OB, CL, BSN, PF        A90
WALTERS, H.L.  LATE ONE EVENING.  4TPT, *PF                       F07
WECKESSER.  BIG GUNS, THE, CAISSON SONG.  4TPT, *PF               B13
WECKESSER.  SOUTHLAND, A MEDLEY.  4TPT, *PF                       B13
```

5 PARTS: WIND(S)-STRING(S)

```
ARNOLD, M.  QUINTET.  HN, FL, BSN, VN, VA                         E58
BARBE.  MINIATUREN ZU EINEN LUSTSPOEL VON SHAKESPEARE            A80
   TPT, TRB, CL, PERC, PF, DB
BRUCKNER, H.-MINTER.  SONATA.  2TPT, 2VN, BC                      E14
CASELLA, A.  SERENATA.  TPT, CL, BSN, VN, VC                      F97
FULEIHAN, A.  QUINTET.  HN, 2VN, VA, VC                           F59
GLAZUNOV, A.K.  IDYLL.  HN, 2VN, VA, VC                           B44
HAUFF, W.G.-WEELINK.  QUINTET (CONCERTO) IN F                    D11
   HN, STR QUAR ET
HAUFF, W.G.-WEELINK.  QUINTET IN E-FLAT.  HN, 2VN, VA, VC         D11
HAYDN, M.-STRASSL.  DIVERTIMENTO IN G-DUR.  HN, FL, VN, VA, DB   B73
HEIDEN, B.  QUINTET.  HN, 2VN, VA, VC                             A38
HENDERSON.  CAPRICCIO (1966).  2TRB, SAX, VN, PF                  A43
HOFFMEISTER, F.A.-STEINBECK.  QUINTETT IN ES-DUR                 B73
   HN, 2VN, VA, VC
HOVHANESS, A.S.  OVERTURE.  TRB, 2VN, VA, VC                      E65
KUFFNER, J.  QUINTET IN E-FLAT.  HN, VN, 2VA, VC                  D11
MOZART, W.A.  QUINTET IN E FLAT, K. 407.  HN(VC), VN, 2VA, VC     A90
MOZART, W.A.  QUINTET IN E FLAT, K. 407.  HN(VC), VN, 2VA, VC     C91
MOZART, W.A.  QUINTET IN E FLAT, K. 407.  HN, VN, 2VA, VC         D08
MOZART, W.A.  QUINTET IN E FLAT, K. 407.  HN, VN, 2VA, VC         E65
MOZART, W.A.  QUINTETT IN ES, K. 386C.  HN, VN, 2VA, VC           A51
MOZART, W.A.  QUINTETTE NO. 3, OP. 407.  HN, VN, 2VA, VC(DB)      F60
PERUTI, C.  ENDGAME.  TRB, 2CL, VC, PF                            F48
PRESSER, W.H.  PASSACAGLIA.  HN, CL, VN, VA, VC                   B38
REICHA, A.  GRANDE QUINTETTO FOR HN, OP.106                      B44
   HN, 2VN, VA, VC, (OPT DB)
REICHA, A.  QUINTET, OP. 105.  HN, 4STR                          E14
ROSETTI, F.A.  NOTTURNO IN D.  HN, FL, VN, VA, VC                 A33
SCHMELZER, J.H.-MINTER.  SONATA IN G "LA CARIOLETTA"             E14
   TPT, TRB, BSN, VN, BC
SCHUMANN, R.  ANDANTE UND VARIATIONEN, OP. 46.  HN, 2CL, 2VC      A90
SERERBRIER, J.  VARIATIONS ON A THEME FROM CHILDHOOD            F59
   TRB, 2VN, VA, VC
SONATE FR DIE BANKELSANGERLIEDER.  2TPT, HN(TRB), TRB, PF        A71
STAMITZ, K.-WINSCHERMANN.  3 QUINTETTE, OP. 11/1 & 2, ES-DUR     F50
   HN, OB, 2VA, VC
STRAUSS, R.-HASENOHRL.  TILL EULENSPIEGEL EINMAL ANDERS          E65
   HN, CL, BSN, VN, DB
WECKMANN, M.  SONATA A 4.  TRB, OB(CORNETTINO), BSN, VN, BC       E14
WEST, G.  LARGO AND ALLEGRO.  TRB, 2VN, VA, VC                    E00
```

5 PARTS: BRASS-MISCELLANEOUS

```
DELANNOY, M.  RAPSODIE.  TPT, PF, VN, VC, ASAX                    C65
HOLEWA, H.  KVINTETT.  TRB, CL, PERC, PF, VC                      B90
HUTCHISON, W.  FANFARE FOR EASTER.  2TPT, HN, TRB, CARILLON       G66
KILPATRICK, J.  WAITING FOR GODOT.  HN, FL, CL, PF, VN            B36
LINDE, B.  MUSICA PER SYLVANUM.  HN, FL, BSN, VN, XYL             B90
MILLS, C.  PAUL BUNYAN (SCORE ONLY).  TPT, PERC, PF, DB, TSAX     E68
NELHYBEL, V.  QUINTETTO CONCERTANTE.  TPT, TRB, PF, VN, XYL       C40
RABE, F.  IMPROMPTU.  TRB, PERC, PF, VC, BCL                      B90
RUYNEMAN, D.  DIVERTIMENTO.  HN, FL, CL, PF, VA                   B23
SHIFRIN, S.J.  SERENADE.  HN, OB, CL, PF, VA                      E65
STERNFELD, F.  THOUGHTS OF C & C.  TRB, FL, CL, BCL, PERC(4)      G66
STEWART, R.  5 MOVEMENTS.  FLG, PF, DB, FL, BSN                   B36
SURINACH, C.  HOLLYWOOD CARNIVAL (SKETCHES IN CARTOON)            F03
    TPT, FL, CL, PERC, DB
SYDEMAN, W.  QUINTET.  TRB, CL, PERC, PF, DB                      G66
VIVALDI, A.  SONATA A 4.  TRB, OB, BSN, VN, BC                    E14
WASHBURN, G.  PASSACAGLIA.  TPT, OB(CL), PERC, PF, VC             G66
WECKMANN, M.-LUMSDEN.  SONATA A 4.  TRB, OB(CTT), BSN, VN, BC     E14
```

SIX-PART MUSIC

6 EQUAL BRASS INSTRUMENTS

AMATO, B. ALLELUIA. 6HN	G66
BACH, J.S.-SHAW. ALLEGRO. 6HN	C78
BACH, J.S. CHORALE PRELUDE-"WIR GLAUBEN ALL'AN EINEN GOTT" 6HN	C78
BUSCH, C. ARIOSO & FANFARE. 6TPT	C13
CHILDS, B. MUSIC FOR TUBAS. 6TU	A13
CRUFT, A.F. FANFARES. 6TPT	C33
HANDEL, G.F.-MARTINET. ALLEGRO MODERATO (WATER MUSIC). 6HN	C78
JOHNSON, R. RITUAL MUSIC. 6HN	F43
JOHNSON, R. SUITE FOR 6 HORNS. 6HN	P49
KERKORIAN, G. SEXTET FOR HORNS. 6HN	C78
LUCAS, T. MUSIC FOR 6 HORNS. 6HN	P49
MAYER, R. FANTASIA. 6HN	F60
OTT, J. SUITE FOR 6 TUBAS. 6TU	A65
PEDERSON, T. BIG SPLASH, THE. 6TRB	M93
PEDERSON, T. CAMELS & CADILLACS. 6TRB	M93
PEDERSON, T. DANCE OF THE DOLPHIN, THE. 6TRB	M93
PEDERSON, T. FROG & THE PUPPY DOG, THE. 6TRB	M93
PEDERSON, T. GOLD DUST & DIAMONDS. 6TRB	M93
PEDERSON, T. HYMN FOR TROMBONES. 6TRB	M93
PEDERSON, T. PRINCE OF ATTICA, THE. 6TRB	M93
PEDERSON, T. SECRETS OF HOYT'S GARAGE, THE. 6TRB	M93
PEDERSON, T. TROMBONE TREE, THE. 6TRB	M93
PEDERSON, T. TURQUOISE & TROMBONES. 6TRB	M93
PHILLIPS, B. PIECE FOR 6 TRBS. 6TRB	D16
PHILLIPS, B. PIECE. 6TRB	M98
PRESSER, W.H. SUITE. 6TU	F80
PURCELL, H.-TANNER. DIDO'S LAMENT. 6TRB	G21
RAVEL, M.-ROBERTSON. PAVANE. 6TRB	B98
RUBBRA. FANFARE, OP. 142. 6TPT	D42
SCHMID, H.K. TURMMUSIK, OP. 105A. 6TPT, (OPT 2PERC)	A89
SCHMIDT. SEQUENTIAL FANFARE. 6TPT	A43
SHINER, M. 2 SEXTETS. 6TRB	D14
SVARDA, W. PIECES FOR 6 TUBAS. 6TU	N61
TANNER, P. CANGREJO, EL. 6TRB	C77
ZONN, P. FANFARE FOR AN UNCOMMON MAN. 6HN	A13

6 MIXED BRASS (BRASS-PERC)

ADSON, J. COURTLY MASQUING AYRES. 3TPT, 3TRB	E14
ALPAERTS, F. HULDE FANFARE. 3TPT, 2TRB, PERC	B12
AMELLER, A.C. LARGAMENTE. 2TPT, HN, 2TRB, TU	D36
APPLEBAUM, S.S. 3 STRATFORD FANFARES. 3TPT, 3TRB	D71
BACH, J.S.-JOHNSON. 4 CHORALES. 2TPT, HN, TRB, EU, TU	F07
BACH, J.S.-OSTLING. CONTRASTS. 2TPT, HN, TRB, EU, TU	G85
BACH, J.S.-LANDES. IN THEE IS GLADNESS 2TPT, HN(TPT), TRB, TU, TU	B40
BACH, J.S.-MOEHLMANN. PRELUDE & FUGUE IN E-FLAT MAJOR 2TPT, HN, TRB, EU, TU	D34
BACH, J.S.-MOEHLMANN. PRELUDE & FUGUE IN E-FLAT MAJOR 2TPT, HN, TRB, EU, TU	F60

```
BARNHOUSE, C.L.-HOLMES.  EVENING IDYLS.  2TPT, HN, TRB, EU, TU    A55
BARNHOUSE, C.L.-HOLMES.  JOY TO THE WORLD                        A55
   2TPT, HN, TRB, EU, TU
BARNHOUSE, C.L.  ON THE MOUNTAIN TOP.  2TPT, HN, TRB, EU, TU     A55
BARTOK, B.-SMELTEKOP.  9 BAGATELLES.  2TPT, HN, 2TRB, TU         E00
BARTOK, B.-SIEKMANN.  BARTOK FOR BRASS.  2TPT, HN, TRB, EU, TU   A55
BARTSCH, C.  FANFARE, CANTILENE ET DANSE.  4TPT, HN, TRB         D67
BEALE, D.  SPIRIT OF ST. LOUIS.  2TPT, HN, TRB, BTRB            P48
BECKER, A.C.  PAEAN.  2TPT, HN, TRB, EU, TU                     H06
BECKERATH, A.V.  TURMMUSIK.  3TPT, 2TRB, BTRB                   E73
BEETHOVEN, L.V.-HOLMES.  ALLEGRO 6TH SYM.                       A55
   2TPT, HN, TRB, EU, TU
BEETHOVEN, L.V.-LOTZENHISER.  CHORALE & MARCH.  6 INST ?        F07
BEETHOVEN, L.V.-HOLMES.  MARCH (FIDELIO)                        A55
   2TPT, HN, TRB, EU, TU
BEETHOVEN, L.V.  MARCIA FUNEBRA.  2TRB, 2EU, 2TU               D94
BEZANSON, P.  PRELUDE & DANCE.  2TPT, HN, 2TRB, TU             C89
BEZANSON, P.  SEXTET.  2TPT, 2HN, 2TRB                        A13
BIZET, G.-HOLMES.  PRELUDE (L'ARLESIENNE)                     A55
   2TPT, HN, TRB, EU, TU
BLISS, A.  2 ROYAL FANFARES.  3TPT, 2TRB, BTRB                E41
BLOCH, E.-LANDES.  CHANTY (POEMS OF THE SEA)                  F23
   2TPT, HN, TRB, EU, TU
BOGAR.  BURLESCA.  3TPT, 2TRB, TU                             B84
BOONE, D.  3 MOODS.  4EU, 2TU                                 M80
BOONE, D.  3 MOODS.  4EU, 2TU                                 P42
BRAHMS, J.-WISE.  JOY OF THY SALVATION.  2TPT, HN, TRB, EU, TU E80
BRIEGEL, G.F.  4 FANFARES.  3TPT, 3TRB                        A91
BRUCKNER, A.-GORDON.  PRAYER AND ALLELUIA                     F60
   2TPT, HN(TRE), TRB, TU, TIMP
BRUGK, H.M.  FANFARE & INTRADE.  3TPT, 3TRB                   E37
BURGHAUSER.  OLD CZECH FANFARES.  2TPT, 3TRB, TIMP            A33
BUSCH, C.  PRELUDE & CHORAL                                   C11
   2TPT, HN, TRB, EU, TU, (OPT TIMP)
BUSH, G.  HOMAGE TO MATTHEW LOCKE.  3TPT, 3TRB                C33
BUTLER.  PAEAN OF PRAISE.  3TPT, 3TRB                         A84
BYRD-MOORE.  CHRIST RISING AGAIN.  2TPT, HN, 2TRB, TU         M71
CABUS, P.N.  INTRADA.  3TPT, HN, 2TRB                         D67
CABUS, P.N.  OPENING FANFARE.  2TPT, 2HN, 2TRB               D67
CADOW, P.  INTRADA.  2TPT, 2HN, 2TRB                         C54
CADOW, P.  PRALUDIUM.  3TPT, 3HN                             C54
CAZDEN, N.  SUITE, OP. 55.  2TPT, HN, TRB, EU, TU            A38
CHASE, A.H.  FUGUE.  2TPT, HN, 2TRB, TU                      B44
CHRISTENSEN, J.  COVENTRY CAROL.  2TPT, HN, TRB, EU, TU      D14
CLAPP, P.G.  SUITE IN E-FLAT.  2TPT, HN, TRB, EU, TU         P23
CONLEY, L.  CHACONNE.  2TPT, HN(TRB), TRB, EU                D14
CONLEY, L.  INTRADA.  2TPT, HN, TRB, EU, TU                  D14
CONLEY, L.  PROMENADE.  3TPT, TRB, EU, TU                    D14
COOKE, A.A.  SEXTET.  2TPT, 2HN, TRB, TU                     B44
CORELLI, A.  PASTORALE FROM CHRISTMAS CONCERTO GROSSO        D16
   2TPT, 2HN(TPT, TRB), 2TRB-TU
CORELLI, A.-THILDE.  SUITE DE DANSES.  2TPT, 4TRB           A71
COUPERIN-VON KANNON.  3 MOVEMENTS FROM LA STEINQUERQUE       D63
   2TPT, HN(TPT), TRB, EU-TU, HN(TRB)
COWELL, H.  TALL TALE.  2TPT, HN, 2TRB, TU                   D74
CRUFT, A.F.  DIVERSION, A.  2TPT, 2HN, 2TRB                  G26
CURZON, F.  FANFARE #4, 5, 6.  6INST ?                       A78
CUSTER, A.R.  3 PIECES.  2TPT, 2HN, 2TRB                     C40
DAHL, I.  FANFARE ON A AND C.  3TPT, HN, TRB, EU            G68
DAHL, I.  MUSIC FOR BRASS INSTS..  2TPT, HN, 2TRB, (OPT TU)  G31
DELP, R.  HYPOSTASIS.  2TPT, TRB, TU, PERC, FLG, VIB        G66
DIETZ, N.C.  MODERN MOODS.  2TPT, HN, TRB, EU, TU           A38
```

```
DUNHAM.  SEXTET.  T, HN, TRB, EU, TU                              2TP
EDMONDSON.  INTRADA & CAPRICE.  2TPT, HN(TET), TRB, EU, TU        D14
EHMANN, W.(CMPL).  ALTE SPIELMUSIK.  6INST ?                      A51
EHMANN, W.  BLASER-INTRADEN AUM WOCHENLIED.  6INST ?              A51
EVANS.  FESTIVAL FANFARE.  3TPT, HN, 2TRB                         P47
FIRST DIVISION BAND COURSE.  CONTRASTS BY BACH.  6INST ?          A62
FIRST DIVISION BAND COURSE.  MARCH ROMAINE.  6INST ?              A62
FIRST DIVISION BAND COURSE.  SOURWOOD MOUNTAIN.  6INST ?          A62
FIRST DIVISION BAND COURSE.  THEME FR AN AMERICAN RHAPSODY        A62
   6INST ?
FISHER, G.  DAY OF '49.  6INST ?                                  A84
FLAGELLO, N.  LYRA.  3TPT, HN, TRB, BTRB                          C40
FLAGELLO, N.  LYRA.  3TPT, HN, TRB, BTRB                          E41
FOSTER, S.C.-HARTZELL.  RING, RING DE BANJO                       F79
   2TPT, HN, TRB, EU, TU
FRANCK, M.-REIN.  INTRADA AUS "NEUE MUSIKALISCHE ...              A89
   3TPT, 3TRB
FRANCK, M.  2 INTRADAS.  2TPT, HN, TRB, EU, TU                    F07
FRANCK, M.-SINGLETON.  2 INTRADAS                                 F59
   2TPT, TPT(HN), TRB(HN), TRB, TU
FRANGKISER, C.  ENTRY OF THE HERALDS.  2TPT, HN, TRB, EU, TU      A78
FREUND, D.  ROMANZA FOR BRASS.  2TPT, 2HN, TRB, TU                G66
GABRIELI, A.-SHUMAN.  AGNUS DEI.  3TPT, 2TRB, TU                  F59
GABRIELI, A.-SHUMAN.  DE PROFUNDIS CLAMAVI(TRB SOLO)           '  F59
   2TPT, 3TRB, TU
GABRIELI, G.  SINFONIA (VENICE 1615).  3TPT, 3TRB                 P19
GARRETT, J.A.  FANFARE.  2EU, 4TU                                 M80
GARRETT, J.A.  FANFARE.  2EU, 4TU                                 P42
GAULT, G.  SERENADE.  2TPT, HN(TPT), TRB(HN), EU, TU             H06
GLASS, P.  BRASS SEXTET.  2TPT, HN, TRB(HN), TRB, TU(TRB)         E41
GLICKMAN, E.  DIVERTIMENTO FOR BRASS & PERC                       D94
   2TPT, HN, TRB, TU, PERC,
GLIERE, R.M.-SIEKMANN.  RUSSIAN SAILORS' DANCE                    A55
   2TPT, HN, TRB, EU, TU
GORDON.  FOUR CENTURIES FOR BRASS.  2TPT, HN, 2TRB, TU            C11
GRAHAM.  REVERIE.  2TPT, HN, TRB, EU, TU                          E80
GRANT, P.  SEXTET, "ON THE HIDDEN RIVER," OP. 57, NO. 2           A13
   2TPT, 2HN, 2TRB
GRIEG, E.H.-TRINKAUS.  SOLVEJG'S SONG, OP.55/4                    H06
   2TPT, HN(TPT), TRB(HN), EU, TU
GUENTZEL, G.  FANTASIE DE CONCERT.  2TPT, HN, TRB, EU, TU         A55
GUENTZEL, G.  FIESTA, LA.  2TPT, HN, TRB, EU, TU                  A55
GUENTZEL, G.  POLONAISE #4.  2TPT, HN, TRB, EU, TU                A55
GUENTZEL, G.  QUIERIDO GAYO, EL.  2TPT, HN, TRB, EU, TU           A55
GUENTZEL, G.  ROYAL FESTIVAL.  2TPT, HN, TRB, EU, TU              A55
GUENTZEL, G.  TURTLE WADDLE, THE.  2TPT, HN, TRB, EU, TU          A55
GUENTZEL, G.  VOLUNTARY.  2TPT, HN, TRB, EU, TU                   A55
HAAN, S.D.  6 SHORT PIECES.  3TPT, 3TRB                           C71
HANDEL, G.F.-PORTER.  MARCH FROM OCCASIONAL OVERTURE              B39
   2TPT, HN, TRB, EU, TU
HANDEL, G.F.-KING.  3 PIECES FROM THE WATER MUSIC                 D16
   2TPT, TPT(TRB), 2HN, TRB-TU
HANDEL, G.F.-WALDECK.  TRUMPET SHALL SOUND, THE                   B44
   3TPT, 2TRB, TU
HARDT, V.H.  SUITE.  2TPT, HN, TRB, EU, TU                        F79
HARRIS, R.W.  3 KROMA.  2TPT, HN, TRB, TU, PERC                   B35
HAUBIEL, C.  BALLADE.  2TPT, HN, TRB, EU, TU                      B38
HAUBIEL, C.  BALLADE.  BRASS SEXTET                               G66
HERRMANN, H.  MUSICA FESTIVA.  3TPT, 3TRB                         E89
HILLERT, R.  3 CHRISTMAS CAROLS.  2TPT, 2HN, 2TRB                 B40
HODGSON, D.(ARR).  3 MARCHES OF AMERICAN REVOLUTIONARY DAYS       B39
   2TPT, HN, TRB, EU, TU
```

```
HOLLOS.  ALTE TURMMUSIK.  3TPT, 2TRB, TU                              F23
HOLMES.  WHEN YOU AND I WERE YOUNG, MAGGIE                            A55
   2TPT, HN, TRB, EU, TU
HOLMES (ARR).  MEMORIES OF STEPHEN FOSTER                            A55
   2TPT, HN, TRB, EU, TU
HOWE, M.C. (ARR).  3 MADRIGALS.  2TPT, HN, TRB, EU, TU                B92
INWOOD.  3 MOVEMENTS.  2TPT, 2HN, TRB, TU                             G66
JARMAN, H.C.  GOOD KING WENCESLAS.  3TPT, TPT(TRB), TRB, BTRB         A82
JARMAN, H.C.  TIME.  4TPT(TRB), TRB, BTRB                             A82
JARMAN, H.C.  WELCOME.  4TPT(TRB), TRB, BTRB                          A82
JOHNSON, C.W.  TONE SKETCH.  2TPT, HN, TRB, EU, TU                    F07
JOHNSON, H.M.  GORDIAN.  2TPT, HN, TRB, EU, TU                        A62
JOHNSON, W.S.  PRELUDE ROMANTIQUE.  2TPT, HN(TPT), TRB, EU, TU        C11
KABALEVSKY, D.B.-BARNES.  SONATINA.  2TPT, HN, TRB, EU, TU            D52
KAUFMANN, W.  PASSACAGLIO & CAPRICCIO.  2TPT, HN, 2TRB, TU            F43
KAZDIN, A. (ARR).  12 DAYS OF CHRISTMAS                               D16
   2TPT, HN, TRB, EU, TU
KELLY.  FANFARES AND SONATINA.  2TPT, HN(TPT), HN(TRB), 2TRB          E41
KELLY, B.  FANFARES & SONATINA.  2TPT, 2HN(TPT, TRB), 2TRB            E41
KERN.  WHO.  2TPT, 2TRB, EU, TU                                       G85
KETTING, O.  3 FANFARES.  3TPT, 3TRB                                  B74
KING, K.L.-HOLMES.  NIGHT IN JUNE.  2TPT, HN, TRB, EU, TU             A55
KOCSAR, M.  SESTETTO D'OTTONI.  3TPT, 2TRB, TU                        B84
KOEPKE, P.  MARCHE VAILLANT.  2TPT, HN, TRB, EU, TU                   F07
KOEPKE, P.  SCHERZO.  2TPT, HN, TRB, EU, TU                           F07
KOERPPEN, A.  2 SATZE UBER "WIR GLAUBEN ALL'AN EINEN GOTT"            A90
   3TPT, 3TRB
KOVACS.  DIVERTIMENTO.  3TPT, 2TRB, TU                                B84
KRAFT, W.  NONET.  2TPT, HN, TRB, TU, PERC(4)                         A43
KROEGER, K.  CANZONA II.  3TPT, 3TRB                                  F88
KROEGER, K.  CANZONA III.  3TPT, 3TRB                                 F88
KROEGER, K.  CANZONA.  2TPT, 2HN, TRB, TU                             F88
KUBIK, G.  FANFARE FOR THE CENTURY.  3TPT, 3TRB                       M98
KUMMER, H.  SONNTAGSMUSIK, EINE, OP. 37.  3TPT, 3TRB                  C54
LANG.  CASSAZIONE.  3TPT, 2TRB, TU                                    A78
LANIER, N.-OSBORNE.  ALMAND & SARABAND                               B05
   2TPT, HN, TRB, TU, BTRB
LASSO-VOLKMANN.  SURREXIT PASTOR BONUS.  2TPT, HN, TRB, EU, TU        B40
LEBOW, L.S.  POPULAR SUITE.  2TPT, HN, TRB, TU, PERC                  F60
LERNER & LOEWE-MORRISSEY.  ON THE STREET WHERE YOU LIVE               B20
   2TPT, HN, TRB, EU, TU
LEVY, F.  FANTASY FOR BRASS QUINTET & TYMPANI                        B44
   2TPT, HN, TRB, TU, TIMP
LEWIS & ODE.  HYMNS, DESCANTS & FANTASIAS                            L74
   2TPT, HN, TRB, EU, TU
LOCKE, M.-KING.  MUSIC FOR KING CHARLES II                           D16
   2TPT, TPT(HN), HN(TRB), TRB, TRB-TU
LOEWE & LERNER-MORRISSEY.  ON THE STREET WHERE YOU LIVE              B20
   2TPT, HN, TRB, EU, TU
LONG, N.H.  NEWELL LONG BRASS SEXTETTE ALBUM                         D18
   2TPT, HN(TPT), TRB, EU, TU
LUBECK, H.  PRINZIPAL-AUFZUGE AUS DEM TROMPETERBUCH.  INST?          A51
MACDOWELL, E.A.-MCKAY.  2 EXPRESSIVE PIECES                          A55
   2TPT, HN, TRB, EU, TU
MACDOWELL, E.A.-JOHNSON.  WOODLAND SKETCHES.  INST ?                 F07
MALIGE.  KLEINE SUITE.  3TPT, 3TRB                                    C75
MALOTTE, A.H.-BEELER.  LORD'S PRAYER, THE.  2TPT, HN, 2TRB, TU        F23
MALTER, L.-AZAROV.  6 RUSSIAN FOLK SONGS.  2TPT, 2HN, EU, TU          D71
MARINI-SMITH.  CANZON OTTAVA A6                                       B98
   2TPT, HN(TRB), TRB, EU, TU(TRB)
MARINI-SMITH.  CANZONA DECIMA A6                                      B98
   2TPT, HN(TRB), TRB, EU, TU(TRB)
```

MASCAGNI, P.-EVERETT. CATHEDRAL SCENE & INTERMEZZO   A62
    2TPT, HN, TRB, EU, TU
MC KAY, F.H.   CONCERT PRELUDE.   2TPT, HN, TRB, EU, TU   A55
MC KAY, F.H.   DRAMATIC PRELUDE.   2TPT, HN, TRB, EU, TU   A55
MC KAY, F.H.   FANTASY.   2TPT, HN, TRB, EU, TU   A55
MC KAY, F.H.   GRANDIOSO IN C MAJOR.   2TPT, HN, TRB, EU, TU   A55
MC KAY, F.H.   NARRATIVE SKETCH.   2TPT, HN, TRB, EU, TU   A55
MC KAY, F.H.   PROLOGUE IN E-FLAT MAJOR.   2TPT, HN, TRB, EU, TU   A55
MC KAY, F.H.   ROMANTIC MURAL, OP.30.   2TPT, HN, TRB, EU, TU   A55
MC KAY, F.H.   SECOND FANTASY.   2TPT, HN, TRB, EU, TU   A55
MC KAY, F.H.   SEXTET IN A MAJOR.   2TPT, HN, TRB, EU, TU   A55
MC KAY, G.F.   LEGENDS.   2TPT, HN, TRB, EU, TU   A55
MC KAY, G.F.   MOODS IN CONTRAST.   2TPT, HN, TRB, EU, TU   A55
MC KAY, G.F.   PRELUDE & ALLEGRO.   2TPT, HN, TRB, EU, TU   A55
MEHUL, E.N.-FINCH. JOSEPH IN EGYPT OVERTURE   C11
    2TPT, HN, TRB, EU, TU
MENDELSSOHN, F.-BARNES. PRELUDE & FUGUE   D52
    2TPT, HN, TRB, EU, TU
MEYER. CHORAL ET FUGA-CANTABILE. 3TPT, HN, TRB, TRB(TU)   D36
MEYER, C. AUTUMN MOODS. 2TPT, HN, TRB, EU, TU   G66
MEYERS, C.D. AUTUMN MOODS. 2TPT, HN, TRB, EU, TU   B38
MEYERS, C.D. RHAPSODY. 2TPT, HN, TRB, EU, TU   A38
MILLER, P.D. SUITE MINIATURE. 2TPT, HN, TRB, EU, TU   A62
MILLS, C. BRASS PIANO, THE. 3TPT, 3TRB, (OPT PERC)   E68
MOSZKOWSKI. SPANISH DANCE. 2TPT, HN, TRB, EU, TU   F07
MOZART, W.A. ALLEGRO FROM EINE KLEINE NACHTMUSIK   D16
    2TPT, HN(TPT), HN(TRB), TRB, TRB-TU
MOZART, W.A.-JOHNSON. DIVERTIMENTO # 5   F07
    2TPT, HN, TRB, EU, TU
NAGEL, R. SONATINA. 2TPT, 2TRB, TU, BTRB   E68
NENNA-EICHMAN. APRI IL SEN ALLE FIAMME   F60
    2TPT, HN(TRB), 2TRB, TU
NENNA-EICHMAN. DOLCE MIO FOCO ARDENTE   F60
    2TPT, HN(TRB), 2TRB, TU
NENNA-EICHMAN. ECCO O MIA DOLCE PENA   F60
    2TPT, HN(TRB), 2TRB, TU
NENNA-EICHMAN. ITENE O MIEI SOSPIR. 2TPT, HN(TRB), 2TRB, TU   F60
NENNA-EICHMAN. OCCHI MIEI CHE VEDESTE   F60
    2TPT, HN(TRB), 2TRB, TU
NERIJNEN, J.V. PASTORALE. 3TPT, 3TRB   D92
ODE & LEWIS. HYMNS, DESCANTS & FANTASIAS   L74
    2TPT, HN, TRB, EU, TU
ORR, R. DIVERTIMENTO. 2TPT, HN(TRB), 2TRE, TU   E14
OSBORNE, W. PRELUDE. 2TPT, TPT(HN), TRB(HN), TRB, TRB-TU   D16
OSBORNE, W. 2 RICERCARI. 2TPT, HN(TPT), HN(TRB), TRB, TRB-TU   D16
OSTRANSKY, L. PASSACAGLIA & SCHERZO. 2TPT, HN, TRB, EU, TU   F07
OSTRANSKY, L. SUITE. 2TPT, HN, TRB, EU, TU   F07
OTTEN, L. CASSATION. 3TPT, 3TRB   B74
OTTEN, L. SUITE. 3TPT, 3TRB   B74
PALESTRINA, G.P.-VOLKMANN. ALLELUIA TULERUNT   B40
    2TPT, HN, TRB, EU, TU
PALESTRINA, G.P. EXALTABO TE, DOMINE. 2TPT, HN, TRB, EU, TU   G21
PALESTRINA, G.P.-WISE. EXALTABO TE, DOMINE. INST ?   M79
PALESTRINA, G.P.-VOLKMANN. LAUDATE DOMINUM   B40
    2TPT, HN, TRB, EU, TU
PALMER, P.-FARKAS. 8 ARTISTIC BRASS SEXTETS   G28
    2TPT, HN, TRB, EU, TU
PATACHICH. RITMI DISPARI. 3TPT, 2TRB, TU   B84
PEASLEE. DEVIL'S HERALD. SOLO TU, 4HN, PERC   G68
PELEMANS, W. SEXTUOR. 2TPT, 2HN, 2TRB   D67
PETERSEN, T. 4 SKETCHES. 3TPT, 3TRB   D14
PFANNENSTIEL, E. FEIERLICHE MUSIK #3. 2TPT, 4TRB   F31

```
PHILLIPS, I.C.  3 HUNTING SONGS.  2TPT, 2HN, 2TRB                        E51
PICHLER.  MUSIK FUR BLASER.  2TPT, 2HN, 2TRB                             B73
PILSS, K.  4 FANFAREN.  3TPT, 3TRB                                       E37
PINTO, C.-HANNAFORD.  TOM THUMB'S MARCH                                  F23
   2TPT, HN, TRB, EU, TU
PISK, P.A.  5 VARIATIONS ON AN OLD TRUMPET HYMN TUNE                     F56
   2TPT, HN, 2TRB, TRB-TU
PITFIELD.  THREE FOR SIX.  2TPT, HN, 2TRB, TU                            D92
PLONER, J.  3 STUCKE.  2TPT, 2HN, EU, TU                                 C54
POLIN, CLAIRE.  JOURNEY OF OWAIN MADOC                                   G66
   BRASS QUINTET, PERC(10)
PREMRU, R.E.  MUSIC FROM HARTER FELL.  3TPT, 3TRB                        B23
PROKOFIEV, S.S.-HANNAFORD.  GAVOTTE, OP. 12/2                            F23
   2TPT, HN, TRB, EU, TU
PROKOFIEV, S.S.-PORTER.  TRIUMPHAL MARCH FR PETER & THE WOLF             B39
   2TPT, HN, TRB, EU, TU
PURCELL, H.-THILDE.  AIR.  3TPT, 3TRB                                    A71
PURCELL, H.-THILDE.  FANFARE.  3TPT, 3TRB                                A71
PURCELL, H.-MAGANINI.  FANTASIA ON ONE NOTE                              B85
   2TPT, HN, 2TRB, TU
PURCELL, H.-THILDE.  PRELUDE AND MINUET.  3TPT, 3TRB                     X99
PURCELL, H.-BROWN.  TRUMPET TUNE & AIR.  2TPT, HN, TRB, EU, TU           F07
RAPHLING, S.  LITTLE SUITE.  3TPT, 3TRB                                  B85
REITER, A.  MUSIK FUR SOLO-POSAUNE UND HORNER.  5HN, TRB                 B73
REYNOLDS.  CONCERTARE I.  2TPT, HN, TRB, TU, PERC                        C11
RIMSKY-KORSAKOV, N.A.  DANCE OF THE TUMBLERS                             P51
   2TPT, HN, TRB, EU, TU
RODGERS, R.-MORRISSEY.  HELLO, YOUNG LOVERS                              B20
   2TPT, 2TRB, EU, TU
RODGERS, R.-MORRISSEY.  SURREY WITH THE FRINGE ON TOP                    B20
   2TPT, 2TRB, EU, TU
RODGERS, R.-MORRISSEY.  YOU'LL NEVER WALK ALONE                          B20
   2TPT, 2TRB, EU, TU
ROOT.  ANDANTE & ALLEGRO.  2TPT, HN, TRB, EU, TU                         F97
RUBANK.  CONCERT REPERTOIRE FOR BRASS SEXTET                             F07
   2TPT, HN, TRB, EU, TU, (OPT CHOIR PARTS)
SAPP, G.  KWAIDAN.  5TPT, TIMP                                           G66
SAUCEDO, V.  TOCCATA.  2TPT, 2HN, 2TRB                                   B91
SCHAEFFER, D.  BRASS CHOIR, THE.  2TPT, HN, TRB, EU, TU                  E80
SCHEIN-SCHMITT.  SUITE ZU 5 STIMMEN.  2TPT, HN(TPT), 2TRB, TU            F23
SCHILLING.  TRIPARTITA.  2TPT, HN(TPT), TRB, TU(TRB), PERC               D36
SCHILLING, H.L.  FANFARE, RICERCARE & HYMNUS....  3TPT, 3TRB             A90
SCHILLING, H.L.  INTRADA.  3TPT, 2TRB, TRB-TU                            A90
SCHMID, H.K.  TURMMUSIK, OP. 105B.  3TPT, 2TRB, BTRB                     A89
SCHMUTZ, A.D.  FANTASY SKETCH.  2TPT, HN, TRB, EU, TU                    C11
SCHNEIDER, W.  MUSIK FUR 6 BLECHBLASER (TURMMUSIK II)                    C54
   3TPT, 3TRB
SCHUMANN, R.-CAFARELLA.  STRANGER, OP. 68/29                             G10
   2TPT, HN, TRB, EU, TU
SHELUKOV, V.-WALTERS.  BALLADE.  2TPT, HN, TRB, EU, TU                   F07
SHERIFF, N.-THOME.  DESTINATION 5.  2TPT, 2TRB, TU, PERC(4)              C93
SHINER, M.  2 SEXTETS.  5TRB, TU                                        D14
SIEGMEISTER, E.  SEXTET.  2TPT, HN, TRB, TU, PERC                        D71
SIMON, A.Y.  4 PIECES.  INST ?                                           F07
SIMPSON, R.W.L.  CANZONA.  2TPT, 3TRB, TU                                D42
SMITH, C.-HOLMES.  IMOGENE.  2TPT, HN, TRB, EU, TU                       A55
SMITH, C.-HOLMES.  WAYFARER, THE.  2TPT, HN, TRB, EU, TU                 A55
SMITH, L.B.  SUITE FROM ARBEAU.  2TPT, HN, TRB, EU, TU                   D18
SPEER, D.  7 BLAESERSTUECKE.  3TPT, 3TRB                                 F23
STEINOHRT.  PROCESSION AND FESTIVAL.  2TPT, HN, TRB, EU, TU              E00
STEWART, R.  CANZONA & RICERCAR.  HN, 2TRB, 2COR, BTRB(EU, TU)           A13
STORP.  MUSIK.  3TPT, 3TRB                                               D98
```

```
SWEELINCK, J.P.-VOLKMANN.   ANGELUS AD PASTORES AIT              B40
    2TPT, HN, TRB, EU, TU
SWEELINCK, J.P.-VOLKMANN.   HODIE CHRISTUS NATUS EST             B40
    2TPT, HN, TRB, EU, TU
SZELENYI.  KAMMERMUSIK.  2TPT, 2HN, 2TRB                         F31
TCHAIKOVSKY, P.I.-TALLMADGE.  LAKE OF THE SWANS                  A62
    2TPT, HN, TRB, EU, TU
TCHAIKOVSKY, P.I.-MCLEOD.  SWAN LAKE.  INST ?                    F27
TCHEREPNIN.  SOMMERMUSIK.  2TPT, 2HN, TRB, TU                    A58
TOWNSEND.  HAPPY CHRISTMAS FOR BRASS                             F27
    2TPT, HN, TRB(HN), EU, TU
UBER, D.A.  BALLETS IN BRASS.  2TPT, HN, 2TRB, TU(BTRB)          D14
UBER, D.A.  BEACHCOMBER'S DANCE.  2TPT, 3TRB, TU                 B85
UBER, D.A.  KINGDOM COMIN', DE, OP. 36                           A94
    2TPT, 2TRB, EU, BTRB(TU)
UBER, D.A.  PANTOMIME.  2TPT, HN, TRB, EU, TU                    B31
UBER, D.A.  SUITE, OP. 20.  2TPT, HN, 2TRB, TU                   A03
ULF, O.  DANCES OF THE 16TH & 17TH CENTURY                      D98
    2TPT(2FLG), HN(AHN), 2TRB(2EU), TU
VERDI, G.-TALLMADGE.  IS IT THOU? FROM OPERA A MASKED BALL       C11
    2TPT, HN, TRB, EU, TU
VERRALL, J.  SUITE.  2TPT, HN, TRB, EU, TU                       D76
VERRALL, J.  SUITE.  2TPT, HN, TRB, EU, TU                       E77
VIECENZ, H.  BLASER-SUITE                                       C75
    2TPT, TPT(ATRB), 2TRB(2HN), TRB(BTRB)
WAGNER, R.-SCHAFER.  KING'S PRAYER AND FINALE                   A38
    2TPT, HN, TRB, EU, TU
WAGNER, R.-TRINKHAUS.  PRAYER FROM RIENZI                       H06
    2TPT, HN(TPT), TRB(HN), EU, TU
WALKER, R.  MARCHE PETITE.  2TPT, HN, TRB, EU, TU               A55
WALKER, R.  SLAVIC PAGEANT.  2TPT, HN, TRB, EU, TU              A55
WALLACE, W.V.-GUENTAEL.  MARITANA EXCERPTS                      A55
    2TPT, HN, TRB, EU, TU
WALTERS.  AIR FOR BRASS.  2TPT, HN, TRB, EU, TU                 E80
WEILL-MORRISSEY.  SEPTEMBER SONG.  2TPT, 2TRB, EU, TU           B20
WHEAR, P.W.  3 CHORALES.  2TPT, 2HN, TRB, EU                    D52
WHITE, D.  DIVERSIONS.  2TPT, HN, 2TRB, TU                      B32
WURZ, R.  ABENDMUSIK (TURMMUSIK #4).  3TPT, 3TRB                A89
WURZ, R.  MORGENMUSIK (TURMMUSIK #3).  3TPT, 3TRB               A89
YOUMANS, V.  GREAT DAY.  2TPT, 2TRB, EU, TU                     P40
YOUMANS, V.  WITHOUT A SONG.  2TPT, 2TRB, EU, TU                P40
ZETTLER.  ALLGAUER SKIZZEN.  2TPT, HN(TPT), TRB, TU, HN         D98
ZIPP, F.  3 FANFAREN.  3TPT, 3TRB                               C60
```

6 PARTS: HORN-WOODWIND

```
ALLERS, H.G.  SUITE.  2HN, FL, OB, CL, BSN                      D98
BEETHOVEN, L.V.-KAHN.  MINUET & MARCH.  2HN, 2CL, 2BSN          D63
BEETHOVEN, L.V.  SCHERZO (MOONLIGHT SONATA, OP.27/2)            G31
    HN, FL, OB, 2CL, BSN
BEETHOVEN, L.V.-SCHOENFELD.  SCHERZO (PF SONATA,OP.2/3)         H06
    HN, FL, OB, 2CL, BSN
BEETHOVEN, L.V.-SCHOENFELD.  SCHERZO IN F MINOR, OP.10/2)       G31
    HN, FL, OB,2CL, BSN
BEETHOVEN, L.V.-SCHOENFELD.  SCHERZO(MOONLIGHT SONATA)          H06
    HN, FL, OB, 2CL, BSN
BEETHOVEN, L.V.-SCHOENFELD.  SCHERZO, OP.2/3                    G31
    HN, FL, OB, 2CL, BSN
```

```
BEETHOVEN, L.V.   SEXTET IN E-FLAT, OP. 71.   2HN, 2CL, 2BSN          A90
BEETHOVEN, L.V.   SEXTET IN E-FLAT, OP. 71.   2HN, 2CL, 2BSN          C03
BEETHOVEN, L.V.   SEXTET IN E-FLAT, OP. 71.   2HN, 2CL, 2BSN          C91
BEETHOVEN, L.V.   SEXTET, OP. 71.   2HN, 2CL, 2BSN                    C71
BRIEGEL, G.F.   MORNING IN THE FOREST.   HN, FL, OB, 2CL, BSN         A91
CADOW, P.   PASTORALE IN ALTEN STIL.   HN, 2OB, 2BSN, EH             C54
CARMICHAEL, H.-KLICKMANN.   STAR DUST.   HN, FL, OB, 2CL, BSN         D84
CASTIL-BLAZE, F.   SEXTET NO. 1.   2HN, 2CL, 2BSN                     E14
DANZI, F.-WOJCIECHOWSKI.   SEXTETT IN E-FLAT.   2HN, 2CL, 2BSN        F50
DRUSCHETZKY, G.   PARTHIA.   2HN, 2CL, 2BSN                           D21
DRUSCHETZKY, G.   SEXTET.   2HN, 2CL, 2BSN                            F31
DUBOIS, P.M.   SINFONIA DA CAMERA.   HN, FL, OB, CL, BSN, ASAX        D36
FROSCHAUER, H.   SEXTETT.   HN, FL, OB, 2CL, BSN                      B73
GAN, N.K.   SUITE (CHILDREN'S PICTURES).   HN, FL, OB, 2CL, BSN       D81
GRIEG, E.H.-SCHOENFELD.   ANITRA'S DANCE (PEER GYNT SUITE)            G31
   HN, FL, OB, 2CL, BSN
GYROWETZ, A.   NOTTURNO.   2HN, 2CL, 2BSN                             E14
HARTLEY, W.S.   CHAMBER MUSIC.   HN, FL, OB, CL, BSN, ASAX            G70
HAYDN, J.-LANDON.   DIVERTIMENTO #2 IN F, H.II:23                     B73
   2HN, 2OB, 2BSN
HAYDN, J.-LUMSDEN.   DIVERTIMENTO #2 IN F, H.II:23                    E14
   2HN, 2OB, 2BSN
HAYDN, J.-LANDON.   DIVERTIMENTO #3 IN C, H. II:7                     B73
   2HN, 2OB, 2BSN
HAYDN, J.-LANDON.   DIVERTIMENTO #5 IN D, H.II:D18                    B73
   2HN, 2OB, 2BSN
HAYDN, J.-LANDON.   DIVERTIMENTO #6 IN G, H.II:3                      B73
   2HN, 2OB, 2BSN
HAYDN, J.-LANDON.   DIVERTIMENTO #7 IN G, H. DEEST                    B73
   2HN, 2OB, 2BSN
HAYDN, J.-LANDON.   DIVERTIMENTO #8 IN D, H. DEEST                    B73
   2HN, 2OB, 2BSN
HAYDN, J.-LANDON.   DIVERTIMENTO IN F, H.II:15.   2HN, 2OB, 2BSN      B73
HAYDN, J.   FELDPARTIE IN C.   2HN, 2OB, 2BSN                         E14
HAYDN, J.-LUMSDEN.   MARCH IN G.   2HN, 2OB, 2BSN                     E14
HAYDN, J.   PARTHIA IN F, H.II.15.   2HN, 2OB, 2BSN                   F23
HAYDN, J.-LUMSDEN.   PARTITA IN F, H.II:23.   2HN, 2OB, 2BSN          E14
JANACEK, L.   YOUTH (MLADI).   HN, FL(PIC), OB, CL, BSN, BCL          C80
KABELAC, M.   SEXTET, OP. 8.   HN, FL, 2CL, BSN, EH                   A33
KABELAC, M.   SEXTETT, OP. 8.   HN, FL, 2CL, BSN, EH                  A51
KELTERBORN, R.   MEDITATIONEN.   2HN, 2CL, 2BSN                       C60
KROMMER, F.-GUITE.   PARTITA.   2HN, 2CL, 2BSN                        C75
MOZART, W.A.   ADAGIO, K. 516.   HN, FL, OB, 2CL, BSN                 C71
MOZART, W.A.-KAHN.   CONTRADANCE IN RONDO FORM.   2HN, 2OB, 2BSN      D63
MOZART, W.A.   DIVERTIMENTO # 8 IN F, K. 213.   2HN, 2OB, 2BSN        A89
MOZART, W.A.   DIVERTIMENTO # 9 IN B-DUR, K. 240                      A89
   2HN, 2OB, 2BSN
MOZART, W.A.   DIVERTIMENTO #12 IN E-FLAT, K. 252                     A89
   2HN, 2OB, 2BSN
MOZART, W.A.   DIVERTIMENTO #13 IN F, K. 253.   2HN, 2OB, 2BSN        A89
MOZART, W.A.   DIVERTIMENTO #14 IN B-FLAT, K. 270                     A89
   2HN, 2OB, 2BSN
MOZART, W.A.   DIVERTIMENTO #16 IN E-FLAT, K. 289                     A89
   2HN, 2OB, 2BSN
MOZART, W.A.   DIVERTIMENTO, K. 213.   2HN, 2OB, 2BSN                 D08
MOZART, W.A.   DIVERTIMENTO, K. 240.   2HN, 2OB, 2BSN                 D08
MOZART, W.A.   DIVERTIMENTO, K. 252.   2HN, 2OB, 2BSN                 D08
MOZART, W.A.   DIVERTIMENTO, K. 253.   2HN, 2OB, 2BSN                 D08
MOZART, W.A.   DIVERTIMENTO, K. 270.   2HN, 2OB, 2BSN                 D08
MOZART, W.A.   DIVERTIMENTO, K. 289.   2HN, 2OB, 2BSN                 D08
MOZART, W.A.   MINUET & TRIO, K. 516.   HN, FL, OB, 2CL, BSN          C71
MOZART, W.A.   SERENADE #11, K. 375.   2HN, 2CL, 2BSN                 E14
```

MOZART, W.A.-SPIEGL. SERENADE IN B FLAT, K. 196F   F31
   2HN, 2CL, 2BSN
MOZART, W.A.-HAAS. SERENADE IN E-FLAT, K. 375   E14
   2HN, 2CL, 2BSN
PLEYEL, I.J. SEXTET IN E-FLAT #1. 2HN, 2CL, 2BSN   E14
REBNER, E.W. SEXTETT. HN, FL, OB, CL, BSN, BCL   D88
RIGHINI, V. SEXTET. 2HN, 2CL, 2BSN   E14
ROSETTI, F.A. 3 PARTHIEN. INST ?   A83
SCHUBERT, F.P. ROSAMUNDE, OP. 26. 2HN, 2CL, 2BSN   A89
SCHUBERT, F.P.-SCHOENBACH. SHEPHERD MELODY #6 FR ROSAMUNDE E77
   2HN, 2CL, 2BSN
SCHUMANN, R. ROMANZA FROM 4TH SYMPHONY. HN, FL, OB, 2CL, BSN A91
SEIBER, M. SERENADE. 2HN, 2CL, 2BSN   H30
STRAVINSKY, I.-STONE. NAPOLITANA. HN, FL, OB, 2CL, BSN   C45
SVENSSON, S.E. SEXTETT. HN, FL, OB, CL, BSN, BCL   B90
TOMASI, H. PRINTEMPS. HN, FL/PIC, OB, CL, ASAX, BSN   D36
ZAGWIJN, H. SUITE. HN, FL, OB, CL, BSN, FA   B99

6 PARTS: BRASS-WOODWIND

ALBAM. ESCAPADE. HN, TRB, FL, OB, CL, BSN   M65
BEREAU, J.S. SEXTUOR. TPT, HN, FL, OB, CL, BSN   B24
BREIT & WARD. BOY WHO WANTED A TUBA, THE   G96
   TPT, TU, FL, CL, NAR
GABRIELI, G. CANZONI A 6. 2TPT, 2TRB, TU, CL   F59
GABRIELI, G.-SCHUMAN. CANZONI A 6. 2TPT, 2TRB, TU, CL   F59
GERSCHEFSKI, E. "AMERICA" VARIATIONS FOR WINDS OP.45/2   E68
   TPT, TU, FL, OB, CL, BSN
GERSCHEFSKI, E. WORKOUT, OP. 18/4. INST ?   E68
GIRON. SEXTET. TPT, HN, FL, OB, CL, BSN   C11
KAINZ. 3 KLEINE STUECKE FUR BLASER. 2TPT, HN, 2TRB, CL   P53
MOLTER, J.M.-GLOVER-TARR. SINFONIA CONCERTANTE #2   M80
   D TPT, 2HN, 2OB, BSN
MOLTER, J.M. SINFONIA CONCERTO MWV VIII, 1   E14
   TPT, 2HN, 2OB, BSN
RUSSELL, A. SUITE CONCERTANTE FOR TUBA & WW   E87
   TU, FL, OB, CL, HN, BSN
SCHMIDT. CONCERTINO FOR TUBA AND WW QUINTET   M79
   TU, HN, FL, OB, CL, BSN
SCHWERTSIK, K. PROVIANT. TPT, HN, FL, OB, CL, BSN   B73
SEREBRIER, J. EROTICA. TPT, HN, FL, OB, CL, BSN   E61
STEWART, R. DIVERTIMENTO FOR WINDS   B35
   TPT, HN, FL, OB, CL, BSN, (OR 5CL, HN)
VILLA¬LOBOS, H. CHOROS #3 "PICA-PAO" (OPT MEN'S CH)   C01
   TPT, 2HN, CL, BSN, ASAX

6 PARTS: WINDS-KEYBOARD

ALBINONI, T.-WOJCIECHOWSKI. CONCERTO C-DUR   F50
   TPT, 3OB, BSN, BC
ALEXANDER, J. FESTIVITIES. 2TPT, HN, TRB, TU, PF   F59
ANDRIESSEN, J. L'INCONTRO DI CESARE E CLEOPATRA   B74
   HN, FL, OB, CL, BSN, PF
BACH, J.C. SEXTET IN C. 2HN, OB, VN, VC, HPCD(PA)   E14

BADINGS, H. SEXTET. HN, FL, OB, CL, BSN, PF   B74
BARBE. MINIATUREN ZU EINEM LUSTSPIEL VON SHAKESPEARE   A51
    TPT, TRB, CL, PERC, PF, DB
BECKLER, S.R. SONGS AND DANCES. HN, FL, CB, CL, BSN, PF   B35
BLUMER, T. SEXTET, OP. 92. HN, FL, OB, CL, BSN, PF   E99
BOISDEFFRE, C.H.R. DE. SEXTUOR, OP. 49   C55
    HN, FL, CB, CL, BSN, PF
BOTTJE, W.G. SEXTET. INST ?   E68
BOUTRY, R. 2 PIECES EN SEXTOUR. HN, FL, CB, CL, BSN, PF   D36
BOWLES, P.F. CONCERTO FOR 2 PIANOS, WINDS & PERC   A15
    TPT, OB/EH, CL/BCL, PERC, 2PF
BRANDON, S. CHACONNE AND VARIATIONS. 2HN, TRB, OB, ASAX, PF   P48
BROWN, R. VARIATIONS. 2TPT, HN, TRB, TU, PF   G21
CASTEREDE, J. PRELUDE ET DANSE. 3TRB, TU, PERC, PF   D36
CONSTANT, M. 4 ETUDES DE CONCERT. TPT, 2HN, TRB, PERC, PF   D36
CRUFT, A.F. DANCE MOVEMENT (BALLABILE), OP. 28   B93
    HN, FL, OB, CL, BSN, PF
CUNNINGHAM, M.G. EPITAPH FOR DYLAN THOMAS   B35
    2TPT, HN, TRB, TU, PF
D'INDY, V. SARABANDE & MINUET, OP. 72   C91
    HN, FL, OB, CL, BSN, PF
D'INDY, V. SARABANDE ET MENUET, OP. 24A   C55
    HN, FL, OB, CL, BSN, PF
DAVID, J.N.-BOHLE. KUME, KUM, GESELLE MIN, OP. 24   A90
    HN, FL, OB, CL, BSN, PF
DI DOMENICA, R. SEXTET. HN, FL, OB, CL, BSN, PF   D63
DIEMER, E.I. SEXTET. HN, FL, OB, CL, BSN, PF   B35
DIONISI, R. DIVERTIMENTO. HN, FL, OB, CL, BSN, PF   G38
DRESDEN, S. KLEINE SUITE IN C (SEXTET #2)   B70
    HN, FL, OB, CL, BSN, PF
DRESDEN, S. SUITE #3. HN, FL, OB, CL, BSN, PF   B70
DRESDEN, S. SUITE NAAR RAMEAU. HN, FL, OB, CL, BSN, PF   B70
DRESDEN, S. SUITE NAAR RAMEAU. HN, FL, OB, CL, BSN, PF   B74
EBEEL, A. SEXTET IN E-FLAT, OP. 47. HN, CL, PF, VN, VA, VC   E14
ERB, D. 3 PIECES. 2TPT, HN, TRB, TU, PF   D76
FOX, F. CONCERTPIECE FOR BRASS QUINTET & PF   D94
    2TPT, HN, TRB, TU, PF
GODRON, H. SERENADE. HN, FL, OB, CL, BSN, PF   B74
HAIEFF, A. DANCE SUITE(PRINCESS ZONDILDA & HER ENTOURAGE)   A58
    TPT, FL, BSN, PF, VN, VC
HEMEL, O.V. SEXTET. HN, FL, OB, CL, BSN, PF   B73
HENRY, J. SEXTET. HN, PF, 2VN, VA, VC   B35
HILL, E.B. SEXTET. HN, FL, OB, CL, BSN, PF   F56
HILL, E.B. SEXTET, OP. 39. HN, FL, OB, CL, BSN, PF   C33
HOLEWA, H. CONCERTINO. HN, CL, PERC, PF, VA, HP   B90
HOVHANESS, A.S. KHALDIS, CONCERT, OP. 91. 4TPT, PERC, PF   D16
HUSA, K. CONCERTO. 2TPT, HN, TRB, TU, *PF   D36
JACOB, G.P.S. SEXTET. HN, FL, OB, CL, BSN, PF   E14
JENTSCH, W. KLEINE KAMMERMUSIK (THEMA MIT VARIATIONEN), OP. 5   E99
    HN, FL, OB, CL, BSN, PF
JONGEN, J. RHAPSODIE, OP. 70. HN, FL, OB, CL, BSN, PF   B12
JUON, P. DIVERTIMENTO, OP. 51. HN, FL, OB, CL, BSN, PF   D46
KAHOWEZ, G. STRUCTURES POUR 6 INSTS.   B73
    HN, FL, OB, CL, BSN, PF
KEITH. JOURNEY OF THE SWAGMAN. HN, FL, OB, CL, BSN, PF   H06
KELKEL, M. APHORISMES POUR 5 INST & PERCUSSION   E98
    TPT, CL, BSN, PERC, PF, VN
KOX, H. SEXTET #3. HN, FL, OB, CL, BSN, PF   B74
KOX, H. SEXTET #4. HN, FL, OB, CL, BSN, PF   B74
LADMIRAULT, P.E. CHORAL ET VARIATIONS   D41
    HN, FL, OB, CL, BSN, PF
LAKNER, Y. SEXTET. HN, FL, OB, CL, BSN, PF   C93

```
LEWIS.  MOVEMENT.  2TPT, HN, TRB, TU, PF                          B98
MEULEMANS, A.  AUBADE.  HN, FL, OB, CL, BSN, PF                   B12
MOZART, W.A.-PIPHER.  FANTASIA FUR EINE ORGELWALZE, K.608         B74
   HN, FL, OB, CL, BSN, PF
MOZART, W.A.  SEXTET.  HN, FL, OB, CL, BSN, PF                    B44
MULDER, E.W.  SEXTET.  HN, FL, OB, CL, BSN, PF                    B74
OSIECK, H.W.  DIVERTIMENTO.  HN, FL, OB, CL, BSN, PF              B74
PERUTI, C.  HALLOWEEN MUSIC.  TPT, TRB, TU, BSN, DB, PF           P48
PIJPER, W.  PHANTASIE (ON A MOZART THEME)                         B74
   HN, FL, OB, CL, BSN, PF
PIJPER, W.  SEXTET.  HN, FL, OB, CL, BSN, PF                      B74
PILLIN.  SERENADE.  HN, FL, OB, CL, BSN, PF                       N43
POULENC, F.  SEXTET.  HN, FL, OB, CL, BSN, PF                     H30
POUWELS, J.  SEXTET.  HN, FL, OB, CL, BSN, PF                     B74
REED, H.O.  SYMPHONIC DANCE.  HN, FL, OB, CL, BSN, PF             D84
REUCHSEL, A.  SEXTUOR.  HN, FL, OB, CL, BSN, PF                   D41
RIEGGER, W.  CONCERTO FOR PIANO & WIND QUINTET, OP. 53            A38
   HN, FL, OB, CL, BSN, PF
ROLDAN, A.  RITMICA #1.  HN, FL, OB, CL, BSN, PF                  F59
ROOS, R. DE.  SEXTUOR.  HN, FL, OB, CL, BSN, PF                   B74
ROSS.  CONCERTO.  2TPT, HN, TRB, TU, PF                           A78
ROUSSEL, A.  DIVERTISSEMENT, OP. 6.  HN, FL, OB, CL, BSN, PF      D08
ROUSSEL, A.  DIVERTISSEMENT, OP. 6.  HN, FL, OB, CL, BSN, PF      F05
SCHMIDT.  CONCERTINO.  2TPT, HN, TRB, TU(TRB), PF                 G21
SCHMIDT, W.  CONCERTINO.  SS QUINTET, PF                          BRA
SCHROEDER, H.  SEXTET, OP. 36.  HN, FL, OB, CL, BSN, PF           F31
SEIBER, M.  JAZZCLETTES.  TPT, TRB, PERC, PF, 2SAX               H30
SMIT, L.  SEXTUOR.  HN, FL, OB, CL, BSN, PF                       B74
STRATEGIER, H.  SEXTET.  HN, FL, OB, CL, BSN, PF                  B74
SUGAR, R.  FRAMMENTI MUSICALI.  HN, FL, OB, CL, BSN, PF           B84
TANSMAN, A.  "DANSE DE LA SORCIERE" FROM LE JARDIN DU PARADIS     C01
   HN, FL, OB, CL, BSN, PF
THUILLE, L.  SEXTET IN B-FLAT, OP.6.  HN, FL, OB, CL, BSN, PF     C91
THUILLE, L.  SEXTETT IN B-DUR, OP. 6.  HN, FL, OB, CL, BSN, PF    A90
TORELLI, G.  SINFONIA CON TROMBA.  TPT, VN, VA, VC, DB, BC        D16
VLIJMEN, J.V.  SERIE PER SEI STRUMENTI                           B74
   TPT, FL, OB, CL, BSN, PF
WEBER, B.  BALLET, OP. 26 (THE POOL OF DARKNESS)                 B36
   TPT, FL, BSN, PF, VN, VC
WEISS, A.A.  SEXTETTE.  HN, FL, OB, CL, BSN, PF                   B36
WINNUBST, J.  KLEINE SERENADE.  HN, FL, OB, CL, BSN, PF           B74
XENAKIS.  EONTA.  2TPT, 3TRB, PF                                  A78
ZAGWIJN, H.  SCHERZO.  HN, FL, OB, CL, BSN, PF                    B74
ZAGWIJN, H.  SUITE.  HN, FL, OB, CL, BSN, PF                      B74
```

6 PARTS: WIND(S)-STRING(S)

```
ARDEVOL, J.  MUSICA DE CAMERA.  TPT, FL, CL, BSN, VN, VC          E53
BACH, J.C.  SEXTET IN C.  2HN, OB, VN, VC, BC                     E14
BARBE.  MINIATUREN ZU EINEM LUSTSPIEL VON SHAKESPEARE             A51
   TPT, TRB, CL, PERC, PF, DB
BEETHOVEN, L.V.  SEXTET IN E-FLAT, OP.81B.  2HN, 2VN, VA, VC      C91
BEETHOVEN, L.V.  SEXTET IN E-FLAT, OP.81B.  2HN, 2VN, VA, VC      D48
BEETHOVEN, L.V.  SEXTETT ES DUR, OP.81B.  2HN, 2VN, VA, VC        C03
BERKELEY, L.  SEXTET.  HN, CL, 2VN, VA, VC                        B23
BIBER, H.I.F.-JANETZKY.  SONATA A 6.  TPT, BC, STR                E14
BOCCHERINI, L.-BORMANN.  SEXTET IN E-FLAT, OP. 42/1               F50
   HN, 2VN, VA, 2VC
```

```
BOCCHERINI, L.-BORMANN.  SEXTET IN E-FLAT, OP. 42/2            F50
   HN, OB(FL), BSN, VN, VA, DB
BOCCHERINI, L.-HAAS.  SEXTET IN E-FLAT, OP. 42/2              E41
   HN, OB, BSN, VN, VA, DB
BOCCHERINI, L.  SEXTET, OP. 42.  HN, 2VN, VA, 2VC            C91
BOCCHERINI, L.  SEXTETT IN E-FLAT, OP. 42.  HN, 2VN, VA, 2VC  A90
CERHA, F.  ENJAMBEMENTS.  TPT, TRB, FL, PERC, VN, DB          F97
DOHNANYI, E. VON.  SEXTET IN C, OP. 37                        D42
   HN, CL, PF, VN, VA, VC
EBERL, A.  SEXTET.  HN, CL, PF, VN, VA, VC                    E14
ERLANGER, G.  SEXTETT, OP. 41.  HN, CL, BSN, VN, VA, VC       D17
FRANCO, J.  PSALM.  3TPT, HN, TRB, HP                         B36
HAIEFF, A.  DANCE SUITE (PRINCESS ZONDILDA AND HER ENTOURAGE) A58
   TPT, FL, BSN, PF, VN, VC
HAYDN, J.-JANETZKY.  SEXTET #14, H. II/40                     E14
   HN, OB, BSN, VN, VA, VC
HAYDN, M.-STRASSL.  NOTTURNO IN F, PERGER-KAT. 106            B73
   2HN, 2VN, VA, DB
HENRY, J.  SEXTET.  HN, PF, 2VN, VA, VC                       B35
HOLEWA, H.  CONCERTINO.  HN, CL, PERC, PF, VA, HP             B90
HOVHANESS, A.S.  CONCERTO #3 DIRAN (THE RELIGIOUS SINGER)     D16
   SOLO EU(TRB, HN), 2VN, VA, VC, DB
HURRELL, C.E.  BRASS RHAPSODY.  TPT, 3TRB, DB(TU), GUIT(PF)   A91
KREISLER, F.  PRAELUDIUM & ALLEGRO.  2TPT, HN, TRB, TU, VN    B04
KUFFNER, J.  QUINTET.  HN, STRINGS                            D11
MARTINU, B.  SERENADEN I.  HN, CL, 3VN, VA                    A51
MARTINU, B.  SERENATA I FOR 6 INSTRUMENTS.  HN, CL, 3VN, VA   A33
MERSSON, B.  MOMENTS MUSICAUX, OP. 21.  TRB, PERC, 2DB, VIB   H03
MOZART, W.A.-LYMAN.  DIVERTIMENTO #17 IN D MAJOR              C03
   2HN, 2VN, VA, DB(VC)
MOZART, W.A.-LYMAN.  DIVERTIMENTO #17 IN D MAJOR              C91
   2HN, 2VN, VA, DB(VC)
MOZART, W.A.  MUSICAL JOKE, A (THE VILLAGE MUSICIANS), K. 522  C91
   2HN, 2VN, VA, DB(VC)
MOZART, W.A.  MUSICAL JOKE, A (VILLAGE MUSICIANS), K. 522     D08
   2HN, 2VN, VA, VC
MOZART, W.A.-WACKERNAGEL.  MUSIKALISCHER SPASS, K. 522        D46
   2HN, 2VN, VA, VC
MOZART, W.A.  MUSIKALISCHER, EIN, K. 522.  2HN, 2VN, VA, VC   F60
PRAAG, H.C.V.  4 REFLEXIONS.  HN, FL, OB, CL, BSN, VN         B74
QUINET, M.  BALLADE.  HN, FL, OB, CL, BSN, VN                 B12
SABATINI, G.  ECSTASY.  2TPT, HN, TRB, TU, SOLO VN            B04
SCHIBLER, A.  PRISONIER, LE (DER GEFANGENE)                   A08
   TPT, TRB, CL, PERC, VN, VC
SCHMIDT.  MUSIC FOR SCRIMSHAWS.  2TPT, HN, TRB, TU, HP        A43
SEIBER, M.  FANTASIA.  HN, FL, 2VN, VA, VC                    G41
SPERGER-MALAFIE.  RONDO.  2HN, FL, VN, VA, DB                 B73
STERNFELD, F.  RETURN TO ISRAEL.  TPT, HN, TRB, CL, DB, PERC  G66
TABACHNIK, M.  PASTEL.  HN, FL, PERC, VC, HP                  E41
TARTINI, G.  ANDANTE CANTABILE FOR SOLO VN & QUINTET          B04
   2TPT, HN, TRB, TU, VN
TELEMANN, G.P.  CONCERTO FOR SOLO VN & WW QUINTET             B04
   HN, FL, OB, CL, BSN, VN
TISNE, A.  STRATES COLOREES.  TPT, TRB, OB, CL, VA, EH        F87
TORELLI, G.  SINFONIA CON TROMBA.  TPT, VN, VA, VC, DB, BC    D16
TORELLI, G.-SCHROEDER.  SONATA A CINQUE #1 IN D MAJOR         B73
   TPT, 2VN, VA, VC, BC
TORELLI, G.-SCHROEDER.  SONATA A CINQUE #7                    B73
   TPT, 2VN, VA, VC, BC
VITALE, T.  CIACONNA FOR SOLO VN & QUINTET                    B04
   2TPT, HN, TRB, TU, VN
WEBER, B.  BALLET, OP. 26 (THE POOL OF DARKNESS)             B36
   TPT, FL, BSN, PF, VN, VC
```

6 PARTS: BRASS-MISCELLANEOUS

```
BELLINI, G.  5 STUDI.  TPT, HN, TRB, FI, CL, PERC              G 38
BROWN, R.  CONCERTINO.  2TPT, HN, TRB, TU, HP                  G 21
FRANKO, J.  PSALM FOR BRASSES & HARP.  3TPT, HN, TRB, HP       E 68
HARTLEY, W.S.  DIVERTIMENTO.  HN, FL, OB, CL, BSN, VC          G 70
HARTLEY, W.S.  SERENADE.  HN, FL, OB, CL, BSN, DB              G 70
MARTINU, B.  REVUE DE CUISINE, LA.  TPT, CL, BSN, PF, VN, VC   D 36
MOSCHELES, F.  SEXTET, OP. 35.  2HN, FL, PF, VN, VC            E 14
MOULAERT, R.  CONCERT.  HN, FL, OB, CL, BSN, HP               B 12
OAKES, R.  SIX BY SIX.  ANY 6 INST                            B 35
RAVEL, M.-RYKER.  PAVANE POUR UNE INFANTE DEFUNTE            D 94
   2TPT, HN, TRB, TU, HP
REIF, P.  SEXTET.  TPT, 3BSN, VC, BCL                         G 66
SALMENHAARA, E.  ELEGIE I.  2TPT, 3FL, DB                     G 66
SCHWARTZ, E.S.  TELLY.  PERC, 5INST ?                          P 37
TOCH, E.  5 PIECES FOR WIND INST & PERC, OP.83                D 84
   2HN, FL, OB, CL, BSN, SDR (INST VARIES BY MOVEMENT)
ZELENKA, I.  FRUH-STUCK.  HN, PERC, AFL, BCL, HP, GUIT        D 88
```

SEVEN-PART MUSIC

7 EQUAL BRASS INSTRUMENTS

```
MOZART, W.A.   AVE VERUM. 7TRB                                  D14
PEDERSON, T.   BLUE TOPAZ. 7TRB                                 M93
PEDERSON, T.   BRAVE BLUES, THE. 7TRB                           M93
PEDERSON, T.   COGENT CAPRICE. 7TRB                             M93
PEDERSON, T.   DOVE SONG. 7TRB                                  M93
PEDERSON, T.   GYPSY GOLD. 7TRB                                 M93
PEDERSON, T.   KALEIDOSCOPE. 7TRB                               M93
PEDERSON, T.   PILL DICKLES. 7TRB                               M93
PEDERSON, T.   TERRIBLE TEMPERED TROMBONE, THE.  7TRB           M93
PEDERSON, T.   TOUCH OF DRASTIC, A.  7TRB                       M93
PEDERSON, T.   TROMBONE THAT ATE THE WORLD, THE.  7TRB          M93
PEDERSON, T.   TROMBONES 'N TOMAHAWKS.  7TRB                    M93
SCHICKELE.  MONOCHROME II.  7TRB                                B92
```

7 MIXED BRASS (BRASS-PERC)

```
ALEXANDER.  FESTIVE FANFARE FOR BRASS.  3TPT, 2HN, TRB, TU       N69
APPLEBAUM, S.S.  STRATFORD FANFARES.  3TPT, 3TRB, TU             G85
BACH, J.S.-THILDE.  FINAL DE LA PASSION SEION ST. JEAN           A71
    3TPT, 3TRB, TU
BACH, J.S.  RICERCAR (MUSICAL OFFERING)                          D16
    3TPT, HN(TRB), 2TRB, TU-TRB
BEETHOVEN, L.V.-SHIMER.   OPUS 18, NO. 2                         D14
    2TPT, HN, 2TRB, EU, TU
BENDER, J.  PHANTASY ON CHORALE "COME, HOLY GHOST...             B40
    3TPT, 2TRB, PERC, BTRB
BENJAMIN, A.  6 CERIMONIAL FANFARES.  EFCOR, 3TPT, 3TRB          A78
BEREZOWSKY, N.  BRASS SUITE, OP. 24.  2TPT, 2HN, 2TRB, TU        D84
BLISS, A.  FANFARE #1.  EFTPT, 3TPT, 2TRB, BTRB                  A78
BLISS, A.  2 ROYAL FANFARES (ROYAL FANFARES #5)                 E41
    3TPT, 3TRB, TU
BLUMENFELD, H.  MOVEMENTS FOR BRASS.  2TPT, 2HN, 2TRB, TU        G66
BORRIS, S.  BLASERMUSIK "FANFARE ...", OP.57/3                   F53
    2TPT, 2HN, 2TRB, TU
BOWDER.  3 FOLKSONGS.  2TPT, 2HN, TRB, EU, TU                    E87
BRACALI.  SEXTUOR.  3TPT, 3TRB, PERC                             D36
BUONAMENTE, G.B.  SONATA FROM "SONATE ET CANZONI, 1636"          D16
    2TPT, HN(TPT), HN(TRB), TRB, EU, TU
BURGHAUSER.  OLD CZECH FANFARES.  4TPT, 2HN, TIMP                A33
BUTTERWORTH, D.N.  TRITON SUITE, A.  3TPT, 3TRB, BTRB-TU         D16
BUTTS, C.M.  FANFARE AND BALLAD.  3TPT, 3HN(3TRB), TU            B98
CAMPO.  SUITE FOR BRASS, OP. 30.  2TPT, 2HN, 2TRB, TU            G21
CLERISSE, R.  FANFARES ROYALES.  3TPT, 3TRB, EU                  D36
COHN, A.  MUSIC FOR BRASS INSTRUMENTS.  4TPT(HN), 2TRB, BTRB     F59
COWELL, H.  RONDO.  3TPT, 2HN, 2TRB                              E65
DANIELS, M.L.  ANDANTE & MARCH.  2TPT, HN, TRB, EU, TU, PERC     B98
DAQUIN, L.C.  NOEL SUISSE.  3TPT, 3HN(3EU), TU                   F79
DART, T. (ARR).  SUITE FROM ROYAL BRASS MUSIC OF KING JAMES I    E51
    2TPT, 4TRB
DE JONG, C.  3 STUDIES.  3TPT, 3TRB, TU                          G21
DELP, R.  HYPOSTASIS.  2TPT, TRB, TU, PERC, FLG, VIB             G66
```

```
DIERCKS, J.   MIRROR OF BRASS.  2TPT, 2HN, 2TRB, TU          F80
DODGSON.  SUITE.  3TPT, 3TRB, TU                             B23
DORWARD.  DIVERTIMENTO FOR BRASS.  2TPT, 2HN, 2TRB, TU       C35
DUBOIS, P.M.  3 PRELUDES IN FANFARE                         B92
    2TPT, 2HN, 2TRB, TU, (OPT TIMP)
DUBOIS, P.M.  SEPTUOR.  2TPT, 2HN, 2TRB, TU, (OPT PERC)      D36
DUNCAN, T. & BENJAMIN.  6 CERIMONIAL FANFARES                A78
    EFCOR, 2TPT, 3TRB, TIMP
FERGUSON, H.  2 FANFARES.  4TPT, 3TRB                        A78
FRANCISQUE, A.  SUITE FROM LE TRESCOR D'ORPHEE               D16
    2TPT, 2HN, 2TRB, TRB-TU
GABRIELI, A.-SCHUMANN.  AGNUS DEI.  3TPT, 3TRB, TU           F59
GABRIELI, G.-THOMAS.  CANZON NO. 5.  4TPT, HN(TRB), 2TRB     E14
GABRIELI, G.-THOMAS.  CANZON NO. 6.  4TPT, HN(TRB), 2TRB     E14
GABRIELI, G.-THOMAS.  CANZON NO. 7.  4TPT, HN(TRB), 2TRB     E14
GABRIELI, G.-MCENKEMEYER.  KANZONE.  3TPT, 2TRB, 2TPT(2TRB)  C60
GATTERMEYER.  DIVERTIMENTO, OP. 118, NO. 1                   B73
    2TPT, 2HN, 2TRB, TIMP
GERSCHEFSKI, E.  SEPTET, OP. 26.  2TPT, 2HN, 2TRB, TU        A13
GLICKMAN, E.  DIVERTIMENTO.  2TPT, HN, TRB, TU, 3PERC, TIMP  D94
GOEB, R.J.  SEPTET.  2TPT, 2HN, 2TRB, TU                     E68
GOEBERT.  EXULTICUS FANFARIUS.  3TPT, 3TRB, PERC             F60
GOERNER.  SUITE FOR BRASS.  3TPT, 2HN, 2TRB                  C75
GOULD.  COLUMBIAN FANFARES.  3TPT, 3TRB, TU                  B20
GRANT, P.  BRASS SEPTET "INSOUCIANCE & REMORSE", OP. 57/1    E68
    2TPT, 2HN, 2TRB, TU
HANNA, J.  SONG OF THE REDWOOD TREE.  2TPT, 2HN, 2TRB, TIMP  D16
HARTLEY, W.S.  CONCERTO.  SOLO TU, PERC(6)                   G68
HEISINGER.  MARCH FOR TIMPANI & BRASS.  2TPT, 2TRB, BTRB, TIMP  C11
HELDENBERG, A.  SEPTET, OP. 6.  4TPT, TRB, EU, TU            A96
HERSCHMANN.  MEDITATIONS FOR BRASS.  4TPT, 3TRB              C03
HUBER, K.  2 SAETZE.  2TPT, 2HN, 2TRB, TU                    F31
KETELBY, A.W.  CORONATION FANFARE                           A82
    4TPT, 2TPT(2TRB), PERC, (OPT HNS & BTRB)
KETELEY, A.W.  FANFARE FOR A CEREMONIAL                     A82
    2TPT(2CL), 2TPT, 2TRB(2HN), TRB, PERC
KETELBY, A.W.  FANFARE FOR A NAVAL OCCASION, #1             A82
    3TPT, 3TRB, PERC
KETELBY, A.W.  FANFARE FOR A NAVAL OCCASION, #2             A82
    3TPT, 3TRB, PERC
KING, R.D.  PRELUDE & FUGUE.  2TPT, 2HN(TRB), 2TRB, TRB-TU  D16
KURZ, S.  SONATINE FUR SIEBEN BLECHBLASER, OP. 18           C75
    2TPT, 2HN, 2TRB, TU
LASSUS, R.D.  PROVIDEBAM DONINUM                            D16
    4TPT, HN(TPT, TRB), TRB(HN), EU-TU
LESCHETITZKI, T.H.  ZUM FEIERABEND MUSIK.  INST ?           E03
LUENING, O.  ENTRANCE & EXIT MUSIC.  3TPT, 3TRB, CYM        E65
LYBBERT, D.  PRAELUDIUM.  3TPT, 3TRB, PERC                  E65
MARX.  TURMMUSIK.  3TPT, 3TRB, TIMP                         A51
MENDELSSOHN, F.-SHINER.  SCHERZO.  3TPT, HN, TRB, EU, TU    D14
MEYER.  HYMNE A L'AURORE.  2TPT, 2HN, 2TRB, TU, OPT TIMP    D36
MONTEVERDI, C.-GREER.  3 SINFONIAS FROM ORFEO               C05
    2TPT, 5TRB, ORG
MOURET-THILDE.  SYMPHONIES DE FANFARES.  3TPT, 3TRB, TU     A71
MUCZYNSKI, R.  ALLEGRO DECISO, OP. 4                        F78
    2TPT, 2HN, TRB, TU, TIMP
NELHYBEL, V.  NUMISMATA.  2TPT, 2HN, 2TRB, TU               C40
NESTICO, S. (ARR).  CHRISTMAS; THE JOY AND THE SPIRIT       D14
    2TPT, HN, 2TRB, EU, TU
PEDERSON, T.  ALL THE LITTLE GIRLS.  6TRB, TU(TRB)          M96
PEDERSON, T.  BOSCO ROSCO.  6TRB, TU(TRB)                   M96
PEDERSON, T.  FARM GIRL.  6TRB, TU(TRB)                     M96
```

PEDERSON, T. I'VE BEEN WORKING ON THE TROMBONE   M96
 6TRB, TU(TRB)
PEDERSON, T. MEXICAN MONDAY. 6TRB, TU(TRE)   M96
PEDERSON, T. SHE HAS GONE. 6TRB, TU(TRB)   M96
PILSS, K. 4 FANFAREN. 3TPT, 3TRB, TU   C60
PURCELL, H.-THILDE. TRUMPET TUNE. 3TPT, 3TRB, TU   A71
PURCELL, H.-THILDE. TRUMPET VOLUNTARY. 3TPT, 3TRB, TU   A71
REITEP, A. MUSIK FUR SOLOTROMPETE. TPT, 3HN, 2EU, TU   B73
RIVIER. BRILLANCES. 2TPT, 2HN, 2TRB, TU   F87
RUBENSTEIN, A.-SPENCER. KAMENNOI OSTROW   A62
 2TPT, HN, TRB, EU, TU, PERC
RUGGLES, C. ANGELS (MUTED BRASS). 4TPT, 3TRB   A15
SACCO, P. INTRODUCTION & LAMENT. 2TPT, 2HN, 2TRB, TU   G21
SCHEUREP, R. SCHERZO FOR BRASS & TIMPANI   E77
 2TPT, 2HN, 2TRB, TIMP
SCHILLING. MUSICA FESTIVA. 3TPT, 3TRB, TIMP   A89
SCHUBERT, F.P.-KING. EINE KLEINE TRAUERMUSIK   D16
 2TPT, 2HN, 2TRB, EU-TU
SCHUMANN, G. BLASERMUSIK I.. 4TPT, 3TRB   F53
SEEBOTH, M. SUITE FUR SIEBEN BLASINSTRUMENTE. 4TPT, 3TRB   C60
SHOSTAKOVITCH, D.D.-BRAZINSKI. SHOSTAKOVITCH SUITE   D71
 2TPT, HN, TRB, EU, TU, BTRB
SPINO. SQUARE DANCE. 2TPT, 2HN, 2TRB, TU   N59
SPURGIN. 4 CEREMONIAL FANFARES. 4TPT, 3TRB   A78
TANNER, P. CANGREJO, EL (THE CRAB). 6TRB, PERC   G21
TCHAIKOVSKY, P.I.-TALLMADGE. CAPRICCIO ITALIEN   A62
 2TPT, HN, TRB, EU, TU, MAR
THOMSON, V. FANFARE FOR FRANCE (FR 10 FANFARES...)   A78
 3TPT, 3TRB, PERC
TISNE, A. OZMA. 2TPT, 2HN, 2TRB, PERC   F87
VITALI, G.B.-FITZGERALD. CAPRICCIO. 2TPT, HN, 2TRB, EU, TU   E77
WEBER, B. COLLOQUY. 2TPT, 2HN, TRB, TU, BTRB   E68
WEBER, B. COLLOQUY, OP. 37. 2TPT, 2HN, 2TRB, TU   A13
WERLE, F.C. VARIATIONS & FUGUE. 3TPT, 2TRB, TU, BTRB   F03
WILSON, G. SONAT HARMONIQUE. 3TPT, 3TRB, TU   B35
WINTER, P. FESTFANFARE. 3TPT, 3TRB, TU, (OPT TIMP)   E65
WUENSCH. MUSIC FOR SEVEN BRASS. 3TPT, 3TRB, TU   A43

7 PARTS: HORN-WOODWIND

BACH, K.P.E.-SIMON. 6 MARCHES   D63
 2HN, 2OB, 2CL, BSN, (OPT PERC)
BACH, K.P.E.-JANETZKY. 6 SONATAS. 2HN, 2FL, 2CL, BSN   E14
BACH, K.P.E.-LORENZ. 6 SONATE PER SETTE STRUMENTI A FIATI   E98
 2HN, 2FL, 2CL, BSN
BUSCH, C. OZARK REVERIE, AN. 2HN, FL, OB, 2CL, BSN   C13
DRIESSLER. APHORISMEN FUR 7 BLASER, OP. 7A   A51
 HN, FL, OB, CL, BSN, EH, BCL
FROMMEL, G. BLASER-SUITE OP. 18. 2HN, FL, OB, 2CL, CBSN   E02
INDY, P.M.V.D'. CHANSONS ET DANSES, OP. 50   B81
 HN, FL, CB, 2CL, 2BSN
MOUQUET, J. SUITE (ADAGIO, AUBADE, SCHERZO)   D41
 HN, FL, OB, 2CL, 2BSN
PAYZIELLE, D. DIVERTISSEMENT FOR A SEPTET OF WIND INST.   E19
 2HN, 2FL, 2CL, BSN
PIERNE, G. PRELUDIO & FUGHETTA, OP. 40/1   C91
 HN, 2FL, CB, CL, 2BSN
PIERNE, G. PRELUDIO ET FUGHETTA, OP. 40, NO. 1   C55
 HN, 2FL, OB, CL, 2BSN

RHENE¬BATON. AUBADE POUR SEPTUOR D'INSTRUMENTS A VENT, OP. 53   B81
   HN, FL, OB, 2CL, 2BSN
ROSETTI, F.A. PARTHIA #3, D-DUR.   2HN, 2OB, 2CL, BSN   D21
ROSETTI, F.A. 3 PARTHIEN FUR BLASINSTRUMENTE. INST?   A83

7 PARTS: BRASS-WOODWIND

BOZZA, E. 4 MOUVEMENTS. TPT, HN, TRB, FL, OB, CL, BSN   D36
CORELLI, A.-KING. CONCERTO GROSSO, OP. 6/11   D16
   2TPT(2OB), 2TPT, HN(TRB), SOLO EU(BSN), EU-TU
GABRIELI, A.-SHUMAN. RICERCARE DEL 12 TONC   F59
   3TPT, 2TRE, TU, CL
HINDEMITH, P. SEPTET. TPT, HN, FL, OB, CL, BSN, BCL   F31
PABLO, L. DE. CORAL, OP. 2. TPT, HN, TRB, FL, OB, CL, BSN   D88
SYLVIUS. SEPTET FOR WINDS. TPT, HN, TRB, FL, OB, CL, BSN   N95
WEISLING. POON LIM-A NIGHT ON THE WAVES   N29
   HN, TRB, TU, 2FL, BSN, BCL
WEISLING, R. POON LIM...A NIGHT UPON THE WAVES   N29
   HN, BTRB, TU, 2FL, BCL, BSN

7 PARTS: WINDS-KEYBOARD

AUSTIN, L. BROKEN CONSORT, A   D86
   TPT, HN, FL, CL, JAZZ DR, PF, JDB
BALLOU, E.W. BRASS SEXTETTE WITH PIANOFORTE. INST ?   E68
BERRY, W. DIVERTIMENTO FOR WIND QUINTET, PIANO & PERC.   B92
   INST ?
COSCIA, S. SEPTET. TPT, HN, TRB, FL, OB, CL, BSN   N45
JANACEK, L. CAPRICCIO FUR KLAV (LEFT HAND)   A51
   2TPT, 3TRB, TU, PF
JANACEK, L. CONCERTINO. HN, CL, BSN, PF, 2VN, VA   C91
MARTINU, B. RONDI. TPT, OB, CL, BSN, PF, 2VN   A51
MASELLI, G. DIVERTIMENTO. TPT, TRB, FL, OB, PF, VN, DB   G41
MOSCHELES, F. SEPTET, OP. 88. HN, CL, PF, VN, VA, VC, DB   E14
NESSLER, R. MOTIONEN. TPT, CL, BSN, PERC, PF, VN, VC   D88
NONO, L. POLIFONICA-MONODIA-RITMICA   F31
   HN, FL, CL, PERC, PF, BCL, ASAX
OVERTON, H. FANTASY. 2TPT, HN, TRB, TU, PERC, PF   E68
PIJPER, W. SEPTET. HN, FL, OB, CL, BSN, FF, DB   B74
PURCELL, H. SONATA FOR TRUMPET & STRINGS   D16
   TPT, 2VN, VA, VC, DB, BC
RIOTTE, J.P. SEPTET. HN, CL, BSN, PF, VN, VA, VC   E14
SAINT¬SAENS, C. SEPTET, OP. 65. TPT, PF, 2VN, VA, VC, DB   C91
SPOHR, L. SEPTET, OP. 147. HN, FL, CL, BSN, PF, VN, VC   E14
VAN DER VELDEN, R. CONCERTINO. 2TPT, HN, TRB, TU, 2PF   B12
WALKER, D. HIROSHIMA EPITAPH. 2TPT, HN, TRB, TU, PF, VIB   D94

7 PARTS: WIND(S)-STRING(S)

```
BAAREN, K.V.  SETTETTO.  HN, FL, OB, CL, BSN, VN, DB                 B74
BEETHOVEN, L.V.  SEPTEO IN E-FLAT, OP. 20                            C91
    HN, CL, BSN, VN, VA, VC, DB
BEETHOVEN, L.V.  SEPTET IN E-FLAT, OP.20                             E65
    HN, CL, BSN, VN, VA, VC, DB
BEETHOVEN, L.V.  SEPTET IN E-FLAT, OP.20                             E98
    HN, CL, BSN, VN, VA, VC, DB
BEETHOVEN, L.V.-HELLMESBERGER.  SEPTET IN E-FLAT, OP.20              F97
    HN, CL, BSN, VN, VA, VC, DB
BEETHOVEN, L.V.  SEPTETO, OP. 20.  HN, CL, BSN, VN, VA, VC, DB       C03
BERWALD, F.A.  STOR SEPTETT.  HN, CL, BSN, VN, VA, VC, DB            C39
BIBER, H.I.F.  SONATA A 6 FOR SOLO TRUMPET                          F23
    TPT, 2VN, VA, VC, DB, BC
BIBER, H.I.F.-JANETZKY.  SONATA A 6.  TPT, 2VN, VA, VC, DB, BC       E14
BJELIK.  SEPTETT.  TPT, 2HN, TRB, 2VC, DB                           B73
BOCCHERINI, L.  SERENADE.  2HN, 2OB, 2VN, DB                        C03
BORTZ, D.  KAMMARMUSIK FOR NIO SPELARE                              B90
    TPT, TRB, FL, CL/BCL,  PERC, VN, VC
CAGE, J.  6 SHORT INVENTIONS.  TPT, CL, VN, 2VA, VC, AFL             E65
DEDRICK, A.  INSPIRATION.  2TPT, 2HN, TRB, CL, VC                    D14
DODGE, C.  FOLIA.  TU, CL, VN, VA, PIC, EH, TIMP                     E68
HADDAD, D.  T-BONE PARTY.  4TRB, PERC, PF, DB                        F43
HANDEL, G.F.  MARCHES.  2TPT, 2VA, 2VC                               D74
HAYDN, J.-LANDON.  CASSATIO IN D-DUR, H. DEEST.                      B73
    4HN, VN, VA, DB
HAYDN, J.-JANETZKY.  DIVERTIMENTO IN D, H.II:8                       C59
    2HN, 2FL, 2VN, VC
HAYDN, J.  HARFEN-SEPTETT, OP. 7.  HN, CL, BSN, VN, VA, VC, HP       C59
HUMMEL, J.N.  MILITARY SEPTET, OP. 114                               E14
    TPT, FL, CL, PF, VN, VC, DB
HUMMEL, J.N.  SEPTETT MILITAIRE, OP. 114                             D46
    TPT, FL, CL, PF, VN, VC, DB
JANACEK, L.  CONCERTINO FOR PIANO & 6 INSTS.                         A33
    HN, CL, BSN, PF, 2VN, VA
JANACEK, L.  CONCERTINO.  HN, CL, BSN, PF, 2VN, VA                   A51
JANACEK, L.  CONCERTINO.  HN, CL, BSN, PF, 2VN, VA                   C91
KOETSIER, J.  SEPTETT, OP. 4.  HN, BSN, PF, VN, VA, VC, DB           B74
KOPER, K.H.  MUSIK FUR 6 BLASINSTRUMENTE U. KONTRABASS              D88
    TPT, HN, TRB, FL, CL, DB, ASAX
KREUTZER, K.  GRAND SEPTUOR, OP. 62                                  B73
    HN, CL, BSN, VN, VA, VC, DB
KREUTZER, K.  SEPTET, OP. 62.  HN, CL, BSN, VN, VA, VC, DB           E14
LAYTON, B.J.  DIVERTIMENTO, OP. 6                                    F23
    TRB, CL, BSN, PERC, VN, VC, HPCD
LECOMBE, P.  SERENADE, OP. 47.  HN, FL, OB, 2VN, VA, VC              C55
MACERO.  ONE-THREE QUARTERS.  TRB, TU, 2PF, VN, VC, PIC              E65
MARTINU, B.  RONDI FOR 7 INSTRUMENTS                                A33
    TPT, OB, CL, BSN, PF, 2VN
MARTINU, B.  RONDI.  TPT, OB, CL, BSN, PF, 2VN                       A51
MASELLI, G.  DIVERTIMENTO FOR HARPSICHORD, WINDS & STRINGS          G41
    TPT, TRB, FL, OB, VN, DB, HPCD(PA)
MOSCHELES, F.  SEPTET, OP. 88.  HN, CL, PF, VN, VA, VC, DB           E14
MOTTE, D. DE LA.  SEPTETT.  TPT, TRB, CL, BSN, PERC, VN, DB          A51
MOZART, W.A.-GERBER.  DIVERTIMENTO #11 IN D, K. 251                  C03
    2HN, OB, 2VN, VA, VC
```

```
NESSLER, R.  MOTIONEN.  TPT, CL, BSN, PERC, PF, VN, VC              D88
NEUKOMM, S.R.V.  SEPTET.  TPT, HN, FL, OB, CL, BSN, DB              D55
PURCELL, H.  SONATA FOR TPT & STGS.  TPT, 2VN, VA, VC, DB, BC       D16
RIOTTE, J.P.  SEPTET.  HN, CL, BSN, PF, VN, VA, VC                  E14
SAINT¬SAENS, C.  SEPTET, OP. 65.  TPT, PF, 2VN, VA, VC, DB          C91
SAINT¬SAENS, C.  SEPTUOR POUR TROMPETTE, OP. 65                     B81
     TPT, PF, 2VN, VA, VC, DB
SCHAT, P.  SEPTET.  HN, FL, OB, PERC, PF, VC, BCL                   B74
SPOHR, L.  SEPTET, OP. 147.  HN, FL, CL, BSN, PF, VN, VC            E14
SPOHR, L.  SEPTETT, OP. 147.  HN, FL, CL, BSN, PF, VN, VC           E65
STOUT, A.  4 ANTIPHONIES.  TRB, FL, PERC, CRG, VN, VA, ASAX         E68
STRAVINSKY, I.  L'HISTOIRE DU SOLDAT                                D08
     TPT, TRB, CL, BSN, PERC, VN, DB
STRAVINSKY, I.  SEPTET.  HN, CL, BSN, PF, VN, VA, VC                A78
SYDEMAN, W.  CONCERTO DA CAMERA.  2TPT, TRB, CL, VN, DB, PERC       A38
TANENBAUM, E.  CONSORT.  HN, FL, PERC, VC, DB, GTR, ASAX            B36
TIESSEN, H.  SEPTETT G-DUR, OP. 20 (AMSEL-SEPTETT                   E99
     HN, FL, CL, BSN, 2VN, VA, VC
VEJVANOVSKY, P.J.  SONATA VENATORIA.  2TPT, 2VN, VA, VC, BC         F67
WINTER, P. VON.  SEPTET.  2HN, FL, CL, VN, VA, VC                   E14
WITT, F.  SEPTET.  HN, CL, BSN, VN, 2VA, VC                         E14
YUN, I.  MUSIK FUR 7 INSTRUMENTE.  HN, FL, OB, CL, BSN, VN, VC      A83
```

7 PARTS: BRASS-MISCELLANEOUS

```
AVIDOM, M.  ENIGMA.  HN, FL, OB, CL, BSN, PERC, PF                  C93
BIBER, H.I.F.  SONATA A 6.  TPT, 2VN, 2VA, VC, BC                   E14
DEDRICK, A.  INSPIRATION.  2TPT, 2HN, CL, VC, BTRB                  D14
HUMMEL, J.N.  MILITARY SEPTET, OP. 114                             E14
     TPT, FL, CL, PF, VN, VC, DB
HUMMEL, J.N.  SEPTET, OP. 74.  HN, FL, OB, PF, VA, VC, DB           E65
KAYN, R.  KAMMERKONZERT.  HN, TRB, FL, OB, CL, BSN, PERC            F50
MOZART, W.A.-KAHN.  DIVERTIMENTO # 5.  3TPT, TRB, 2CL, TIMP         D63
MOZART, W.A.-KAHN.  DIVERTIMENTO # 6.  3TPT, TRB, 2CL, TIMP         D63
THORNE.  SIMULTANEITIES.  2TPT, HN, 2TRB, GTR, PERC                 C40
```

EIGHT-PART MUSIC

8 EQUAL BRASS INSTRUMENTS

BABAN, G.-REYNOLDS. VOCE MEA AD DOMINUM. 8HN	C78
BACH, J.S.-HUNSBERGER. PASSACAGLIA IN C MINOR, S. 582	B98
6TRB, 2BTRB	
BACH, J.S.-SHAW. PRELUDE & FUGUE IN A MINCR. 8HN	C78
CHASE, A.H. RONDO. 8TRB	D16
CHASE, A.H. SONATA. 8TRB	G78
DI LASSO, O.-FATCH. ECHO SONG. 8HN	G78
HANDEL, G.F.-SMITH. MAGNUM MYSTERIUM, A. 8TRB	D14
HARRIS, A. THEME AND VARIATIONS. 8HN	D16
HARRIS, A. VARIATIONS. 8HN	D16
HARRIS, A.(ARR). 7EDLEY OF CHRISTMAS SONGS, A. 8HN	P49
HARTLEY, W.S. CANZONA. 8TRB	B98
MASSAINO, T. CANZON. 8TRB	E14
MASSAINO, T. CANZONA. 8TRB	E65
MASSAINO, T.-SILLIMAN. CANZONA. 7TRB, BTRB(TU), (OPT ORG)	B98
MAYER, R. FESTMUSIK. 8HN	P49
MC GOVERN, M. OCTIPHONY. 8HN	P49
MENDELSSOHN, F.-OSTRANDER. HOLY IS GOD THE LORD. 8 OR 12 TRB	B98
MEULEMANS, A. BRUGGE-SUITE. 8TPT	B12
OTT, J. SUITE. 8TRB	A65
PALESTRINA, G.P. ECCE VENIET DIES ILLA. 8TRB	D16
PEDERSON, T. ORATORS, THE. 8TRB	M93
REYNOLDS, V. CANTO #1. 8HN	F60
REYNOLDS, V. CANTO #2. 8HN	F60
REYNOLDS, V. CANTO #3. 8HN	F60
REYNOLDS, V. CANTO #4. 8HN	F60
REYNOLDS, V. FANFARES 1969. 8TPT	A43
SHAW. ANDANTE & ALLEGRO. 8HN	C78
VILLA¬LOBOS, H.-SMITH. PRELUDIO (BACHIANAS BRAZILEIRAS #1)	A38
8TRB	
WAGNER, I.L. (ARR). CHRISTMAS CAROLS. 8TRB (OPT HN, EU, TU)	A02
WESSELL, M. LENTO AND ALLEGRO. 8HN	P49

8 MIXED BRASS (BRASS-PERC)

ADAMS, S. HOLY CITY. 2TPT, 2HN, 2TRB, EU, TU	A91
ALTENBURG, J.E.-KING. CONCERTO FOR CLARINI & TIMP	D16
5TPT, 2TPT(2HN), TIMP	
BACH, J.S. SUITE DE DANSES. 4TPT, 4TRB	A71
BANCHIERI, A.-CRABTREE. BATTAGLIA, LA	N47
3TPT, 3TRB, TPT(HN), TRB(HN)	
BANCHIERI, A.-CRABTREE. ORGANISTA BELLA "IN ECHO", LA	N38
4TPT, TRB, 2TRB(2HN), TRB(TU)	
BARTOLINI, O. CANZONA 30. 4TPT, 4TRB	E14
BENJAMIN & DUNCAN. 6 CEREMONIAL FANFARES. 5TPT, 3TRB	A78
BENJAMIN, A. FANFARE #2. INST ?	A78
BERGER, A. CANZONA FOR EIGHT VOICES. 4TPT, HN, 2TRB(2TU), EU	D82
BERNARDO-VOLKMANN. BENEDIXISTI. 2TPT, 2HN, 2TRB, EU, TU	B40
BLISS, A. 6 BRILLIANT FANFARES. 5TPT, 3TRB	A78
BLISS, A. ROYAL FANFARES. 3TPT, 3TRB, TU, PERC	E14
BONELLI, A.-KING. TOCCATA "ATHALANTA" (IL PRIMO LIBRO, 1602)	D16
2TPT, 2HN(2TPT), 2TRB(2HN), 2EU-2TU	

```
BOYD, C.N.   4 PIECES FOR BRASS CHOIR.  2TPT, 2HN, 3TRB, TU          G31
BRADLEY, W.  HONEYSUCKLE & CLOVER.  4TPT, 2TRB, TU, BTRB             E30
BRAHMS, J.-TEUBER.   FESTIVE & COMMEMORATIVE MUSIC                   F43
   3TPT, 2HN, 2TRB, TRB(TU)
BRAMIERE-WINTER.  CANZON "LA FOCCARA".  4TPT, 4TRB                   E65
BRESGEN, C.  BLAESERMUSIK.  4TPT, 3TRB, PERC                         G06
BRINGS, A.  CANZONE                                                 G66
BRUGK, H.M.  SUITE FUR 7 BLECHBLASER UND PAUKEN                      C60
   3TPT, 3TRB, TU, PERC
BURKHARD, W.  2 CHORALPARTITEN, OP.75.  3TPT, 2HN, 2TRB, TU          A51
BUXTEHUDE, D.  FANFARE AND CHORUS (IHR LIEBEN CHRISTEN)              D16
   4TPT, HN(TPT), HN(TRB), TRB, TRB-TU
BUXTEHUDE, D.-KING.  FANFARE AND CHORUS                              D16
   4TPT, HN(TRB), TRB, EU(TRB), TU, HN(TPT)
CABUS, P.N.  SUITE VOOR KOPERS.  4TPT, 3TRB, TU                      D67
CHILESE, B.  CANZONAS 31. 32.  4TPT, 4TRB                            E14
CLARKE, J.  TRUMPET VOLUNTARY                                        D58
   3TPT, HN(TRB), TPT(HN), 2HN(2TRB, 2EU, 2TU), BTRB(TU)
COLGRASS, M.  CONCERTINO FOR TIMPANI.  3TPT, 3TRB, TU, TIMP          E08
COWELL, H.  RONDO.  3TPT, 2HN, 3TRB                                  E65
DE LONE P.  INTRODUCTION & CAPRICCIO                                 F43
   2TPT, 2HN, 2TRB, TU, PERC, TIMP
DESPREZ, F.  MARCHE TRIOMPHALE.  4TPT, 4TRB, (OPT PERC)              D67
DUBOIS, P.M.  3 PRELUDES IN FANFARE                                  B92
   2TPT, 2HN, 2TRB, TU, (OPT TIMP)
DUBOIS, P.M.  3 PRELUDES IN FANFARE                                  D36
   2TPT, 2HN, 2TRB, TU, PERC
DUNCAN, T. & BENJAMIN.  6 CEREMONIAL FANFARES.  5TPT, 3TRB           A78
ELGAR, E.W.  THEME FR POMP & CIRCUMSTANCE #1                         A78
   4TPT, 3TRB, BTRB
FRANK.  CONTRASTS.  3TPT, 2HN, 2TRB, TU                              A84
FRESCOBALDI, G.  CANZONA 29.  4TPT, 4TRB                             E14
FRESCOBALDI, G.-INGEIFIELD.  SUITE FROM FIORI MUSICALI               N74
   2TPT, HN(TPT), HN(TRB), 2TRB, EU, TU
GABRIELI, A.-CRABTREE.  ALLA BATTAGLIA                               N47
   2TPT, HN(TPT), TRB, TPT(HN), TRB(HN), TRB(EU), TRB(TU)
GABRIELI, A.  CANZONA  NO. 27.  4TPT, 4TRB                           E14
GABRIELI, A.  CANZONA #28.  4TPT, 4TRB                               E14
GABRIELI, G.  ANTIPHONY #2.  2TPT, 2HN, 2TRB, BTRB, EU              E77
GABRIELI, G.-GHEDINI.  CANSON DUODECIMI TONI A 8                     E98
   4TPT, 2TRB, 2ATRB
GABRIELI, G.  CANZON DUO DECIMI TONI A 8.  4TPT, 4TRB                E14
GABRIELI, G.-BLOCK.  CANZON DUODECIMI TONI A8.  4TPT, 4TRB           E14
GABRIELI, G.-THOMAS.  CANZON NO. 8.  3TPT, 5TRB                      E14
GABRIELI, G.-THOMAS.  CANZON NO. 9.  3TPT, HN(TRB), 4TRB             E14
GABRIELI, G.-THOMAS.  CANZON NO.10.  4TPT, 2HN(2TRB), 2TRB           E14
GABRIELI, G.-THOMAS.  CANZON NO.11.  4TPT, 4TRB                      E14
GABRIELI, G.-THOMAS.  CANZON NO.12.  2TPT, 2HN(2TRB), 4TRB           E14
GABRIELI, G.-THOMAS.  CANZON NO.13.  4TPT, 2HN(2TRB), 2TRB           E14
GABRIELI, G.  CANZON NONI TONI A 8.  4TPT, 4TRB                      E14
GABRIELI, G.  CANZON NONI TONI.  4TPT, 2HN(2TRB), 2TRB-2TU           D16
GABRIELI, G.  CANZON PRIMI TONI A 8.  4TPT, 4TRB                     E14
GABRIELI, G.-KING.  CANZON PRIMI TONI A 8                            D16
   2TPT, 2TPT(2HN), 2TRB(2HN), 2TRB
GABRIELI, G.-KING.  CANZON SEPTIMI TONI #2 (SACRAE SYMPH, 1597)      D16
   0
   2TPT, 2TPT(2HN), 2TRB(2HN), 2TRB
GABRIELI, G.  CANZON SEPTIMI TONI A 8, NO. 1.  4TPT, 4TRB            E14
GABRIELI, G.  CANZON SEPTIMI TONI A 8, NO. 2.  4TPT, 4TRB            E14
GABRIELI, G.-GHEDINI.  CANZON SEPTIMI TONI A 8                       E98
   4TPT, TRB, ATRB, 2BTRB
GABRIELI, G.-KING.  CANZON SEPTIMI TONI NO. 1                        D16
   2TPT, 2TRB, 2TPT(2HN), 2TRB(2HN)
```

```
GABRIELI, G.  CANZONA #2.  INST ?                                       E65
GABRIELI, G.  CANZONI 27, 28.  4TPT, 2TRB(2HN), 2TRB                    E14
GABRIELI, G.-WOLTERS.  JUBILATE DEO.  4TPT, 4TRB                        D98
GABRIELI, G.-SMITH.  LIETO GODEA.  2TPT, 2HN(2TPT), 4TRB                B98
GABRIELI, G.-DRAPER.  O MAGNUM MYSTERIUM.  3TPT, 3HN, 2TRB              E51
GABRIELI, G.-SMITH.  SONATA NO. 13.  4TPT, 2HN(2TRB), 2TRB              B98
GABRIELI, G.-WINTER.  SONATA NR. XIII.  4TPT, 4TRB                      E65
GABRIELI, G.-STEIN.  SONATA PIAN'E FORTE (SACRAE SYMPH, 1597)           E65
    2TPT, 2HN, 3TRB, TRB(TU)
GABRIELI, G.  SONATA PIAN'E FORTE A 8.  2TPT, 6TRB                      E14
GABRIELI, G.-GHEDINI.  SONATA PIAN'E FORTE A 8                          E98
    TPT, 3TRB, VA, 2ATRB, BTRB
GABRIELI, G.-KING.  SONATA PIAN'E FORTE                                 D16
    TPT, TPT(HN), HN(TRB), TRB, TRB(HN, VA), 2TRB(2HN), EU-TU
GABRIELI, G.-MILLER.  SONATA PIAN'E FORTE                               E51
    2TPT, 2HN, 3TRB, TU
GABRIELI, G.-WINTER.  SONATA XIII.  4TPT, 4TRB                          E65
GALLUS, J.  REPLETI SUNT.  4TPT, 3TRB, TU                               B44
GOUNOD, C.F.  MARCHE PONTIFICALE.  2TPT, 2HN, 2TRB, EU, TU              A91
GRAINGER, P.-BAINUM.  AUSTRALIAN UP-COUNTRY TUNE                        F23
    2TPT, 2HN, 2TRB, EU, TU
GRILLO, G.B.  CANZONA #2.  3TPT, 4TRB, TU                               E65
GRILLO, G.B.-THOMAS.  CANZONA QUARTA.  4TPT, 2HN(2TRB), 2TRB            E14
GRILLO, G.B.-WINTER.  CANZONE I.  3TPT, 4TRB, TU                        E65
GUAMI, G.  CANZONAS #25, 26.  4TPT, 4TRB                                E14
GUAMI, G.-CRABTREE.  LUCHESINA, LA.  2TPT, 2HN(2TPT), 4TRB              F60
GUSSAGO-WINTER.  PORCELLAGA, LA.  3TPT, 5TRB                            E65
HADDAD, D.  KNOXVILLE 1974.  5EU, 3TU                                   G66
HANDEL, G.F.-SMITH.  O MAGNUM MYSTERIUM.  4TRB, 2EU, 2TU                D14
HASSLER.  SUITE.  4TPT, 2HN, 2TRB, OPT TU                               E77
HORVIT.  ANTIQUE SUITE.  2TPT, 2HN, 2TRB, EU, TU                        F43
HOWARTH.  2 PROCESSIONAL FANFARES                                       B23
    3TPT, TPT(HN), TRB(HN), 3TRB
JACOB, G.P.S.  INTERLUDES (MUSIC FOR A FESTIVAL)                        A78
    4TPT, 3TRB, TIMP
JAGER.  CHORALE & FUGUE.  2TPT, 2HN, 2TRB, EU, TU                       D14
KAUDER, H.  LITTLE SUITE.  2TPT, 2HN, 3TRB, TU                          F60
LAPPI, G.  CANZONA 26.  4TPT, 4TRB                                      E14
LAPPI, G.  CANZONAS #11, 12.  4TPT, 4TRB                                E14
LAPPI, P.  NEGRONA, LA.  5TPT, 3TRB                                     E65
LASSUS, R.D.  ECHO CANZONA.  4TPT, 4TRB                                 P19
LEBOW, L.S.  SUITE FOR BRASS.  3TPT, HN, 3TRB, TU                       F72
LESEMANN.  CAOINE.  2TPT, 2HN, 3TRB, TU                                 G68
LEWIS, R.H.  TANGENTS.  4TPT, 2HN, 2TRB                                 E77
LOCKE, M.-BAINES.  MUSIC FOR HIS MAJESTY'S SACKBUTS & CORNETTS          E51
    INST ?
MASSAINO, T.-KING.  CANZON.  6TRB, TRB(HN), TRB(TU)                     D16
MASSAINO, T.  CANZONA 33.  4TPT, 4TRB                                   E14
MASSAINO, T.  CANZONAS 33, 34, 35.  4TPT, 4TRB                          E14
MASSAINO, T.-WINTER.  CANZONE.  4TPT, 3TRB, TRB(TPT)                    E65
MENDELSSOHN, F.-SHINER.  SCHERZO.  3TPT, 2HN, TRB, EU, TU               D14
MEULEMANS, A.  5 OPROEPEN.  3TPT, 3TRB, TU, PERC                        B12
MOENKEMEYER.  2 CANZONAS.  4TPT, 4TRB                                   C60
MOERENHOUT, J.  FANFARES I & II.  3TPT, 3TRB, TU, PERC                  D80
NELSON, P.  CHRISTMAS MUSIC FOR ANTIPHONAL BRASS                        P49
    3TPT, 2HN, 3TRB
OTTO.  CHORALE VARIATIONS.  4TPT, 3TRB, TU                              B32
PALESTRINA, G.P.-WALDECK.  ORATIO HIEREMIAE                             B44
    2TPT, 2HN, 3TRB, TU
PAYNTER, J.P.  FANFARODADE.  4TPT, 3TRB, TU                             D18
PFANNENSTIEL, E.  FEIERLICHE MUSIK #2.  3TPT, 4TRB, BTRB                F31
RASSE, F.  FANFARE.  3TPT, 3TRB, TU, PERC                               B12
```

```
ROGNONI-TAEGGIO, R.  PORTA, LA (CANZONA)                            E65
    2TPT, 2TPT(2TRB), 4TRB
SACCO, P.  STUDY FOR BRASS & PERCUSSION                             G21
    3TPT, 2TRB, EU, TU, PERC
SCHILLING.  CAPRICCIO ARMONICO.  3TPT, 3EU, TU, PERC                N28
SCHUTZ, H.-ANTHONY.  ANTIPHONY #1.  4TPT, 4TRB                      E77
SCHUTZ, H.-HANCOCK.  ANTIPHONY NO. 1.  4EU, 4TU                     N92
SERIL, F.  MUNCHENER PETERSTURMMUSIKEN (4 VOL)                      C60
    3TPT, 3TRB, TU, PERC
SIMPSON, R.W.L.  CANZONA FOR BRASS.  4TPT, 3TRB, TU                 D42
STEWART, R.  DIVERTISSEMENT (OMNIBUS).  2TPT, 2HN, 3TRB, TU         A13
STOUT, A.  PIETA, OP. 7A.  4TPT, 3TRB, TU                           E68
TISNE, A.  OZMA.  2TPT, 2HN, 2TRB, 2PERC                            F87
UBER, D.A.  DOUBLE ROUND.  4TPT, 3TRB, TU                           B85
UBER, D.A.  GETTYSBURG SUITE.  4TPT, 3TRB, TU                       B85
VAN DE VATE, N.  3 SOUND PIECES.  2TPT, 2HN, 2TRB, TU, PERC(6)      P48
VAN VACTOR, L.  BRASS OCTET.  2TPT, 2HN, 2TRB, 2TU                  P44
VIADANA, L.G.D.-THOMAS.  SINFONIA "LA BERGAMASCA"                   E14
    4TPT, 2HN(2TRB), 2TRB
VIADANA, L.G.D.-THOMAS.  SINFONIA "LA PADOVANA"                     E14
    4TPT, 2HN(2TRB), 2TRB
WAGNER, I.L. (ARR).  CHRISTMAS CAROLS.  2HN, 4TRB, EU, TU           A02
WAGNER, R.  MEISTERSINGER: INTRO. TO ACT III                       D16
    2TPT, HN(EU), 3TRB, EU, TU
WALTON, W.T.  QUEEN'S FANFARE, A.  5TPT, 3TRB                       E51
WERLE.  4 SKETCHES.  4TPT, 3TRB, TU                                 A03
WHEAR, P.W.  3 CHORALES.  2TPT, 2HN, 2TRB, EU, TU                   D36
WURZ, R.  TURMMUSIK #1 (INTRADA).  4TPT, 4TRB                       A89
WURZ, R.  TURMMUSIK #2.  4TPT, 4TRB                                 A89
ZILLIG, W.  SERENADE I FUR 8 BLECHBLASER.  2TPT, 3HN, 2TRB, TU      A51
```

8 PARTS: HORN-WOODWIND

```
BEETHOVEN, L.V.-SEDLAK.  FIDELO.  2HN, 2OB, 2CL, 2BSN              E14
BEETHOVEN, L.V.  OCTET FOR WINDS IN E-FLAT, OP.103                 A98
    2HN, 2OB, 2CL, 2BSN
BEETHOVEN, L.V.  OCTET IN E-FLAT, OP.103.  2HN, 2OB, 2CL, 2BSN     A90
BEETHOVEN, L.V.  OCTET, OP.103.  2HN, 2OB, 2CL, 2BSN              C03
BEETHOVEN, L.V.  OCTET, OP.103.  2HN, 2OB, 2CL, 2BSN              E14
BEETHOVEN, L.V.  RONDINO ES-DUR, OP.POSTH                          A90
    2HN, 2OB, 2CL, 2BSN
BEETHOVEN, L.V.  RONDINO IN E-FLAT.  2HN, 2OB, 2CL, 2BSN          C91
BEETHOVEN, L.V.  RONDINO IN E-FLAT                                 D74
    2HN, OB(FL), OB, 2CL, BSN, BSN(BCL)
BEETHOVEN, L.V.  RONDINO IN E-FLAT, OP. POSTH                      C03
    2HN, 2OB, 2CL, 2BSN
BEETHOVEN, L.V.  RONDINO IN MI BEM, OP. POSTH                      E98
    2HN, 2OB, 2CL, 2BSN
BOZZA, E.  OCTANPHONIE.  2HN, 2OB, 2CL, 2BSN                       D36
BRUN, G.  PASSACAILLE.  2HN, 2FL, OB, 2CL, BSN                     D41
FAURE, G.U.  NOCTURNE #1, OP.33/1.  2HN, FL, 2OB, 2CL, BSN         C55
HAYDN, J.-KAHN.  ALLEGRO (OCTET).  2HN, 2OB, 2CL, 2BSN             D63
HAYDN, J.-JANETZKY.  DIVERTIMENTO F-DUR, H. II, 16                 C75
    2HN, 2EHN, 2BSN, 2VN
HAYDN, J.-BOUDREAU.  DIVERTIMENTO NO. 1 (CHORALE ST. ANTONI)       E65
    2HN, 2OB, 3BSN, CNTBSN(DB)
HAYDN, J.  MUSIK F-DUR FUR 8 BLASINSTRUMENTE                       A83
    2HN, 2BL(2OB), 2CL, 2BSN
```

```
HAYDN, J.   OCTET IN F MAJOR.  2HN, 2OB, 2CL, 2BSN              C91
HAYDN, J.-GRUTZMACHER.  OCTET, H.II:F7.  2HN, 2OB, 2CL, 2BSN    D05
HUMMEL, J.N.  CCTET-PARTITA IN E-FLAT.  2HN, 2OB, 2CL, 2BSN     E14
JACOB, G.P.S.  DIVERTIMENTO FOR WIND OCTET                      E14
    2HN, 2OB, 2CL, 2BSN
KRAMAR.  OCTET, OP. 57.  2HN, 2OB, 2CL, 2BSN                    E14
KRAMAR.  OCTET, OP. 67.  2HN, 2OB, 2CL, 2BSN                    E14
KRAMAR.  OCTET, OP. 69.  2HN, 2OB, 2CL, 2BSN                    E14
KRAMAR.  OCTET, OP. 79.  2HN, 2OB, 2CL, 2BSN                    E14
LACHNER, F.  OCTET, OP. 156.  2HN, FL, OB, 2CL, 2BSN            E14
LADERMAN, E.  OCTET FOR WINDS.  2HN, 2OB, 2CL, 2BSN             E51
MILLS, C.  CONCERTO SERENO, OP. 77.  2HN, 2OB, 2CL, 2BSN        A13
MOZART, W.A.-DE WENT, G.   ABDUCTION FROM THE SERAGLIO          A51
    2HN, 2OB, 2BSN, 2EH
MOZART, W.A.-EINSTEIN.  DIVERTIMENTI IN E-FLAT, K.S. 182        E65
    2HN, 2OB, 2CL, 2BSN
MOZART, W.A.  DIVERTIMENTI, E-FLAT, K. 196E                     E14
    2HN, 2OB, 2CL, 2BSN
MOZART, W.A.-EINSTEIN.  DIVERTIMENTO IN E-FLAT, K.196E          E65
    2HN,2OB, 2CL, 2BSN
MOZART, W.A.  DIVERTIMENTO, K. 196.  2HN, 2OB, 2CL, 2BSN        E14
MOZART, W.A.-GEIGLING.  ENTFUHRUNG AUS DEM SERAIL               A51
    2HN, 2OB, 2BSN, 2EH
MOZART, W.A.   HARMONY-COSI FAN TUTTI.  2HN, 2OB, 2CL, 2BSN     E14
MOZART, W.A.   HARMONY-DON GIOVANNI.  2HN, 2OB, 2CL, 2BSN       E14
MOZART, W.A.   HARMONY-FIGARO.  2HN, 2OB, 2CL, 2BSN             E14
MOZART, W.A.   HARMONY-MAGIC FLUTE.  2HN, 2OB, 2CL, 2BSN        E14
MOZART, W.A.   HARMONY-SERAGLIO.  2HN, 2OB, 2CL, 2BSN           E14
MOZART, W.A.   HARMONY-TITUS.  2HN, 2OB, 2CL, 2BSN              E14
MOZART, W.A.-DE WENT.  12 PIECES (DON GIOVANNI)                 A51
    2HN, 2OB, 2BSN, 2FH
MOZART, W.A.   SERENADE #11 IN E-FLAT, K. 375                   A89
    2HN, 2OB, 2CL, 2BSN
MOZART, W.A.   SERENADE #11 IN E-FLAT, K. 375                   A98
    2HN, 2OB, 2CL, 2BSN
MOZART, W.A.   SERENADE #11 IN E-FLAT, K. 375                   C03
    2HN, 2OB, 2CL, 2BSN
MOZART, W.A.   SERENADE #11 IN E-FLAT, K. 375                   E14
    2HN, 2OB, 2CL, 2BSN
MOZART, W.A.   SERENADE #12 IN C MINOR, K. 338                  A89
    2HN, 2OB, 2CL, 2BSN
MOZART, W.A.   SERENADE #12 IN C MINOR, K. 388                  E14
    2HN, 2OB, 2CL, 2BSN
MOZART, W.A.   SERENADE #12, C MINOR, K. 388                    A98
    2HN, 2OB, 2CL, 2BSN
MYSLIVECEK, J.  3 OKTETTE.  2HN, 2OB, 2CL, 2BSN                 A51
PLEYEL, I.J.  OCTET 1.  2HN, 2OB, 2CL, 2BSN                     E14
REINECKE, C.  OCTET, OP. 216.  2HN, FL, OB, 2CL, 2BSN           E14
RIGHINI, V.  OCTET-PARTHIA.  2HN, 2OB, 2CL, 2BSN                E14
SAINT-SAENS, C.-TAFFANEL.  FEUILLET D'ALBUM, OP. 81             B81
    2HN, FL, OB, 2CL, 2BSN
SCHNEIDER, G.A.  HARMONIEMUSIK F-DUR FUR 8 BLASINSTRUMENTE      A83
    2HN, 2FL, 2CL, 2BSN
SCHUBERT, F.P.-KAHN.  MINUET, D. 803.  2HN, 2OB, 2CL, 2BSN      D63
STIEBER, H.  SPIELMUSIK NR. 3.  HN, FL, 2OB, 2CL, 2BSN          C75
```

8 PARTS: BRASS-WOODWIND

```
ANGERER, P.   QUINTA TON FUR BLASER                              F97
   2TPT, HN, TRB, FL, OB, CL, BSN
BORRIS, S.   BLASER-OKTETT, OP. 55                               F53
   TPT, 2HN, FL, OB, CL, BSN, BCL
BRUSSELMANS, M.   PRELUDE ET FUGUE                               F16
   TPT, HN, FL, OB, CL, BSN, EH, BCL
COUPERIN, F.-PETIT.   STEINKERQUE, LA                            A71
   2TPT, HN, TRB, FL, OB, CL, BSN
FELLEGARA, V.   OTTETTO PER STRUMENTI A FIATO                    G41
   2TPT, HN, TRB, FL, OB, CL, BSN
GABRIELI, G.-SHUMAN.   CANZON SEPTINI TONI #1                    F59
   3TPT, 3TRB, TU, CL
GAL, H.   DIVERTIMENTO, OP. 22.   TPT, 2HN, FL, OB, 2CL, BSN     D44
HAYDN, J.   3 ENGLISH MARCHES, H.VIII, 1-3 (OPT DRUMS)           E14
   TPT, 2HN, 2CL, 2BSN, SER(BSN)
HAYDN, J.-LANDON.   MARSCHE.   TPT, 2HN, TU, 2CL, 2BSN           B73
HERMANS, N.   BAGATELLEN.   TPT, 2FL, 2OB, 2CL, BSN              B74
HOMS, J.   OCTET DE VENT.   TPT HN, TRB, TU, FL, OB, CL, BCL     G66
KOHN.   IMPROMPTUS.   2TPT, 2TRB, FL, CL, 2BSN                   C11
LAZAROF.   OCTET.   TPT, HN, TRB, FL, OB, CL, BSN, BCL           A38
LESSARD.   OCTET.   2TPT, 2HN, TRB, FL, CL, BSN                  C40
PASCAL, C.   OCTUOR A INSTRUMENTS A VENT                         B81
   TPT, HN, 2FI, OB, CL, 2BSN
PIERNE, G.   PASTORALE VARIEE, OP. 30                            B81
   TPT, HN, 2FI, OB, CL, 2BSN
PLUISTER, S.   DIVERTIMENTO (MUZIEK VOOR STAATMUZIKANTEN)        B74
   TPT, HN, TRB, 2FL, OB, CL, BSN
SCHAT, P.   OCTET.   2TPT, HN, TRB, FL, OB, CL, BSN              B74
STRAVINSKY, I.   OCTET.   2TPT, 2TRB, FL, CL, 2BSN               G68
```

8 PARTS: WINDS-KEYBOARD

```
DUPONT, J.   OCTUOR.   HN, CL, BSN, PF, 2VN, VA, VC              C55
GREEN, R.   3 PIECES FOR A CONCERT                               A15
   2TPT, TRB, FL, 2CL, PERC, PF
HAMMERSCHMIDT.   MY SOUL, NOW BLESS THY MAKER.   3TPT, 4TRB, BC  B40
HILL, J.(ARR).   LEEDS TRB GET-TOGETHER                          D37
   2TRB, PERC, PF, DB, GUIT
HILL, J. (ARR).   LEEDS TRUMPET GET-TOGETHER (2-4 TPTS)          D37
   2TPT, PERC, PF, DB, GUIT
JANACEK, L.   CAPRICCIO (LEFT-HAND PF, TENOR TU)                 E14
   2TPT, 3TRB, EU, FL(PIC), PF
JANACEK, L.   CAPRICCIO.   2TPT, 3TRB, EU, FI, PF                A33
JUON, P.   OKTETT B-DUR, OP. 27A                                 D46
   HN, OB, CL, BSN, PF, VN, VA, VC
JUON, P.   OKTETT B-DUR, OP. 27A                                 F24
   HN, OB, CL, BSN, PF, VN, VA, VC
KUBIK, G.   DIVERTIMENTO #2                                      B32
   TPT, TRB, 2FL, OB, CL, BSN, PF, VA
LOUIS FERDINAND OF PRUSSIA, PRINCE.   OCTET                      E14
   2HN, CL, PF, 2VA, VC, DB
```

NATANSON, T.   3 PICTURES FOR 7 INST & PERC   A31
    TPT, TRB, OB, BSN, PERC, PF, VC, ASAX
RIES, F.   OCTET, A-FLAT, OP. 128   E14
    HN, CL, BSN, PF, VN, VA, VC, DB
SCHMELZER, J.H.   SONATA A 7.   2TPT, 3TRB, 2CTT(2TPT), BC(ORG)   E14
WHITE.   COMPOSITION.   T, 2HN, 2TRB, 2PERC, PF   2TP
WILLIS, R.   PASSAGGI.   2TPT, HN, TRB, TU, 2PERC, PF   G66
WUORINEN, C.   OCTET.   HN, TRB, OB, CL, PF, VN, VC, DB   D55

8 PARTS: WIND(S)-STRING(S)

BADINGS, H.   OCTET.   HN, CL, BSN, 2VN, VA, VC, DB   B74
BERLIN, D.   OCTET.   HN, TPT, TRB, FL, CL, PERC, VN, DB   P48
BORRIS, S.   OKTETT, OP. 99/4.   HN, CL, BSN, 2VN, VA, VC, DB   F53
DUPONT, J.   OCTUOR.   HN, CL, BSN, PF, 2VN, VA, VC   C55
FRANCHETTI, A.   3 ITALIAN MASQUES.   3TPT, 2TRB, PERC, PF, DB   C33
INDY, P.M.V.D'.   SUITE IN OLDEN STYLE, OP. 24   C91
    TPT, 2FL, BSN, 2VN, VA, VC
JOUBERT, J.   OCTET, OP. 33.   HN, CL, BSN, 2VN, VA, VC, DB   E41
JUON, P.   OKTETT B-DUR, OP. 27A   D46
    HN, OB, CL, BSN, PF, VN, VA, VC
KUBIK, G.   DIVERTIMENTO #2 FOR 8 PLAYERS   B32
    TPT, TRB, 2FL, OB, CL, BSN, PF, VA
KUBIK, G.   DIVERTIMENTO II.   TPT, TRB, FL, OB, CL, BSN, PF, VA   D71
LOUIS FERDINAND OF PRUSSIA, PRINCE.   OCTET   E14
    2HN, CL, PF, 2VA, VC, DB
MIHALOVICI, M.   VARIATIONS.   2TPT, 2TRB, 4STR, (OPT ORCH)   A16
PILSS, K.   OKTETT.   HN, CL, BSN, 2VN, VA, VC, DB   B73
REICHA, A.   OCTET, OP. 96.   HN, OB, CL, BSN, 2VN, VA, VC   E14
REVUELTAS, S.   OCHO POR RADIO   F59
    TPT, CL, BSN, PERC, 2VN, VC, DB
REVUELTAS, S.   TOCCATA (WITHOUT A FUGUE)   F59
    TPT, HN, CL, VN, PIC, EFCL, BCL, TIMP
RIES, F.   OCTET IN A-FLAT, OP. 128   E14
    HN, CL, BSN, PF, VN, VA, VC, DB
SCHUBERT, F.P.   OCTET IN F, OP. 166   C91
    HN, CL, BSN, 2VN, VA, VC, DB
SCHUBERT, F.P.   OCTET IN F, OP. 166, D. 803   C03
    HN, CL, BSN, 2VN, VA, VC, DB
SCHUBERT, F.P.   OCTET, OP. 166, F MAJOR   E65
    HN, CL, BSN, 2VN, VA, VC, DB
SCHUBERT, F.P.   OKTETT F-DUR, OP. 166   A90
    HN, CL, BSN, 2VN, VA, VC, DB
SPOHR, L.   OCTET, OP. 32.   2HN, CL, VN, 2VA, VC, DB   E14
SPOHR, L.-UHLENDORFF.   OKTETT IN E, OP. 32   A51
    2HN, CL, VN, 2VA, VC, DB
SPOHR, L.   OKTETT, OP. 32.   2HN, CL, VN, 2VA, VC, DB   D46
SYDEMAN.   CONCERTO DA CAMERA #3.   2TPT, TRB, CL, 2PERC, VN, DB   A38
TANENBAUM, E.   TRIOS I, II, III   B36
    TPT, HN, TRB, PERC, VN, VA, VC, DB
THARICHEN, W.   OKTETT, OP. 40.   HN, CL, BSN, INST ?   A83
UHL, A.   4 TANZSTUCKE.   HN, CL, BSN, 2VN, VA, VC, DB   B73
VARESE, E.   OCTANDRE.   TPT, HN, TRB, FL, OB, CL, BSN, DB   B32
VEJVANOVSKY, P.J.   SONATA VENATORIA.   2TPT, 2VN, VA, VC, BC   A33
WHISTLER, H.S. & HUMMEL.   ENSEMBLE TIME   F07
    TPT(TSAX), HN, TRB(TU), FL(OB), CL(BCL), PF, VN, ASAX(BARSAX)
WILDER, A.   HORNS O'PLENTY.   4HN, PF(HPCD), DB, TDR, GUIT   D86
WUORINEN, C.   OCTET.   HN, TRB, OB, CL, PF, VN, VC, DB   D55

8 PARTS: BRASS-MISCELLANEOUS

```
CROLEY.  CONCERTO FOR FLUTE & METAL ORCHESTRA                    G83
    4TRB, TU, FL, PERC, PF
FRANCHETTI, A.  3 ITALIAN MASQUES.  3TPT, 2TRB, PERC, PF, DB     C33
GABRIELI, G.-GHEDINI.  SONATA PIAN E FORTE A 8                   E98
    TPT, 3TRB, VA, 2ATRB, BTRB
GERBER, R.  CONCERTINO.  TPT, 2HN, FL, OB, CL, PERC, PF          H03
GRILLO, G.B.-WINTER.  CANZONA 2.  INST ?                         E65
LAPPI, P.-WINTER.  NEGRONA, LA.  INST ?                          E65
MOZART, W.A.  DIVERTIMENTO # 5, K. 187                           A89
    3TPT IN C, 2TPT IN D, 2FL, PERC
MOZART, W.A.  DIVERTIMENTO # 6.  5TPT, 2FL, TIMP(4)              M79
MOZART, W.A.  DIVERTIMENTO # 6, K. 187                           A89
    3TPT IN D, 2TPT IN D, 2FL, PERC
MOZART, W.A.-BLECK.  DIVERTIMENTO #6.  5TPT, 2FL, TIMP          M79
MOZART, W.A.  DIVERTIMENTO C-DUR, K. 188.  5TPT, 2FL, TIMP      A89
MOZART, W.A.  DIVERTIMENTO, K. 188.  5TPT, 2FL(2CL), TIMP       E14
NATANSON, T.  3 PICTURES                                         A31
    TPT, TRB, OB, BSN, PERC, PF, VC, ASAX
ROGNONI-TAEGGIO, G.D.-WINTER.  LA PORTA (CANZONE).  INST ?      E65
STARZER, J.  MUSICA DA CAMERA MOLTO PARTICULARE                E14
    5TPT, 2FL(2CL), TIMP
STERNFELD, R.  RETURN TO ISRAEL.  TPT, HN, TRB, CL, 3PERC, DB   G66
STERNFELD, R.  THOUGHTS OF C & C.  TRB, FL, CL, 4 PERC, BCL     G66
WILLIS, R.  PASSAGGI.  2TPT, HN, TRB, TU, 2PERC, PF             G66
```

NINE-PART MUSIC

9 EQUAL BRASS INSTRUMENTS

WEBER-SHINER. ANDANTE MAESTOSO (EURYANTHE). 9TRB   D14
WEBER, C.M.V.-SHINER. ANDANTE MAESTOSO (EURYANTHE). 9TRB   D14

9 MIXED BRASS (BRASS-PERC)

ADLER, S. PRAELUDIUM. 2TPT, 2HN, 2TRB, EU, TU, TIMP   D16
ARNELL, R. CEREMONIAL & FLOURISH. 3TPT, 3HN, 3TRB   A38
BUCCHI. BATTAGLIA. 6TPT, 2TRB, PERC   B07
CAMPRA, A.-WETZLER. RIGAUDON. 3TPT, 2HN, 3TRB, TU   B40
CANNING, T.S. RONDO FOR PERCUSSION & BRASS   E68
  2TPT, 2HN, 3TRB, TU, PERC
CLERISSE, R. SYMPHONIE POUR LES SOUPIRS DU ROY   E36
  2TPT, HN, 3TRB, EU, TU, PERC
DONATO, A. NONET. 3TPT, 3TRB, 3PERC   P36
DONDEYNE, D. 3 ESQUESSES DE FANFARE. 3TPT, 2HN, 3TRB, TU   F87
DVORAK. LAMENT AND RESPONSE. 2TPT, 2HN, 3TRB, EU, TU   B32
ERB, D. FANFARE. 3TPT, 2HN, 2TRB, TU, PERC   E77
FRANCO, J. FANFARE. 3TPT, 3HN, 3TRB   A13
GORNER, H.G. INTRADA ET HYMNUS, OP. 20. 3TPT, 3HN, 3TRB   C60
HASSLER, L.-OWEN. LAUDATE DOMINUM   D14
  2TPT, 2HN, 3TRB, TU, TRB(EU)
HEUSSENSTAMM, G. 2 FANFARES. 5TPT, 4TRB   G66
HIBBARD, W. VARIATIONS FOR BRASS NONET. 3TPT, 3HN, 3TRB   D86
IRELAND, J.-STEPP. HOLY BOY, THE. 3TPT, 2HN, 2TRB, EU, TU   A78
LACHNER, F.-JANETZKY. NONETT. 2TPT, 4HN, 3TRB   C75
MAILMAN, M. 2 FANFARES, OP. 49. 3TPT, 3HN, 3TRB   F60
MEYEROWITZ, J. SHORT SUITE. 3TPT, 3HN, 2TRB, TU   F03
MOERENHOUT, J. FANFARE I & II. 3TPT, 3TRB, 2TU, PERC   D80
MONTEVERDI, C.-KING. SONATA SOPRA SANCTA MARIA ORA PRO NOBIS D16
  4TPT, 2TRB, EU, EU-TU
MORGAN, F. 2 FANFARES. 3TPT, 2HN, 2TRB, PERC, BTRB   A78
NELHYBEL, V. CHORALE FOR BRASS & PERCUSSION   C40
  3TPT, 3TRB, EU, TU, TIMP, BDR, SDR, CYM
NELHYBEL, V. 3 INTRADAS FOR BRASS CHOIR. 3TPT, 2HN, 3TRB, TU C40
NOWAK, L. FESTIVAL, A PROCESSIONAL   E68
  4TPT, 4TRB, TIMP, BDR, SDR, XYL, CYM, WOOD BLOCK
NYSTEDT, K. PIA MEMORIA   A38
  2TPT, 2HN, 3TRB, EU, TU, (OPT CHIMES)
PARRIS, R. LAMENTATIONS & PRAISES. 3TPT, 2HN, 2TRB, TU, BTRB E65
REITER, A. MUSIK FUR BLASER. 3TPT, 2HN, 2TRB, EU, TU   B73
RIEGGER, W. NCNET, OP. 49. 3TPT, 2HN, 3TRB, TU   A38
ROGER, K.G. SUITE FOR BRASS & KETTLEDRUMS, OP. 62   D90
  4TPT, 4TRB, TIMP
ROGER, K.G. SUITE FOR BRASS CHOIR. 4TPT, 4TRB, PERC   F31
SHELLY, R.W. (ARR). DECK THE HALL. 4TPT, 2HN, TRB, EU, TU   D14
SHULMAN, A. 2 CHORALES. 2TPT, 2HN, 2TRB, 2EU, TU   N93
STEFFEN, W. FESTLICHE FANFARE. 4TPT, 3TRB, TU, BTRB   F53
THARICHEN, W. BLASERMUSIK, OP. 43. 4TPT, 4TRB, TU   A83
THOMSON. ODE TO THE WONDERS OF NATURE. 3TPT, 2HN, 3TRB, PERC F23
WEINBERGER, J. CONCERTO FOR THE TIMPANI   A38
  4TPT, 3TRB, TRB(TU), TIMP

XENAKIS. LINAIA-AGON. 3HN, 3TRB, 3TU   F16
ZAGWIJN, H. CORTEGE (AUFZUGMUSIK)   B74
    5TPT, BACH TPT, 2TRB, TIMP

9 PARTS: HORN-WOODWIND

BEETHOVEN, L.V.-HESS. ADAGIO F-DUR FUR DIE SPIELUHR   A90
    2HN, FL, 2OB, 2CL, 2BSN
BRAUTIGAM, H. KLEINE JAGDMUSIK, OP. 11   A89
    2HN, FL, 2OB, 2CL, 2BSN
BYRD, W.-VINARDI. PAVANA. HN, 2FL, 2OB, 2CL, 2BSN   E98
COLE, H. SERENADE FOR 9 WIND INSTS.   E41
    2HN, FL, CB, OB(CL), 2CL, 2BSN
GOUNOD, C.F. LITTLE SYMPHONY. 2HN, FL, 2CB, 2CL, 2BSN   C91
GOUNOD, C.F. PETITE SYMPHONIE. 2HN, FL, 2OB, 2CL, 2BSN   A71
HOFFMEISTER, F.A.-HESS. SERENADE IN E-FLAT   D21
    2HN, 2OB(2FL), 2CL, 2BSN,DB(CNTBSN)
KROMMER, F.-JANETZKY. NONETT, OP. 79   C75
    2HN, 2OB, 2CL, 2BSN, CNTBSN
OTTEN, L. DIVERTIMENTO #3. 2HN, FL, 2OB, 2CL, 2BSN   B74
SCHRECK, G. NONETT (DIVERTIMENTO), OP. 40   A90
    2HN, 2FL, OB, 2CL, 2BSN

9 PARTS: BRASS-WOODWIND

FLOWERS, G. MINIATURE SUITE. 2TPT, 2TRB, FL, OB, 2CL, BSN   E41
FROHLICH, F.T.-SCHERCHEN. WALZER FUR NEUN BLASER   F31
    2HN, TRB, FL, OB, 2CL, 2BSN
GOOSSENS, E. FANTASY FOR 9 WIND INSTS., OP. 40   D36
    TPT, 2HN, FL, OB, 2CL, 2BSN
HAYDN, J.-WEBER. DIVERTIMENTO MIT CHORAL ST. ANTONI   F82
    2HN, 2OB, 3BSN, SER(CNTBSN)
HOVHANESS, A.S. MOUNTAINS & RIVERS WITHOUT END   E65
    TPT, TRB, FL, OB, CL, 3PERC, HP
HOVHANESS, A.S. TOWER MUSIC, OP. 129   A98
    TPT, 2HN, TRB, TU, FL, OB, CL, BSN
SCHUBERT, F.P. EINE KLEINE TRAUERMUSIK   B98
    2HN, 2TRB, 2CL, 2BSN, BCL
SCHUBERT, F.P. EINE KLEINE TRAUERMUSIK   D55
    2HN, 2TRB, 2CL, 2BSN, CNTBSN
SCHUBERT, F.P. EINE KLEINE TRAUERMUSIK, D. 79   E14
    2HN, 2TRB, 2CL, 2BSN, CNTBSN
TREMBLOT DE LA CRPIX. DIVERTIMENTO   D36
    2TPT, HN, TRB, FL, OB, CL, BSN, PERC

9 PARTS: WINDS-KEYBOARD

BASSETT, L.R. NONET. TPT, HN, TRB, TU, FL, OB, CL, BSN, PF E65
BENTZON, N.V. CHAMBER CONCERTO, OP. 52   B23
    2TPT, CL, BSN, PERC, 3PF, DB

GERHARD, R.   NONET   G85
    TPT, HN, TRB, TU, FL, OB, CL, BSN, ACCORDIAN
GHEZZO. PONTICA II. 2TPT, 2HN, TRB, FL, SAX, PF, NAR   G66
GUDMUNDSEN¬HOLMGREEN, P. 2 IMPROVISATIONS, OP. 9   C17
    TPT, HN, TRB, FL, CL, PERC, PF, DB, VIB
HAYDN, J.-HAAS. ENGLISH MILITARY MARCHES, H.VIII, 1-3   E14
    TPT, 2HN, 2CL, 2BSN, DR, SER
IVES, C.E. SCHERZO: OVER THE PAVEMENTS   E14
    TPT, 3TRB, CL, BSN, PERC, PF, PIC
LADERMAN, E. NONETTE. TPT, HN, TRB, FL, CL, BSN, PF, VN, VC   E51
STEWART, R. NONET. TPT, HN, FL, CL, BSN, PF, VN, VA, VC   B36

9 PARTS: WIND(S)-STRING(S)

ANGERER, P. COGITATO (KAMMERMUSIK FUR 9 SCLOINSTRUMENTE)   B73
    HN, FL, OB, CL, BSN, VN, VA, VC, DB
BLAND, W.K. SONICS I-III. TPT, HN, TRB, TU, PF, 2VN, VA, VC   B35
BORKOVEC, P. NONET. HN, FL, OB, CL, BSN, VN, VA, VC, DB   A33
CHAVEZ. ENERGIA FOR 9 INSTRUMENTS   G85
    TPT, HN, TRB, FL, BSN, VA, VC, DB, PIC
CHILDS, B. JACK'S NEW BAG   F68
    TPT, TRB, FL, PERC, 2PF, VN, VC, DB
CLEMENTI, A. CONCERTINO IN FORMA DI VARIAZIONI   G41
    HN, FL, OB, BSN, PF, VN, VC, DB, CNTBSN
CUSTER, A.R. CYCLE FOR 9 INSTRUMENTS   D63
    TPT, HN, FL, VN, VA, VC, DB, BCL, ASAX
DAVID, T.C. KONZERT FUR 9 SOLOINSTRUMENTE   B73
    HN, FL, CB, CL, BSN, VN, VA, VC, DB
DEPELSENAIRE, J.M. DIVERTISSEMENT NOCTURNE   D41
    TPT, 2FL, PF, 2VN, VA, VC, DB
FELD, J. NONETTO (SUITE DE CHAMBRE)   D36
    HN, FL, OB, CL, BSN, VN, VA, VC, DB
FISHER, S. MUSIC FOR 9 INSTRUMENTS   D86
    TPT, HN, TRB, TU, CL, BSN, VN, VC, DB
FOERSTER, J.B. NONET. HN, FL, OB, CL, BSN, VN, VA, VC, DB   D55
FOERSTER, J.B. NONETT, OP. 147   A51
    HN, FL, OB, CL, BSN, VN, VA, VC, DB
FOLPRECHT, Z. CONCERTINO, OP. 21   A33
    HN, FL, OB, CL, BSN, VN, VA, VC, DB
FOLPRECHT, Z. CONCERTINO, OP. 21   A51
    HN, FL, OB, CL, BSN, VN, VA, VC, DB
GILSE, J.V. NONET. HN, OB, CL, BSN, 2VN, VA, VC, DB   B74
GIURANNA, B.E. ADAGIO E ALLEGRO DI CONCERTO   E98
    HN, FL, OB, CL, BSN, VN, VA, VC, DB
GORECKI, H.M. CONCERTO, OP. 11   A31
    TPT, FL, CL, 2VN, VA, VC, XYL, MND
GRANDIERT, J. NONETT. TPT, HN, TRB, FL, OB, CL, BSN, VC, EU   B90
GUDMUNDSEN¬HOLMGREEN, P. 2 IMPROVISATIONS, OP. 9   C17
    TPT, HN, TRB, FL, CL, PERC, PF, DB, VIB
HABA, A. NONETT #3, OP. 82   A51
    HN, FL, OB, CL, BSN, VN, VA, VC, DB
HAYDN, J.-LANDON. DIVERTIMENTO IN F, H.II:20   B73
    2HN, 2OB, 2VN, 2VA, DB
HOFFMEISTER, F.A. SERENADE. 2HN, 2OB, 2CL, 2BSN, DB(CNTBSN)   F52
JAROCH, J. KINDERSUITE. HN, FL, OB, CL, BSN, VN, VA, VC, DB   A51
KORNAUTH, E. CHAMBER MUSIC, OP. 31   F97
    HN, FL, OB, CL, 2VN, VA, VC, DB
KORNAUTH, E. KAMMERMUSIK, OP.31   B73
    HN, FL, OB, CL, 2VN, VA, VC, DB

KUBIZEK, A. SINFONIA DA CAMERA, OP. 26B   B73
  HN, FL, OB, CL, BSN, VN, VA, VC, DB
LADERMAN, E. NONETTE. TPT, HN, TRB, FL, CL, BSN, PF, VN, VC   E51
LEGRAND. PORCELAINE DE SAXE   D84
  TRB, PERC, DB, 2SSAX(2CL), ASAX, TSAX, BARSAX, BSAX(BSN)
LUTYENS, E. CHAMBER CONCERTO #1   B23
  TPT, HN, TRB, OB, CL, BSN, VN, VA, VC
MARTINU, B. NONETTO. HN, FL, OB, CL, BSN, 2VN, VA, VC   A51
MULDER, E.W. FUGA #4 UIT "ARS CONTRAPUNCTICA"   B74
  HN, FL, OB, CL, 2VN, VA, VC, DB
MUSGRAVE, T. CHAMBER CONCERTO   B23
  TPT, HN, TRB, OB, CL, BSN, VN, VA, VC
NAUMANN, S.E. CADENZE PER 9 STRUMENTI   B90
  TPT, HN, TRB, FL, CL, PERC, VN, VC, BCL
NOVAK, J. BALETTI A 9. HN, FL, OB, CL, BSN, VN, VA, VC, DB   A51
POULENC, F. MOUVEMENTS PERPETUEIS   B23
  HN, FL, OB/EH, CL, BSN, VN, VA, VC, DB
RHEINBERGER, I. NONET, OP. 139   E14
  HN, FL, OB, CL, BSN, VN, VA, VC, DB
RIDKY, J. NONETT, OP. 39/2   A51
  HN, FL, OB, CL, BSN, VN, VA, VC, DB
ROCHBERG, G. CHAMBER SYMPHONY FOR 9 INSTRUMENTS   E77
  TPT, HN, TRB, FL, CL, BSN, VN, VA, VC
RUDZINSKI, W. NONET. HN, FL, OB, CL, BSN, VN, VA, VC, DB   A31
SALIERI, A.-HOCKNER. 2 BLASERSERENADEN   B73
  2HN, 2FL, 2OB, 2BSN, DB
SALVIUCCI, G. SERENATA. TPT, FL, OB, CL, BSN, 2VN, VA, VC   E98
SPOHR, L. NONET. HN, FL, OB, CL, BSN, VN, VA, VC, DB   D55
SPOHR, L. NONET, OP. 31 IN F   D48
  HN, FL, OB, CL, BSN, VN, VA, VC, DB
SPOHR, L. NONET, OP. 31. HN, FL, OB, CL, BSN, VN, VA, VC, DB   C03
SPOHR, L. NONETT, OP. 31   D46
  HN, FL, OB, CL, BSN, VN, VA, VC, DB
STEWART, R. NONET. TPT, HN, FL, CL, BSN, PF, VN, VA, VC   B36
SZABELSKI, B. APHORISMS "9"   A31
  TPT, TRB, FL/PIC, OB, CL, PERC, VN, VA, VC
TADEUSZ, M. 3 VIRTUOSO STUDIES FOR CHAMBER ENSEMBLE   A31
  TPT, HN, 2FL, OB, CL, BSN, DB, TIMP
WELIN, K.E. NR. 3. TPT, HN, TRB, FL, OB, CL, DB, BCL   A08
WOLFF, C. NINE. TPT, HN, TRB, FL, CL, PF, 2VC, CEL   E65
ZILLIG, W. SERENADE 2   A51
  TPT, HN(COR), TRB, CL, VN, VA, VC, EFCL, BCL

                9 PARTS: BRASS-MISCELLANEOUS

ALPAERTS, F. TREURDICHT. 2TPT, 4HN, 2BSN, GNG   B12
BENTZON, N.V. CHAMBER CONCERTO, OP. 52   H30
  2TPT, CL, BSN, PERC, 3PF, DB
BIANCHI, G. 4 STUDI DA MALU   E98
  TPT, HN, FL, OB, CL, BSN, PERC, 2PF
BIBER, H.I.F.-HARNONCOURT. SONATA A 7   B73
  6TPT, DB, TIMP, HPCD(ORG)
CHILDS, B. JACK'S NEW BAG   E68
  TPT, TRB, FL, PERC, 2PF, VN, VC, DB
FISHER, S. MUSIC FOR 9 INSTRUMENTS   D86
  TPT, HN, TRB, TU, CL, BSN, VN, VC, DB
GUDMUNDSEN-HOLMGREEN, P. 2 IMPROVISATIONS, OP. 9   N53
  TPT, HN, TRB, FL, CL, PERC, PF, DB, VIB

HAYDN, J.-HAAS. 3 ENGLISH MILITARY MARCHES, H.VIII, 1-3   F14
    TPT, 2HN, 2CL, 2BSN, PERC, SER
LOEBNER. MUSIK FUR BLECHBLAESER. 2TPT, 2HN, 2TRB, PERC, 2PF   C41
REYNOLDS. BLIND MEN. 3TPT, 3TRB, TU, PERC, PF   E65
SCHMELZER, J.H. SONATA SECUNDA A 8   F14
    3TRB, 2VN, VA, VC, CTT(TPT), BC(ORG)
SCHUBERT, F.P. EINE KLEINE TRAUERMUSIK   B98
    2HN, 2TRB, 2CL, 2BSN, CNTBSN

MUSIC WITH TEN OR MORE PARTS

10 OR MORE EQUAL BRASS INSTRUMENTS

```
ADLER, S.  5 VIGNETTES.  12TRB                                   E51
CHASE, A.H.  PASSACAGLIA.  10TRB                                 B98
GOTTSCHALK, A.  SUBSTRUCTURES 1.  1 TO 10 TUBAS                  G66
MALONE.  TUBA FANFARE.  12 TO 100 TUBAS                          N92
MAXWELL, C.  MUSIC FOR HORNS.  10HN                              P49
MAYER, R.  SUITE IN FOUR PARTS.  12HN                           P49
MENDELSSOHN, F.-OSTRANDER.  HOLY IS GOD THE LORD.  12TRB         B98
PEDERSON, T.  VELVET LASER, THE.  12TRB                          M93
SCHULLER, G.  LINES AND CONTRASTS.  16HN                         D86
```

10 OR MORE MIXED BRASS (BRASS-PERC)

```
ADLER, S.  BRASS FRAGMENTS.  6TPT, 5HN, 6TRB, EU, 2TU            F60
ADLER, S.  CONCERT PIECE.  3TPT, 2HN, 3TRB, 2EU, TU, TIMP        D16
ADLER, S.  DIVERTIMENTO.  3TPT, 3HN, 3TRB, 2EU, TU              D16
ADLER, S.  HISTRIONICS.  4TPT, 4HN, 4TRB, EU, TU, PF            F60
ALPAERTS, F.  FANFARE D'INAUGURATION                            D80
   3TPT, 4HN, 3TRB, TU, TIMP
ALPAERTS, F.  OLYMPISCHE SPELEN TO ANTWERPEN.  12TPT, PERC      B12
ALWYN, W.  FANFARE FOR A JOYFUL OCCASICN                        E51
   3TPT, 4HN, 2TRB, TU(BTRB), PERC
AMELLER.  FANFARES POUR TOUS LES TEMPS.  4TPT, 2HN, 4TRB, TU    D36
ANDERSON, L.  SUITE OF CAROLS.  4TPT, 4HN, 3TRB, EU, TU, BTRB   D84
ANDRIESSEN.  ENTRATA FESTIVA.  3TPT, 4HN, 3TRB, TIMP, GNG       B74
ANDRIESSEN.  IN POMPA MAGNA.  4TPT, 6HN, 4TRB, TU, PERC         B74
ARNAUD.  BUGLER'S DREAM.  4TPT, 4HN, 3TRB, TU, PERC             F43
ARNELL, R.  CEREMONIAL AND FLOURISH, OP. 43.  3TPT, 4HN, 3TRB   A38
AUBIN, T.  CRESSIDA FANFARE.  3TPT, 4HN, 3TRB, 2EU, TU, PERC    D36
BACH, J.S.-GILLIS.  BACH CHORALES.  4TPT, 4HN, 3TRB, EU, TU     F60
BACH, J.S.  JESU CHRIST, MEIN'S LEBENS LICHT (CANTATA 118)      D16
   4TPT, 2HN(TPT, TRB), 2TRB(2HN), TRB, TRE-TU
BACH, J.S.-ROSENTHAL.  PRELUDE AND FUGUE IN C MAJOR             G21
   3TPT, 4HN, 3TRB, EU, TU
BACH, J.S.-WALKER.  SARABANDE AND BOURREE                       F60
   3TPT, 4HN, 3TRB, EU, TU
BACH, J.S.-TULL.  VON HIMMEL HOCH                               F60
   3TPT, 2HN, 2TRB, EU, TU, TIMP
BAERVOETS, R.  FANFARE HEROIQUE & FANFARE JOYEUSE               D80
   3TPT, 4HN, 3TRB, TU, PERC
BARATTO.  ANDANTE RELIGIOSO.  5TPT, 4HN, 3TRB, EU, TU           N40
BARBER, S.  MUTATIONS FROM BACH.  3TPT, 4HN, 3TRB, TU, TIMP     F23
BARNES, C.P. (ED).  ROBBINS COLLECTION...FOR BRASS CHOIR        A70
   3TPT, 4HN, 3TRB, EU, TU, PERC
BEACH, B.C.  FANFARE AND CHORALE.  3TPT, 2HN, 3TRB, 2EU, TU     E80
BEADELL, R.  INTRODUCTION AND ALLEGRO                           D16
   3TPT, 3HN, 3TRB, EU, TU, TIMP
BECKHELM, P.  TRAGIC MARCH.  4TPT, 4HN, 3TRB, EU, TU, PERC      D16
BEETHOVEN, L.V.-PEARSON.  BEETHOVEN FOR BRASS                   F23
   3TPT, 4HN, 3TRB, EU, TU
BEETHOVEN, L.V.-KING.  SYMPHONY #7 (ALLEGRETTO)                 D16
   3TPT, 2HN, 3TRB, EU, TU, TIMP
```

```
BERLIN, D.  MUSIC FOR BRASS AND PERCUSSION                          P48
    6TPT, 4HN, 3TRB, 2EU, TU, PERC
BERNSTEIN, L.-ERICKSON.  PRESTO BARBARO (ON THE WATERFRONT)         M66
    4TPT, 4HN, 3TRB, EU, TU, PERC, PF, TIMP
BERNSTEIN, L.-ERICKSON.  SHIVAREE.  4TPT, 6HN, 3TRB, TU            M66
BEVERSDORF, T.  CATHEDRAL MUSIC.  3TPT, 4HN, 3TRB, EU, TU          F60
BEYER, H.  SUITE FOR BRASS INSTRUMENTS.  3TPT, 4HN, 3TRB, TIMP     D16
BILIK.  SONATA FOR BRASS.  5TPT, HN(EU), 3TRB, EU, TU, 3HN         C29
BINKERD.  3 CANZONAS.  3TPT, 3HN, 3TRB, TU                         A78
BLANK, A.  PAGANINI CAPRICE (XIV).  3TPT, 4HN, 3TRB, TU            A13
BLATTER.  SUITE.  4TPT, 2HN, 2TRB, EU, TU                          B30
BLISS, A.  FANFARE FOR A COMING OF AGE                             D16
    3TPT, 4HN, 3TRB, TU, TIMP, CYM
BLISS, A.  FANFARE FOR THE LORD MAYOR OF LONDON                    D16
    3TPT, 4HN, 3TRB, TU, PERC
BLISS, A.  FANFARE, HOMAGE TO SHAKESPEARE                          D16
    5TPT, 3TRB, TU, PERC
BLISS, A.  GREETINGS TO A CITY.  4TPT, 4HN, 6TRB, TU, PERC         D16
BOEHLE, W.R.  BRASS SUITE.  3TPT, 3HN, 3TRB, TU, PERC              C85
BONNEAU, P.  FANFARE.  3TPT, 3HN, 2TRB, TU, TIMP                   D36
BONONCINI, G.-MOORE.  CANON FOR 12 BRASS INSTS.                    G21
    5TPT, 5TRB, 2TU
BONTA.  RENAISSANCE MUSIC.  4TPT, 2HN, 3TRB, EU                    F23
BOTTJE, W.G.  SYMPHONIC ALLEGRO                                    D16
    6TPT, 4HN, 3TRB, EU, TU, PERC
BOZZA, E.  FANFARE HEROIQUE, OP. 46                                D36
    3TPT, 4HN, 3TRB, TU, PERC
BOZZA, E.  MESSE SOLENNELLE DE STE. CECILE                         D36
    3TPT, 4HN, 3TRB, TU, PERC, ORG
BOZZA, E.  OVERTURE POUR UNE CEREMONIE                             D36
    3TPT, 4HN, 4TRB, TU, PERC
BRENTA, G.  FANFARE (1935).  3TPT, 4HN, 3TRB, TU                   B12
BRENTA, G.  FANFARE HEROIQUE (1945)                                B12
    3TPT, 4HN, 3TRB, TU, PERC
BRIAN, H.  FESTIVAL FANFARE.  4TPT, 4HN, 3TRB, 2TU                 P45
BROWN, R.  FANTASY-FUGUE.  6TPT, 4HN, 4TRB, TU, PERC               G21
BROWN, R.  5 PIECES                                                G21
    4TPT, 4HN, 4TRB, EU, TU, PERC, ORG, TIMP, HP
BROWN, R.  PRELUDE AND FUGUE.  4TPT, 4HN, 4TRB, EU, TU, PERC       G21
BRUGK, H.M.  SUITE FUR 10 BLECHBLASER, OP. 8                       C60
    3TPT, 3HN, 3TRB, TU
BRUMBY.  FANFARE.  3TPT, 4HN, 3TRB, TU, PERC                       N86
BURGHAUSER.  OLD CZECH FANFARES.  4TPT, 2HN(2TPT), 3TRB, TIMP      A33
BYRD, W.-OSBORNE.  FANTASY IN 6 PARTS                              D16
    6TPT, 4HN, 3TRB, 2BAR, EU, BTRB, 2TU
CABUS, P.N.  FANFARE.  3TPT, 4HN, 3TRB, TU, TIMP                   D76
CABUS, P.N.  RHAPSODIE.  5TPT, 4HN, 3TRB, TU, PERC                 D67
CARMICHAEL.  BEAUTY OF THE EARTH, THE LORD IS MY SHEPHERD          P46
    4TPT, 4HN, 4TRB, TU, PERC
CARMICHAEL.  GUIDE ME, O THOU GREAT JEHOVAH...                     P46
    4TPT, 4HN, 4TRB, TU, PERC
CARMICHAEL.  HOW FIRM A FOUNDATION, THE VALLEY OF BLESSING         P46
    4TPT, 4HN, 4TRB, TU, PERC
CARMICHAEL & CONKEY.  IN THE CROSS OF CHRIST I GLORY               P46
    4TPT, 4HN, 4TRB, TU, PERC
CASALS-STOKOWSKI.  O VOX OMNES.  3TPT, 4HN, 2TRB, TU               P38
CESTI, M.A.-FITZGERALD.  PRELUDE (IL POMO D'ORO)                   E77
    3TPT, 4HN, 3TRB, TU, 3COR, EU
CHOPIN, F.-SCHMIDT.  NOCTURNE.  4TPT, 4HN, 5TRB, EU, TU, PERC      D14
CHOU, WEN-CHUNG.  SOLILOQUY OF A BHIKSUNI                          E65
    TPT, 4HN, 3TRB, TU, 3PERC
CLARKE, J.-CLARK, F.  PURCELL'S TRUMPET VOLUNTARY                  B85
    4TPT, 2HN, 2TRB, EU, TU, (OPT ORG)
```

```
COBINE, A.  VERMONT SUITE.  4TPT, 3HN, 4TRB, EU, TU             D16
CONKEY & CARMICHAEL.  IN THE CROSS OF CHRIST I GLORY            P46
   4TPT, 4HN, 4TRB, TU, PERC
COPLAND, A.  FANFARE FOR THE COMMON MAN                         A78
   3TPT, 4HN, 3TRB, TU, PERC, TIMP
CORELLI, A.-KING.  CONCERTO GROSSO, OP. 6, NO. 11               D16
   2TPT, HN(TRB), TRB(EU), -TU, EU(BSN), 2TPT(2OB)
COWELL, H.  FANFARE FOR THE FORCES...ALLIES                     A78
   3TPT, 4HN, 3TRB, PERC
DE YOUNG, L.  DIVERTISSEMENT.  4TPT, 4HN, 3TRB, EU, TU, PERC    D16
DEBUSSY, C.  MARTYRE DE SAINT SEBASTIEN FANFARES, LE            B81
   4TPT, 6HN, 3TRB, TU, TIMP
DEVREESE, G.  FANFARE.  3TPT, 4HN, 3TRB, TU, PERC               B12
DI LASSO, C.-FATCH.  ECHO SONG                                 G78
   4TPT, 2HN(2TRB), 2TRB, 2TU(2BTRB)
DIAMOND, D.  CEREMONIAL FANFARE                                 F59
   4TPT, 6HN, 3TRB, TU, PERC, 2TIMP
DIAMOND, D.  ELEGY IN MEMORY OF M. RAVEL                        F59
   3TPT, 4HN, 3TRB, TU, PERC, HP
DIEMENTE, E.  LOVE SONG FOR AUTUMN.  6TPT, 4HN, 3TRB, TU        G66
DIEMER, E.I.  DECLAMATION                                      B92
   4TPT, 2HN, TRB, EU, TU, BTRB, TIMP, SDR, CYM
DUBOIS, P.M.  3 PRELUDES EN FANFARE.  TIMP                      D36
DUKAS, P.  FANFARE (LA PERI).  3TPT, 4HN, 3TRB, TU             B81
DUREY.  INTERLUDE.  4TPT, 4HN, 3TRB, TU, PERC                   F87
DURY, M.  3 FANFARES.  3TPT, 4HN, 3TRB, PERC                    D67
ERB, D.  SCNNERIES.  4TPT, 4HN, 3TRB, TU                        D76
FLAGELLO.  CONCERTINO.  2TPT, 4HN, 3TRB, TU, PF, TIMP           C40
FLAGELLO, N.  CHORALE AND EPISODE FOR 10 BRASS INSTS.           C40
   2TPT, 4HN, 2TRB, TU, BTRB
FREED, I.  SYMPHONY #2.  4TPT, 4HN, 3TRB, 2TU                   F78
FRESCOBALDI, G.-BINKERD.  BATTLE, THE.  4TPT, 3HN, 4TRB, PERC   A78
GABRIELI, G.-KING.  CANZON A 12                                D16
   5TPT, 2HN(2TRB), 2TRB, 2TRB(2HN), BTRB
GABRIELI, G.  CANZON DUO DECIMI TONI A 10, NO. 4.  6TPT, 4TRB   E14
GABRIELI, G.  CANZON DUODECIMI TONI (SACRAE SYMPHONIAE, 1597)   D16
   4TPT, 2HN(2TPT), 2TRB(2HN), TRB(EU), TRB-TU
GABRIELI, G.-BLOCK.  CANZON DUODECIMI TONI A 10 NO. 1           E14
   6TPT, 4TRB
GABRIELI, G.-BLOCK.  CANZON DUODECIMI TONI A 10 NO. 2           E14
   6TPT, 4TRB
GABRIELI, G.-BLOCK.  CANZON DUODECIMI TONI A 10 NO. 3           E14
   5TPT, 5TRB
GABRIELI, G.-KING.  CANZON IN DOUBLE ECHO                       D16
   6TPT, 3TRB, 3TRB(3HN)
GABRIELI, G.-THOMAS.  CANZON NO.14.  6TPT, 4TRB                 E14
GABRIELI, G.-THOMAS.  CANZON NO.15.  4TPT, 2HN(2TRB), 4TRB      E14
GABRIELI, G.-THOMAS.  CANZON NO.16.  6TPT, 3HN(3TRB), 3TRB)     E14
GABRIELI, G.-THOMAS.  CANZON NO.17.  6TPT, 6TRB                 E14
GABRIELI, G.-THOMAS.  CANZON NO.18.  4TPT, 2HN(2TRB), 8TRB      E14
GABRIELI, G.-THOMAS.  CANZON NO.19.  3TPT, 3HN(3TRB), 9TRB      E14
GABRIELI, G.-THOMAS.  CANZON NO.20.  5TPT, 4HN(4TRB), 13TRB     E14
GABRIELI, G.  CANZON NONI TONI A 12.  6TPT, 6TRB               E14
GABRIELI, G.-FENNELL.  CANZON NONI TONI A 12                    B98
   6TPT, 3HN(3TRB), 3TRB
GABRIELI, G.-BOUDREAU.  CANZON NONI TONI                        E65
   6TPT, 3TRB(3HN), 3TRB(3TU)
GABRIELI, G.-BLOCK.  CANZON PRIMI TONI A 10                     E14
   5TPT, 3TRB, 2TPT(2TRB)
GABRIELI, G.  CANZON QUARTI TONI (SACRAE SYMPHONIAE, 1597)      D16
   TPT, 2HN(2TPT), 2HN(2TRB), 2TRB(2HN), 4TRB, 3TU
GABRIELI, G.  CANZON QUARTI TONI A 15.  3TPT, 9TRB, 3TRB        E14
```

```
GABRIELI, G.-GREER.  CANZON QUARTI TONI.  4TPT, 4HN, 6TRB, TU       C05
GABRIELI, G.-BLOCK.  CANZON SEPTIMI OCTAVE TONI A 12                E14
   6TPT, 6TRB
GABRIELI, G.  CANZONA #10.  INST ?                                  E65
GABRIELI, G.-WINTER.  CANZONE NO. 7.  6TPT, 4TRB                    E65
GABRIELI, G.  SONATA OCTAVI TONI (SACRAE SYMPHONIAE, 1597)          D16
   2TPT, 2TPT(2HN), 2HN(2TRB), 2TRB, EU
GABRIELI, G.  SONATA OCTAVI TONI A 12.  2TPT, 8TRB, 2TRB(2HN)       E14
GABRIELI, G.-SMITH.  SONATA 19.  6TPT, 3HN, 3TRB, 3TU              A38
GALLUS-KANDEL.  ALLELUIA.  3TPT, 3HN, 4TRB, 2EU, 2TU              A38
GANZ, R.  BRASSY PRELUDE, OP. 33/1.  3TPT, 4HN, 3TRB, TU          D84
GEORGE, T.F.  SUITE DE CHANSONS DE NOEL.  4TPT, 4HN, 4TRB, TU     E87
GERAEDTS, J.  KORAAL-FANFARE.  3TPT, 4HN, 3TRB, TU, PERC          B74
GIGGY, F.D.  TRIADIC.  3TPT, 3HN, 3TRB, TU                        B35
GIUFFRE, J.  PHAROAH, THE.  6TPT, 4HN, 3TRB, 2EU, TU, TIMP        D86
GLAZOUNOV & LIADOW.  FANFARES.  2TPT, 4HN, 3TRB, TU, TIMP         N20
GOLDMAN, E.F.  MARCH FOR BRASSES                                  B20
   3TPT, 2HN, 3TRB, EU, TU, PERC
GOLDMAN, R.F.  HYMN FOR BRASS CHOIR                               D16
   4TPT, 4HN, 3TRB, EU, TU, TIMP
GOODENOUGH, F.  FANFARCE.  3TPT, 4HN, 3TRB, TU                    A13
GOTTSCHALK, A.  SUBSTRUCTURES I.  2EU, 8TU                        G66
GRANT, P.  PRELUDE AND DANCE, OP. 39.  3TPT, 4HN, 3TRB, TU        E68
GRIEG, E.H.-EMERSON.  FUNERAL MARCH                               D16
   3TPT, 4HN, 3TRB, TU, PERC, EU
GRIEG, E.H.-ERICKSON.  GRIEG FOR BRASS                            F23
   3TPT, 4HN, 3TRB, EU, TU
GROOT, H.D.  N.O.S. "FIRATO FANFARE"                              B74
   12TPT, 16HN, 8TRB, 2TU, 7PERC
GUSTAFSON, D.(ARR).  WHEN I CAN READ MY TITLE CLEAR               F43
   3TPT, 3HN, 3TRB, EU, TU
HADDAD, D.  FUGUE IN D MINOR.  3TPT, 3HN, 3TRB, TU, PERC          F43
HANDEL, D.  VARIATION ON "ERSCHIENEN IST DER HERRLICH TAG"        F23
   4TPT, 4HN, 3TRB, EU, TU
HARDIN, B.E.  REGAL FESTIVAL MUSIC.  3TPT, 4HN, 3TRB, EU, TU      B35
HARRIS, R.G.  3 THREE-PARTS.  4TPT, 3HN, 3TRB, EU, TU             A13
HARTLEY, W.S.  SINFONIA NO. 3.  5TPT, 4HN, 3TRB, EU, TU           F80
HARTMEYER, J.  NEGEV, TONE POEM FOR BRASS                         D16
   3TPT, 3HN, 3TRB, EU, TU, TIMP
HASSLER, L.-OWEN.  LAUDATE DOMINUM                                D14
HATTON-CARMICHAEL.  JESUS SHALL REIGN                             P46
   4TPT, 4HN, 4TRB, TU, PERC
HAVERGAL-CARMICHAEL.  GOLDEN HARPS ARE SOUNDING                   P46
   4TPT, 4HN, 4TRB, TU, PERC
HAZZARD, P.  MENTOR.  4TPT, 4HN, TU, 3PERC, TIMP                  G66
HENDERSON.  FANFARE 1964.  3TPT, 4HN, 3TRB, TU, TIMP              A43
HERBERIGS, R.  SUITE NO. 1.  3TPT, 4HN, 3TRB                      B12
HERBERIGS, R.  SUITE NO. 2.  3TPT, 4HN, 3TRB                      B12
HEUSSENSTAMM, G.  LABYRINTH.  8TPT, 4HN, 4TRB, 4TU                G66
HEUSSENSTAMM, G.  TOURNAMENT                                      G66
   8TPT, 4HN, 4TRB, 4EU, 4TU, 4PERC
HOGG, M.E.  SONATA.  4TPT, 3HN, 3TRB, EU, TU                      N59
HOLCOMBE.  AMERICAN CHRISTMAS FOLK SONG SUITE                     M84
   4TPT, 2HN, 3TRB, EU, TU
HOLCOMBE.  CEREMONIAL FOR CHRISTMAS BRASS                         M84
   4TPT, 2HN, 3TRB, EU, TU
HOLCOMBE.  12 DAYS OF CHRISTMAS.  4TPT, 2HN, 3TRB, EU, TU         M84
HOLCOMBE.  FANFARE AND TOCCATA.  4TPT, 2HN, 3TRB, EU, TU          M84
HOLCOMBE (ARR).  BRYN CALFARIA.  3TPT, 2HN, 3TRB, EU, TU          M84
HOLMES, P.  SUITE FOR BRASS.  3TPT, 4HN, 3TRB, TU                 F43
HOLST, G.  3 CHRISTMAS CAROLS.  3TPT, 4HN, 3TRB, EU, TU           F23
HOVHANESS, A.S.  REQUIEM & RESURRECTION                           E65
   2TPT, 4HN, 3TRB, TU, PERC
```

```
HUSA, K.  DIVERTIMENTO.  3TPT, 4HN, 3TRB, TU, PERC              A38
IMBRIE.  HERE WE STAND.  6TPT, 8HN, 6TRB, 2TU                   F43
JACOB.  SALUTE TO U.S.A..  3TPT, 4HN, 3TRB, TU, TIMP            D16
JENNI, D.  ALLEGRO.  3TPT, 4HN, 3TRB, EU, TU                    A13
JESSON, R.  VARIATIONS AND SCHERZO                             D16
   4TPT, 3HN, 3TRB, EU, TU, TIMP, SDR
JOLIVET, A.  FANFARES POUR BRITANNICUS                         A78
   4TPT, 4HN, 4TRB, TU, PERC
JONGEN, J.  FANFARE HEROIQUE, OP. 110                          B12
   3TPT, 4HN, 3TRB, EU, TU, PERC
KAUFMANN, L.J.-JANETZKY.  MUSIK.  3TPT, 4HN, 3TRB, TU          C75
KEE.  BLIJDE INCOMSTE.  3TPT, 2HN, 3TRB, TU, PERC              B74
KELLY, F.  CHORALE & FUGUE                                     E68
   4TPT, 4HN, 4TRB, 2TU, 4COR, 2EU, TIMP
KETTING, O.  COLLAGE NO. 9.  5TPT, 6HN, 3TRB, EU, TU, 5PERC    B74
KETTING, O.  FANFARES.  8TPT, 4HN, 3TRB, TU, PERC              B74
KETTING, O.  INTRADA FESTIVA.  3TPT, 4HN, 3TRB, TU, 2PERC      B74
KING, P.D.  7 CONVERSATION PIECES.  4TPT, 4TRB, 2EU, TU        D16
KLAUSS.  PRELUDE FOR BRASS CHOIR.  8TPT, 4HN, 8TRB, 4TU        F79
KNIGHT.  VARIETIES FOR BRASS.  3TPT, 4HN, 3TRB, TU             N61
KNIGHT, M.  VARIETIES FOR BRASS.  3TPT, 4HN, 2TRB, BTRB, TU    N61
KNOX, C.  SYMPHONY FOR BRASS & PERCUSSION                      G83
   3TPT, 4HN, 3TRB, EU, TU, PERC
KNOX, C.  SYMPHONY.  3TPT, 4HN, 3TRB, EU, TU, PERC, TIMP       P19
KOEPKE, P.  MARCHE VAILLANT.  4TPT, 3HN, 3TRB, EU, TU          F07
KUPFERMAN.  CONCERTINO.  4TPT, 2HN, 4TRB, TU                   C40
LEBOW, L.S.  SUITE FOR BRASS.  3TPT, 3HN, 3TRB, EU, TU, PERC   F72
LEE.  SUITE FOR BRASS.  3TPT, 4HN, 3TRB, TU, PERC              H30
LEES.  FANFARE FOR A CENTENNIAL.  3TPT, 4HN, 3TRB, TU, PERC    A78
LEVY, F.  SYMPHONY FOR 16 BRASS & PERC.  INST ?               G66
LEWIS, J.  FANFARES I & II.  4TPT, 4HN, 2TRB, TU, PERC         D86
LIADOW & GLAZOUNOW.  FANFARES.  2TPT, 4HN, 3TRB, TU, TIMP      N20
LOUEL, J.  FANFARE J.M..  3TPT, 4HN, 3TRB, TU, PERC            B12
LOUEL, J.  FANFARES.  3TPT, 4HN, 3TRB, TU, PERC               B12
LOWRY-CARMICHAEL.  CHRIST AROSE.  4TPT, 4HN, 4TRB, TU, PERC    P46
LUENING, O.  FANFARE FOR A FESTIVE OCCASION                   E65
   3TPT, 3HN, 3TRB, PERC
MAGANINI, Q.E.  SHENANDOAH.  3TPT, 2HN, 3TRB, EU, TU          B85
MARKS, J.  INTRODUCTION AND PASSACAGLIA                       D16
   3TPT, 3HN, 3TRB, EU, TU, TIMP
MARKS, J.  MUSIC FOR BRASS AND TIMPANI                        D16
   3TPT, 4HN, 3TRB, EU, TU, TIMP
MAXWELL, C.  MUSIC FOR HORNS & TRB.  6HN, 4TRB                P49
MC KAY, G.F.  BRAVURA PRELUDE.  4TPT, 4HN, 4TRB, 2EU, TU      A38
MENDELSSOHN, F.-EMERSON.  FUNERAL MARCH                       D16
   3TPT, 4HN, 3TRB, EU, TU, TIMP
MERILAINEN, U.  PARTITI.  4TPT, 4HN, 3TRB, TU                 D16
MERRIMAN, T.  THEME AND FOUR VARIATIONS                       A38
   4TPT, 2HN, 3TRB, EU, TU
MEULEMANS, A.  FANFARE VOOR DE INAUGURATIE VAN K.V.S.         B12
   3TPT, 4HN, 3TRB, TU, PERC
MEULEMANS, A.  FANFARE.  7TPT, 4HN, 3TRB, TU, PERC            B12
MEULEMANS, A.  8 PANFARES.  7TPT, 8HN, 3TRB, TU, PERC         B12
MEULEMANS, A.  INAUGURALE FANFARE.  7TPT, 4HN, 3TRB, TU, PERC B12
MEULEMANS, A.  LENTE FANFARES, ZOMER FANFARES                B12
   7TPT, 4HN, 3TRB, TU, PERC
MISSAL, J.M.  FANFARE, CHORALE AND PROCESSION                C25
   4TPT, 4HN, 4TRB, 2TU, TIMP
MISSAL, J.M.  JERICHO SUITE.  4TPT, 4HN, 4TRB, EU, TU, PERC   F60
MORLEY, T.-O'REILLY.  3 MADRIGALS.  3TPT, 4HN, 3TRB, EU, TU   F23
MOULAERT, R.  FANFARE D'HONNEUR                              B12
   3TPT, 2HN, 3TRB, EU, 2TU, PERC
```

```
MOZART, W.A.-WALDECK.  KYRIE.  5TPT, 5TRB                             B44
NELHYBEL, V.  ANCIENT HUNGARIAN DANCES                               B32
   3TPT, 2HN, 3TRB, 2EU, TU
NELHYBEL, V.  CHORALE.  3TPT, 2HN, 3TRB, EU, TU                      C40
NELHYBEL, V.  CONCERTO ANTIFONALE.  4TPT, 3HN, 5TRB, 2TU             B32
NELHYBEL, V.  DESIGNS FOR BRASS.  3TPT, 4HN, 3TRB, EU, TU            A78
NELHYBEL, V.  MOTET AND PAVANE.  3TPT, 2HN, 2TRB, 2EU, TU            B32
NELHYBEL, V.  SLAVIC MARCH.  3TPT, 3HN, 3TRB, EU, TU, PERC           C40
NIBLOCK, J.  TRIPTYSH FOR BRASS                                     B52
   3TPT, 4HN, 3TRB, EU, TU, TIMP
NOVY, D.  SONATINA.  3TPT, 3HN, 3TRB, TIMP                          D16
OTT, J.  MUSIC FOR BRASS AND PERCUSSION                             A65
   4TPT, 4HN, 4TRB, 2EU, 2TU, 4PERC
PALESTRINA, G.P.-KANDEL.  LAUDATE DOMINUM IN TYMPANIS               A38
   4TPT, 2HN, 4TRB, 2EU, 2TU
PALESTRINA, G.P.-READ.  LAUDATE DOMINUM IN TYMPANIS                 B32
   3TPT, 3HN, 3TRB, 3EU, 3TU
PARRIS, H.M.  4 RHAPSODIES.  3TPT, 4HN, 3TRB, TU                    B92
PEASLEE.  DIVERTIMENTO.  3TPT, 2HN, 3TRB, TU, PERC                  G68
PILSS, K.  HELDENKLAGE.  8TPT, 8TRB, 2EU, 2TU, 2PERC                D16
PISK, P.A.  CORTEGE, OP. 53B.  3TPT, 2HN, 3TRB, EU, TU, 3COR        A13
PISTON, W.  CEREMONIAL FANFARE.  4TPT, 6HN, 3TRB, TU, PERC          A38
PISTON, W.  FANFARE(10 FANFARES BY 10 COMPOSERS)                    A78
   3TPT, 4HN, 3TRB, TU 3PERC, TIMP
POLIN, C.  JOURNEY OF OWAIN MADOC, THE                              G66
   2TPT, HN, TRB, TU, 10 PERC
POLIN, CLAIRE.  JOURNEY OF OWAIN MADOC                              G66
   BRASS QUINTET, PERC(10)
PRESSER, W.H.  PASSACAGLIA AND FUGUE                                F80
   3TPT, 4HN, 3TRB, EU, TU, 2PERC
PRESSER, W.H.  RESEARCH.  3TPT, 3HN, 3TRB, 2EU, TU                  F80
PRICHARD-CARMICHAEL.  COME THOU LONG-EXPECTED JESUS                 P46
   4TPT, 4HN, 4TRB, TU, PERC
PROKOFIEFF, S.S.  MARCH FR LOVE OF 3 ORANGES                        G68
   2TPT, 4HN, 3TRB, EU, TU, PERC
PROKOFIEV, S.S.-TULL.  2 PIECES FROM LT. KIJE                       A78
   6TPT, 4HN, 3TRB, 2EU, 2TU, PERC
PURCELL, H.-SURTEES.  PURCELL SUITE, A                              B20
   3TPT, 3HN, 2TRB, 3EU, 2TU, BTRB
PURCELL, H.-SMITH.  SYMPHONY (FAIRY QUEEN, ACT IV)                  D16
   6TPT, 2HN(2TRB), 3TRB, EU-TU, TIMP
PURCELL, H.-CLARK.  TRUMPET VOLUNTARY                               B85
   4TPT, 2HN, 2TRB, EU, TU, ORG
RAUTAVAARA, E.  REQUIEM IN OUR TIME, A                              D16
   4TPT, 4HN, 3TRB, EU, TU, PERC, TIMP
READ, G.  CHORALE AND FUGHETTA, OP. 83A                            D16
   4TPT, 4HN, 2TRB, 2EU, TU, BTRB
READ, G.  SOUND PIECE FOR BRASS & PERC, OP. 82                      D16
   4TPT, 4HN, 3TRB, EU, 2TU, PERC
REED.  SYMPHONY FOR BRASS & PERCUSSION                              C25
   4TPT, 4HN, 4TRB, 2EU, 2TU, PERC, 2COR
REGER, M.-WERLE.  FROM MY DIARY, OP. 82.    4TPT, 2HN, 3TRB, TU     A78
REYNOLDS, V.  PRELUDE AND ALLEGRO                                   D16
   3TPT, 4HN, 3TRB, 2EU, TU, TIMP
REYNOLDS, V.  THEME AND VARIATIONS                                  D16
   3TPT, 3HN, 3TRB, EU, TU, TIMP
RIEGGER, W.  MUSIC FOR BRASS CHOIR, OP. 45                          D74
   10TPT, 4HN, 10TRB, 2TU, PERC
RILEY, J.  SUITE FOR BRASS CHOIR.  3TPT, 4HN, 3TRB, EU, TU          F80
ROSSEAU, N.  FANFARE, OP. 58.  3TPT, 4HN, 3TRB, TU, PERC            B12
ROSSI-ADLER.  PSALM 92.  3TPT, 5HN, 3TRB, TU                        F23
ROY, K.G.  TRIPARTITA, OP. 5.  3TPT, 2HN, 3TRB, 2EU, TU             D16
```

```
SCHMIDT, W.  3 CHANSONS DINCENNES                                    A43
   4TPT, 4HN, 3TRB, EU, TU, PERC, PERC
SCHMIDT, W.  CHORALE, MARCH AND FUGATO                               G21
   3TPT, 4HN, 3TRB, EU, TU, PERC
SCHMIDT, W.  4 SONGS FOR BRASS & PERC.                               A43
   3TPT, 4HN, 3TRB, EU, TU, PERC, OPT HP
SCHMITT, F.  FANFARE, LE CAMP DE POMPEE, OP. 69                      B87
   3TPT, 4HN, 3TRB, TU, TIMP, CYM, TDR
SCHUBERT, F.P.-SURTEES.  SCHUBERT SUITE, A                           B20
   3TPT, 3HN, 2TRB, 3EU, 2TU, BTRB
SCHULLER, G.  SYMPHONY FOR BRASS & PERCUSSION, OP.16                 E43
   6TPT, 4HN, 3TRB, 2EU(2TU), TU, PERC
SCHUMANN, G.  SUITE FUR BLECHBLASER UND PAUKEN                       F53
   4TPT, 4HN, 4TRB, PERC, BTRB
SCHUMANN, R.-STEPHENS.  SCHUMANN SUITE, A                            B20
   3TPT, 3HN, 2TRB, 3EU, 2TU, BTRB
SCOTT, W.  RONDO GIOJOSO.  3TPT, 4HN, 4TRB, EU, TU, PERC             D16
SERVAIS, H.  INTRADA                                                D80
   2TPT, HN, TRB, EU, 2TU, FL, 2COR, 2BUGLE, PERC
SHAHAN, P.  LEIPZIG TOWERS.  4TPT, 4HN, 4TRB, EU, TU, PERC           D16
SHAHAN, P.  SPECTRUMS.  4TPT, 4HN, 4TRB, EU, TU, PERC                D16
SHELUKOV, V.-WALTERS.  BALLADE.  4TPT, 3HN, 3TRB, EU, TU             F07
SHULMAN, A.  TOP BRASS, 6 MINUTES FOR 12.  4TPT, 4HN, 3TRB, TU       F78
SOSNIK.  LONESOME SOLDIER, THE.  3TPT, 4HN, 3TRB, EU, TU, PERC       A84
SPINO, P.  SLOW WALTZ FOR TEN BRASS.  3TPT, 3TRB, 3HN, TU            N59
STABILE.  SUITE.  6TPT, 6TRB, TU, TIMP                               G21
STARER, R.  SERENADE FOR BRASS.  3TPT, 4HN, 3TRB, TU                 F59
STEWART, R.  MUSIC FOR BRASS NO. 4                                   A13
   4TPT, 2HN, 2TRB, EU, TU, BTRB
STEWART, R.  MUSIC FOR BRASS NO. 4.  4TPT, 2HN, 2TRB, EU, BTRB       E68
STOLTE, S.  FANFARE DES FRIEDENS.  3TPT, 2HN, 3TRB, TU, PERC         E14
STOUT, A.  PIETA.  6TPT, 3TRB, TU                                    G68
STRAUSS, R.  FANFARE...STADT WEIN...                                 A78
   6TPT, 8HN, 6TRB, 2TU, 2TIMP
STRAUSS, R.  FEIERLICHER EINZUG.  9TPT, 4HN, 4TRB, 2TU, 6TPT         D46
STRAUSS, R.  WIENER PHILHARMONIKA FANFARE                           A78
   6EFTPT, 8HN, 6TRB, 2TU, 2TIMP
SULLIVAN, A.S.-KING.  OVERTURE TO THE MIKADO                         D16
   3TPT, 2HN, 3TRB, EU, TU, PERC
SUMERLIN, M.  FANFARE, ANDANTE AND FUGUE                             G21
   2TPT, 3HN, 3TRB, EU, TU, PERC
TAYLOR, C.H.  INSCRIPTIONS IN BRASS                                 F23
   3TPT, 4HN, 3TRB, EU, TU, PERC
TCHAIKOVSKY, P.I.-CORLEY.  ROMANCE, OP. 5                            D16
   3TPT, 2HN, 3TRB, EU, TU, PERC
TCHEREPNIN, A.N.  FANFARE.  3TPT, 4HN, 2TRB, TU, PERC, BTRB          A78
THOMSON.  METROPOLITAN MUSEUM FANFARE                               F23
   5TPT, 4HN, 3TRB, TU, PERC
TIPPETT, M.  FANFARE NO. 1.  3TPT, 4HN, 3TRB                         F31
TIPPETT, M.  PRAELUDIUM.  3TPT, 6HN, 3TRB, 2TU, PERC                 F31
TOMASI, H.  FANFARES LITURGIQUES                                    D36
   3TPT, 4HN, 3TRB, TU, PERC, BTRB
TSCHESNOKOFF-HOLCOMBE.  RUSSIAN LITANY FOR BRASS                     M84
   3TPT, 2HN, 3TRB, EU, TU
TULL, F.  LITURGICAL SYMPHONY                                       A43
   6TPT, 4HN, 4TRB, 2EU, 2TU, PERC
TULL, F.  SOUNDINGS.  6TPT, 6HN, 4TRB, 2EU, 2TU, PERC, TIMP          F43
TULL, F.  VARIATIONS ON AN ADVENT HYMN                             A43
   6TPT, 4HN, 4TRB, 2EU, 2TU, PERC
TUROK, P.  ELEGY IN MEMORY OF K. RATHAUS                            E14
   3TPT, 2HN, 3TRB, EU, TU
TYRA, T.N.  SUITE.  3TPT, 4HN, 3TRB, EU, TU, TIMP                    F60
```

UBER, D.A. CANZONA MODERNA IN HOMAGE TO G. GABRIELI   N59
    4TPT, HN, 3TRB, EU, 2TU, HN(TRB)
UBER, D.A. CHRISTMAS FESTIVAL OF CAROLS, A   N59
    4TPT, 2HN, 3TRB, TU
UBER, D.A. CHRISTMAS IN BRASS. 4TPT, 4HN, 3TRB, EU, TU   F23
UBER, D.A. EVOLUTION I. 4TPT, 4HN, 3TRB, EU, TU, TIMP   F59
UBER, D.A. GLORIA IN EXCELSIS. 4TPT, 2HN, 3TRB, EU, TU, TIMP N59
UBER, D.A. HYMN (THE POWER AND THE GLORY)   F59
    4TPT, 2HN, 3TRB, EU, TU, TIMP
UBER, D.A. LITURGY, OP. 50. 4TPT, 2HN, 3TRB, EU, TU, TIMP   B98
UBER, D.A. PRELUDE (THE POWER AND THE GLORY)   F59
    4TPT, 2HN, 3TRB, EU, TU, TIMP
UBER, D.A. RITUAL DANCE (THE POWER AND THE GLORY)   F59
    4TPT, 2HN, 3TRB, EU, TU, TIMP
UBER, D.A. SPIRITUAL (THE POWER AND THE GLORY)   F59
    4TPT, 2HN, 3TRB, EU, TU, TIMP
UBER, D.A. TWENTIETH CENTURY ANTIPHONAL, OP. 38   F59
    4TPT, 2HN(2TPT), HN, HN(TRB), 2TRB, EU, BTRB, 2TU
ULDALL, H. MUSIK   D44
    2TPT, 2HN, 2TRB, TU, PERC, 2FLG(2TPT), 2AHN(2HN)
VAN DER VELDEN, R. FANFARE. 3TPT, 4HN, 3TRB, TU, PERC   B12
VAN DER VELDEN, R. FANFARE. 3TPT, 4HN, 3TRB, TU, PERC   D80
VOELKEL, E.A. TURMMUSIK, OP. 111. 4TPT, 4TRB, TU, PERC   E96
WAGNER, L. FANFARE, SCHERZO AND ALLEGRO   D16
    6TPT, 4HN, 3TRB, EU, TU, PERC
WAGNER, R.-SHINER & SCHMIDT. EVENING STAR   D14
    4TPT, 3HN, 5TRB, EU, TU
WAGNER, R. FUNERAL MARCH (DIE GOTTERDAMMERUNG)   D16
    3TPT, 2HN, 3TRB, EU, TU, PERC
WAGNER, R.-FITZGERALD. PRIZE SONG & FINALE   F60
    6TPT, 4HN, 4TRB, 2EU, TU
WALTON, W.T. ANNIVERSARY FANFARE   E51
    9TPT, 4TRB, PERC, 3BTRB, TIMP
WALTON, W.T. FANFARE FOR THE QUEEN. 8TPT, 4TRB   E51
WALTON, W.T.-SARGENT. FANFARE. 3TPT, 4HN, 3TRB, TU, PERC   E51
WARD, W.R. FANTASIA. 3TPT, 4HN, 2TRB, TU, BTRB, TIMP   C68
WILDGANS, F. FESTLICHE MUSIK. 8TPT, 6TRB, 2TU, PERC   B73
WOOLLEN, R. TRIPTYCH, OP. 34. 4TPT, 2HN, 3TRB, TU   E65
WYETH-CARMICHAEL. COME THOU FOUNT. 4TPT, 4HN, 4TRB, TU, PERC P46
ZADOR, E. SUITE. 4TPT, 4HN, 2TRB, TU, BTRB   C03
ZANINELLI. JUBILATE DEO. 4TPT, 4HN, 4TRB, TU   F43
ZANINELLI. MUSIC FOR A SOLEMN OCCASION. 5TPT, 4TRB, TU, PERC E77
ZINDARS, E. BRASS SQUARE, THE. 4TPT, 4HN, 3TRB, TU, TIMP   D16

10 OR MORE PARTS: HORN-WOODWIND

ANDRIESSEN, J. RESPIRATION-SUITE. 2HN, 2FL, 2OB, 2CL, 2BSN   B74
BALLOU, E.W. SUITE FOR WINDS. 2HN, 2FL, 2OB, 2CL, 2BSN   A13
BERNARD, J.E.A. DIVERTISSEMENT, OP. 36   B81
    2HN, 2FL, 2OB, 2CL, 2BSN
ENESCO, G. DIXTUOR, OP. 14. 2HN, 2FL, OB, 2CL, 2BSN, EH   D55
JACOB, G.P.S. OLD WINE IN NEW BOTTLES   E51
    2HN, 2FL, 2OB, 2CL, 2BSN
KLAUSS, N. JAKARTA. SOLO HN, CL CHOIR   B35
LEWIS, P.T. SESTINA. 2HN, 2FL, 2OB, 2CL, 2BSN, BCL   A13
LILIEN, I. SONATINE APOLLINIQUE. 2HN, 2FL, 2OB, 2CL, 2BSN   B74
LUTYENS, E. MUSIC FOR WIND. 2HN, 2FL, 2OB, 2CL, 2BSN   F31
MOSER, F. SUITE FUR SIEBZEHN BLASINSTRUMENTE, OP. 37   F82
    4HN, 3FL, 3OB, 4CL, 3BSN

MOZART, W.A. DIVERTIMENTO # 3, ES-DUR, K. 166   A89
   2HN, 2OB, 2CL, 2BSN, 2EH
MOZART, W.A. DIVERTIMENTO # 4, B-DUR, K. 186   A89
   2HN, 2OB, 2CL, 2BSN, 2EH
MOZART, W.A. SERENADE B-DUR, NO. 10, K.361   A89
   4HN, 2OB, 2CL, 2BSN, CONTBSN, 2BASSET HN(2CL)
PONSE, L. EUTERPRE, OP. 37. 2HN, 2FL, 2OE, 2CL, 2BSN   B74
SCHMITT, F. LIED ET SCHERZO, OP. 54 (SOLO HN PART)   B81
   2HN, FL, OB, 2CL, 2BSN, PIC, EH
STRAUSS, R. SUITE F-DUR FUR 13 BLASINSTRUMENTE, OP. 4   D44
   4HN8 2FL, 2CB, 2CL, 2BSN, CNTBSN
STRAUSS, R. SUITE. 4HN, 2FL, 2OB, 2CL, 2ESN   D55
TANEYEV, A.S. ANDANTE FOR DOUBLE WOODWIND QUINTET   D55
   2FL, 2OB, 2CL, 2HN, 2BSN
VAN OTTERLOO, W. SYMPHONIETTA. 4HN, 3FL, 3OB, 3CL, 3BSN   B74

10 OR MORE PARTS: BRASS-WOODWIND

ARRIEU, C. DIXTUOR. TPT, HN, TRB, 2FL, OB, 2CL, 2BSN   A71
CIEMENTE, E. CELEBRATION   G66
FINKE, F.F. SUITE, MUSIK FUR 11 BLASER   A89
   2TPT, 2HN, 2TRB, TU, FL, OB, CL, BSN
GABRIELI, A.-GHEDINI. ARIA DELLA BATTAGLIA   E98
   3TPT, 4HN, 3TRB, TU, 3FL, 3OB, 4CL, 3BSN
GWILT, D. SUITE FOR WOODWIND & BRASS INST (PERC OPT)   F41
   2TPT, 2HN, 2TRB, 2FL, OB, 2CL, PERC, CNTBSN
HARTLEY, W.S. DOUBLE CONCERTO (SOLO TU & ASAX))   G83
   2TPT, HN, TRB, TU, FL, OB, CL, BSN, ASAX
HEMEL, O.V. CONCERTO PER STRUMENTI A FIATO   B74
   3TPT, 4HN, 3TRB, TU, 3FL, 2OB, 3CL, 3BSN
HOVHANESS, A.S. TOWER MUSIC   F03
   2TPT, 2HN, TRB, TU, FL, OB, CL, BSN
JADIN, L.E.-GLASENAPP. SYMPHONIE (TPTS IN F)   C75
   2TPT, 2HN, TRB, 2FL, 2CL, 2BSN, SER(BSN, CNTBSN)
JENNI, D. ALLEGRO. 4TPT, 4HN, 3TRB, TU, 2BARSAX   E68
KLEBE, G. MISSA, MISERERE NOBIS, OP. 45   A83
   2TPT, 3HN, 3TRB, TU, 2FL, OB, 3CL, 2BSN
LEEUW, T.D. SYMPHONIES OF WIND INSTRUMENTS   E65
   4TPT, 4HN, 4TRB, TU, 4FL, 4OB, 4CL, 4BSN
MAYER, W.R. ESSAY FOR BRASS & WINDS   A78
   2TPT, 2HN, TRB, TU, FL, OB, CL, BSN
MC CAULEY, W. 5 MINIATURES FOR TEN WINDS   D94
   2TPT, 2HN, TRB, TU, FL, OB, CL, BSN
PERSICHETTI, V. SERENADE NO. 1   B92
   2TPT, 2HN, TRB, TU, FL, OB, CL, BSN
SCHULLER, G. DOUBLE QUINTET   A38
   2TPT, 2HN, TRB, TU, FL, OB, CL, BSN
STRAUSS, R. SERENADE IN E-FLAT, OP. 7   C91
   4HN, 2FL, 2OB, 2CL, 2BSN, CONTBSN(TU)
STRAUSS, R. SERENADE IN E-FLAT, OP. 7   D08
   4HN, 2FL, 2OB, 2CL, 2BSN, CONTBSN(TU)
STRAUSS, R. SERENADE IN E-FLAT, OP. 7   F97
   4HN, 2FI, 2CB, 2CL, 2BSN, CONTBSN
STRAVINSKY, I. SYMPHONIES OF WIND INSTRUMENTS   A78
   3TPT, 4HN, 3TRB, TU, 3FL, 2OB, 3CL, 2BSN, EH, CONTBSN
VAUGHAN-WILLIAMS, R. SCHERZO ALLA MARCIA   E51
   2TPT, 2HN, 3TRB, FL, 2OB, 2!>(, PIC
VRANICKY, A. JAGERMARSCHE. TPT, 2HN, 2OB, 2CL, 2BSN, CONTBSN   A51

WASHBURN, R.   CONCERTINO FOR WIND & BRASS QUINTETS   E51
   2TPT, 2HN, TRB, T1, FL, OB, CL, BSN
WEBER, C.M.V.   MARCH FOR HARMONIE   E14
   2TPT, 2HN, TRB, FL, 2OB, 2CL, 2BSN

10 OR MORE PARTS: WINDS-KEYBOARD

DUBOIS, F.   ESPACES A REMPLIR   F65
   TPT, TRB, TU, 2CL, PERC, PF, DB, SAX, VIB
FRID, G.   12 METAMORPHOSEN, OP. 54A   B74
   2HN, 2FL, 2CB, 2CL, 2BSN, PF
GERHARD.   HYMNODY.   TPT, HN, TRB, TU, FL, CB, CL, 2PF, PERC   E51
HEMEL, O.V.   DIVERTIMENTO NO. 2   B74
   2TPT, 2HN, 2FL, 2OB, 2CL, 2BSN, PF
KOPP, F.   TERROR SUITE.   T, 3HN, 3TRB, TU, PERC, PF, 3SAX   3TP
REVUELTAS, S.   3 SONATOS   F59
   2TPT, HN, TU, 2CL, BSN, PF, BCL, TAM
REYNOLDS.   QUICK ARE THE MOUTHS OF THE EARTH   E65
   TPT, 2TRB, 3FL, OB, PERC, PF, 3VC

10 OR MORE PARTS: WIND(S)-STRING(S)

AMATO, B.   BASSES AND BRASS. 5TPT, 4HN, 3IB   G66
ANDRIESSEN, J.   HOMMAGE A MILHAUD   B74
   TPT, HN, TRB, FL, CL, OB, BSN, SAX, VN, VA, VC
BRAHMS, J.   SERENADE #2 IN A MAJOR   D08
   2HN, 2FL, 2OB, 2CL, 2BSN, VA, VC, DB
BUTTING, M.   KAMMERSYMPHONIE, OP. 25   F81
   HN, FL, OB, CL, BSN, 3VN, 2VA, VC, DB, EH, BCL
CAGAN.   DIVERTISSEMENT OVERTURE   E61
   TPT, TRB, FL/PIC, OB, CL/BCL, BSN, 2PERC, VC, DB
DUBOIS, F.   ESPACES A REMPLIR   E65
   TPT, TRB, TU, 2CL, PERC, PF, DB, SAX, VIB
DVORAK, A.   SERENADE, OP. 44. 3HN, 2OB, 2CL, 3BSN, VC, DB   C91
DVORAK, A.   SERENADE, OP. 44. 2HN, 2OB, 2CL, 2BSN, VC, DB   D08
DVORAK, A.   SERENADE, OP. 44, IN D   E14
   3HN, 2OB, 2CL, 2BSN, VC, DB
GUACCERO.   UN ITER SEGNATO   B00
   TPT, TRB, OB, CL, BSN, 2VN, VA, VC, DB
HASQUENOPH, P.   DIVERTISSEMENT POUR DIXTOUR   B73
   HN, FL, OB, CL, BSN, 2VN, VA, VC, DB
IVES, C.E.-SCHULLER.   CHROMATIMELODTUNE   D86
   TPT, HN, TRB, TU, OB, CL, BSN, PF, 3VN, VA, VC, DB
LUTYENS, E.   6 TEMPI FOR 10 INSTRUMENTS, OP. 42   D84
   TPT, HN, FL, OB, CL, BSN, VN, VA, VC, DE
MOOR, F.   SUITE, OP. 103   F16
   HN, FL, OB, CL, BSN, 2VN, VA, VC, DB
MOZART, W.A.   SERENADE #10, B-FLAT, K. 361   E14
   4HN, 2OB, 2CL, 2BSN, CNTBSN(DB), 2BASSET HN(2CL)
PHILLIPS, P.   CHIMER.   D86
   TPT/FLG, HN, TRB, TU, FL/PIC, CL, VN, VA, VC, DB, EH, CNTBSN
PLUISTER, S.   DIVERTIMENTO   B74
   TPT, HN, TU, 2FL, OB, CL, BSN, PERC, DB
PRAAG, H.C.V.   DIXTUOR.   HN, FL, OB, CL, BSN, 2VN, VA, VC, DB   B74

```
PRATELLA, F.B.   PER UN DRAMMA ORIENTALE, OP. 40                        E98
     HN, FL, OB, CL, BSN, PF, 2VN, VA, VC
RAWSTHORNE, A.   CONCERTO FOR 10 INSTRUMENTS                            E51
     HN, FL, OB(EH), CL, BSN, 2VN, VA, VC
REYNOLDS.  QUICK ARE THE MOUTHS OF THE EARTH                           E65
     TPT, 2TRB, 3FL, OB, PERC, PF, 3VC
SCHISKE, K.  DIVERTIMENTO, OP.49                                       B73
     TPT, HN, TRB, CL, BSN, 2VN, VA, VC, DB
STACHOWIAK, L.  3 IMPROVISATIONS.  2HN, 3FL, 3CL, 2VN, VA, VC          A31
STRAVINSKY, I.  CONCERTINO                                             H30
     2TPT, TRB, FL, OB, CL, 2BSN, VN, VC, BTRB, EH
STRAVINSKY, I.  8 INSTRUMENTAL MINIATURES                              B23
     HN, 2FL, 2OE, 2CL, 2BSN, 2VN, 2VA, 2VC
VALCARCEL.  DICOTOMIA III.  2TPT, 2HN, 2TRB, 2VN, 2VA, 2VC             F59
ZILLIG, W.  SERENADE 4                                                 A51
     TPT,HN,TRB,FL,OB,CL,BSN,PERC,2VN,VA,VC,DB,CEL,CEMB
```

10 OR MORE PARTS: BRASS-MISCELLANEOUS

```
ANDRIESSEN, J.  ROUW PAST ELEKTRA...                                   B74
     2TPT, HN, 2TRB, FL, 2OB, CL, 2BSN, PERC
ANTONIOU, T.  CONCERTINO, OP. 21                                       A51
     TPT, 2HN, FL, OB, 3CL, 2BSN, PERC, PF
AUBIN.  VITRAIL, FANFARE...ST.LOUIS TO BASILICA OF SAINT-DENIS         D36
     3TPT, 4HN, 3TRB, TU, 2FL, PERC
AUBIN, T.  CRESSIDA, FANFARE.  3TPT, 4HN, 3TRB, TU, 2BSN, PERC         D36
BADINGS, H.  SYMPHONIE VOOR 16 SOLO-INSTRUMENTEN                       B74
     TPT, 2HN, 2FL, 2OB, 2CL, 2BSN, 2VN, VA, VC, DB
BEACH, B.C.  5 INTAGLI.  4TPT, 4HN, 3TRB, TU, PERC                     F60
BOEDIJN, G.H.  VIJF CONCERTANTE EPIGRAM-SCHETSEN, OP. 159              B74
     2TPT, 2HN, 2FL, 2OB, 3CL, 2BSN, PERC, PF
BOIS, R.D.  CERCLE.  TPT, 2HN, FL, OB, 2CL, 2BSN, PERC, PF             B74
BONSEL, A.  FOLKLORISTISCHE SUITE                                      B74
     2TPT, 2HN, 2FL, 2OB, 3CL, 2BSN, PERC
BOZZA, E.  OVERTURE FOR A CEREMONY                                     D36
     3TPT, 4HN, 3TRB, TU, PERC, BTRB, ASAX, TSAX, BARSAX
BROWN, R.  CONCERTO.  6TPT, 4HN, 6TRB, TU, PERC, 2PF                   G21
BRUGGEMANN, K.  HUMORISTISCHE MARSCHE FUR ELASORCHESTER                F53
     3TPT, 4HN, 3TRB, 2TU, 3FL/3PIC, 3OB, 3CL, 2BSN, PERC, BCL
BUSH, G.  FANFARE & MARCH: THE PRINCE OF MOROCCO                       F41
     2TPT, 2HN, 3TRB, TU, 2FL, OB, 2CL, BSN, PERC, DB
CASTEREDE, J.  3 FANFARES POUR DES PROCLAMATIONS DE NAPOLEON           D36
     3TPT, 4HN, 3TRB, TU, PERC, NAR
COPE, D.  MUSIC FOR BRASS, STRINGS AND PERCUSSION                      G66
COPE, D.  TOWERS                                                      N29
DAVIDOVSKY, M.  INFLEXIONS                                             D63
     TPT, TRB, 2FL, CL, 4PERC, PF, VN, VA, VC, DB
DEVIENNE, F.  OUVERTURE FUR BLASINSTRUMENTE (2 TPT IN F)               C75
     2TPT, 2HN, 2OB, 2CL, 2BSN, PERC, PIC, SER(BSN, CNTBSN)
DIJK, J.V.  SERENADE                                                   B74
     2TPT, 2HN, 3FL, 3OB, 3CL, 2BSN, PERC, PF
DUCKWORTH.  PITCH CITY                                                 N29
FELDERHOF, J.  MUZIEK VOOR 15 BLAASINSTRUMENTEN                        B74
     2TPT, 2HN, TRB, TU, 2FL, 2OB, 2CL, 2BSN, PERC, ASAX
FINKE, F.F.  SUITE IN 3 SATZEN                                         A89
     2TPT, 2HN, 3TRB, TU, 2FL, 2OB, 2CL, 2BSN, PERC
GABRIELI, G.-WINTER.  CANZONE X.  10 INST ?                            E65
GIURANNA, B.E.  EPISODE                                               E98
     2TPT, 2HN, 2FL, 2OB, 2CL, 2BSN, PF, TIMP
```

GOEB, R.J. ENCOMIUM F68
 3TPT,4HN,3TRB,TU,2FL,2OB,2CL,2BSN,6PERC,PIC,EH,BCL,TIMP
GORECKI. MUZYCZKA 2. 4TPT, 4TRB, PERC, 2PF E72
GORECKI, H.M. GENESIS, OP.19,II A31
 TPT, FL, 2PERC, 2PF, 2VN, 3VA, PIC, GUIT, MND
HANDEL, G.F. MUSIC FOR THE ROYAL FIREWORKS C65
 3TPT, 3HN, 3OB, 3BSN, PERC, DB, TIMP
HANDEL, G.F. WATER MUSIC E65
 3TPT, 2HN, 3FL/3AFL, 3OB/3EH, 5BSN/CNTBSN, TIMP
HAYDN, J.-LANDON. CASSATION IN G-DUR, H.II:G1 B73
 2HN, 2OB, 2VN, 2VA, VC, DB
HEMEL, O.V. 3 CONTRASTS FOR WIND INST & PERC B74
 3TPT, 4HN, 3TRB, TU, 3FL, 3OB, 3CL, 3BSN, PERC, ASAX
HINDEMITH, P. KONZERTMUSIK, OP. 49 (SOLO PF) F31
 3TPT, 4HN, 2TRB, TU, PF, 2HP
HOGG, M.F. CONCERTO. 3TPT, 3HN, 3TRB, EU, TU, TIMP D16
HUTCHESON, J.T. DESIGNS FOR FOURTEEN E65
 4TPT, 2HN, 3TRB, 2TU, 3PERC
HUYBRECHTS, A. DIVERTISSEMENT. 4TPT, 4HN, 3TRB, TU, PERC B35
JOHNSON, J.J. POEM FOR BRASS D86
 7TPT, 4HN, 4TRB, 2EU, TU, PERC, DB
KAPR. OMAGGIO ALLA TROMBA G81
 2TPT, 3HN, TRB, TU, FL, CL, PF, PIC, CNTBSN, BCL, TIMP
KETTING, O. VARIAZIONI PER ORCHESTRA B74
 3TPT, 2HN, 2FL, 2OB, 3CLAR, 2BSN, PERC, HP
KOELLREUTTER, H.J. CONCRETION D88
 TPT, FL, OB, CL, BSN, PERC, PF, VN, VA, CEL
KOELLREUTTER, H.J. CONSTRUCTIO AD SYNESIN D88
 TPT, FL/PIC, OB/EH, CL/BCL, PERC, PF, VN, CNTBSN, HP, CEM
KORTE, K. I THINK YOU WOULD HAVE UNDERSTOOD G66
 4TPT, 4TRB, 4SAX, GUIT, DB, PERC, PF
KRENEK, E. LITTLE SUITE, OP. 70A F97
 2TPT, 2HN, 2TRB, TU, 2FL, 2OB, 2CL, 2BSN, PERC, TIMP
KURKA, R.F. POLKA & WALTZ (GOOD SOLDIER SCHWEIK) G17
 2TPT, 3HN, TRB, FL, OB, CL, BSN, PIC, EH, BCL, CNTBSN, TIMP
LANZA. EIDESIS II. 2HN, 2TRB, TU, 3PERC, 3VC, 2DB A78
LEE. 4 SKETCHES FOR BRASS H30
 4TPT, 4HN, 3TRB, 2EU, TU, PERC, DB
LEWIS, A. PIECES OF EIGHT B35
 HN, EU, FL, 2OB, 3CL, BSN, PERC, 2TSAX
LEWIS, J. EXCERPTS FROM THE COMEDY D86
 4TPT, 4HN, 2TRB, TU, PERC, PF, DB
LEWIS, J. GOLDEN STRIKER, THE. 4TPT, 4HN, 2TRB, TU, PERC, DB D86
LEWIS, J. 3 LITTLE FEELINGS D86
 7TPT, 4HN, 3TRB, 2EU, TU, DB, TIMP
LUTYENS, E. 6 TEMPI D84
 TPT, HN, FL, OB, CL, BSN, PF, VN, VA, VC
MALTBY, R. BALLAD FOR BRASS & PERC C11
 4TPT, 4HN, 4TRB, TU, PERC, DB, GUIT
MAYER. ESSAY FOR BRASS AND WINDS A89
 2TPT, 2HN, 2TRB, TU, FL, OB, CL, BSN, PERC
MC BETH, F. CANTICLE. 4HN, 3TRB, EU, TU, 2FL, PERC F60
MELLERS, W.H. NOCTAMBULE AND SUN DANCE E41
 2TPT, 2HN, 2TRB, 2FL, 2OB, 2CL, 2BSN, PERC, PF
MORAWETZ. SINFONIETTA. 3TPT, 4HN, 2FL, 2CL, BSN, TIMP D37
MOULAERT, R. FANFARES. 3TPT, 4HN, 3TRB, TU, 2BSN, PERC B12
MOYSE, L. DIVERTIMENTO D55
 2HN, 2FL, 2OB, 2CL, 2BSN, 2VC, DB, TIMP
MOZART, W.A. DIVERTIMENTO # 6. 5TPT, 2FL, 4TIMP M79
MOZART, W.A.-EINSTEIN. FALIMATHIAS MUSICUM, K.32... C65
 2HN, 2OB, BSN, PF, 2VN, VA, VC
PHIFER. CONSTRUCTION NO. 2 N29

```
POULENC, F.  SUITE FRANCAISE.  2TPT, 3TRB, 2OB, 2BSN, PERC        B81
RECK, D.  NUMBER 1                                               D86
    HN, FL, CL, 3PERC, PF, VA, DB, GTR, TSAX, VIB
REIMANN, A.  MONUMENTA                                           A83
    2TPT, 3HN, 2TRB, 2FL, OB, 2CL, 2BSN, EH, PERC
REYNOLDS.  WEDGE.  2TPT, 2TRB, TU, 2FL, PERC, PF, DB, CEL        E65
ROREM, N.  SINFONIA (OPT PERC)                                   E65
    2HN, 2FL, 2CB, 4CL, 3BSN, PERC, PIC, EH, (OPT PERC)
SCHILLER, H.  MUSIC NO. 2                                        A31
    TPT, FL, 2CL, BSN, PERC, PF, VN, VC, DB
SCHUMAN, R.  YOUNG DEAD SOLDIERS, THE.  HN, S, 8WW, 9STR         E77
SCHWERTSIK, K.  SALOTTO ROMANO, OP. 5                            D88
    HN, TRB, TU, DB, PERC, VC, DB, BCL, STR, BARSAX, GUIT
SKALKOTTAS, N.  ANDANTE SOSTENUTO                                F97
    TPT, HN, TRB, TU, FL/PIC, OB, CL, !SN, PERC, EH, CNTBSN, TIMP
STOCKHAUSEN, K.H.  FROM THE 7 DAYS.  INST ?                      F97
STOCKHAUSEN, K.H.  PLUS MINUS.  INST ?                           F97
STOCKHAUSEN, K.H.  SOLO.  INST ?                                 F97
STRAVINSKY, I.  RAGTIME                                          B23
    TPT, HN, TRB, FL, CL, PERC, 2VN, VA, DB, CIMBALOM(PF)
TCHEREENINE, N.N.  SONATINE, OP. 61                              A58
    2TPT, HN, TRB, 2FL, 2OB, CL, 2BSN, PERC, XYL
TICCIATI, N.  FANFARE FOR WIND AND PERCUSSION                    C71
    4TPT, 4HN, 3TRB, 3FL, 3OB, 3CL, 2BSN, PERC
VAN DELDEN, L.  PICCOLO CONCERTO, OP. 67                         B74
    2TPT, 2HN, 2FL, 2OB, 2CL, 2BSN, PERC, PF
VAN OTTERLOO, W.  INTRADA.  4TPT, 4HN, 4TRB, TU, BSN, PERC       B74
VARESE, E.  DESERTS                                             B32
    3TPT, IHN, 3TRB, 2TU, 2BL, 2CL, PERC, PF, RECORDED TAPE
VARESE, E.  HYPERISM.  2TPT, 3HN, 2TRB, FL, CL, PERC            B32
VARESE, E.  INTEGRALES                                         B32
    2TPT, HN, TRB, 2TU, 2FL, OB, 2CL, PERC
VERNON.  SUITE.  3TPT, 3HN, 3TRB, PERC                          F23
VOGT, H.  CONCERTINO.  TPT, 2HN, FL, OB, 2CL, 2BSN, PERC, PF    A51
WAGNER, R.  TRAUERSINFONIE(ON ARRIVAL WEBER'S REMAINS...)       A89
    2TPT, 4HN, 3TRB, TU, FL, 2OB, 4CL, 2BSN, PERC
WARREN, R.  MUSIC FOR HARLEQUIN                                 E41
    2TPT, 2HN, 2TRB, FL, OB, 2CL, PERC
WEISS, A.A.  TONE POEM                                          E68
    4TPT, 4HN, 3TRB, TU, 4PERC, TIMP, 2ASAX
WROCHEM, K. VON.  ORATORIUM MEUM PLUS PRAEFERTURI               B35
    TPT, PERC, 2VN, VA, VC, 3V, ASAX, PNEUMATIC DRILL
WUORINEN, C.  EVOLUTIO TRANSCRIPTA                              D55
    TPT, HN, TRB, FL, OB, CL, BSN, PF, 4VN, 2VA, 2VC, DB
WUORINEN, C.  MUSICA DUARUM PARTIUM ECCLESIASTICA               E68
    BRASS, PF, ORG, TIMP
ZYKAN, O.M.  3 SATZE                                            D88
    3TPT, 2HN, 2TRB, TU, FL/PIC, OB, CL, BSN, 3PERC8 PF
```

ADDITIONAL BRASS ENSEMBLE CATEGORIES

BRASS CHOIR

ASHE. FOURTH ADVENTURE	F60
BACH, J.S.-MAYES. 4 CHORALES. 4-PART BRASS	F97
BENOY. CHRISTMAS HYMNS AND CAROLS. 4-PART BRASS	E51
BENOY. 50 HYMNS (SONGS OF PRAISE). 4-PART BRASS	E51
CABUS, P.N. RHAPSODIE. SOLO TPT, SOLO TRB, BRASS CHOIR	D67
GARLICK, A. SINFONIETTA. BRASS CHOIR, PERC	G66
GASSMANN, A.I. A D'R AELPLER-CHILBI	C80
GASSMANN, A.I. FLOTTE TROMPETER, DER. 1 TO 7 BRASS	C80
HANDEL, G.F.-MAYES. MINUET (WATER MUSIC)	F97
HEUSSENSTAMM, G. MUSEUM PIECE. 2 BRASS CHOIRS, PERC	G66
KREISLER, A.V. 2 CHORALES	F60
LASSUS, R.D. ECHO-SONG. DOUBLE BRASS CHOIR, 12 PARTS	F64
MENDELSSOHN, F.-FITZGERALD. EXCERPTS (ELIJAH)	F60
MOZART, W.A.-MAYES. PANTOMIME (LES PETITS RIENS)	F97
PFANNENSTIEL, E. FESTIVE MUSIC	D98
REED. SACRED SUITE, A	D63
SCHAEFFER, D. (ARR). BRASS CHOIR, THE	E80
USOV, A.I. (CMEL). SIGHTREADING OF PEDAGOGICAL REPETOIRE	E19

BRASS ENSEMBLE-BAND

ALFE, M.W. EXCELSIOR. TRB, EU, *BAND	A78
ALLIER. JEAN ET JEANNETTE POLKA. 2COR, *BAND	D64
ALLIER. PIERRE ET PIERRETTE POLKA. 2COR, *BAND	D64
ANDERSON, L. BUGLER'S HOLIDAY. 3TPT, *BAND	D84
ANDRIEU. BLANC ET ROSE POLKA. 2COR, *BAND	D64
ANDRIEU. DEUX BAVARDS POLKA, LES. 2COR, *BAND	D64
ANDRIEU. SABRE ET LANCE VALSE. 2COR, *BAND	D64
BACH, J.S.-PETERSEN. CRUCIFIXUS (MASS IN B MINOR) 2TPT, 2TRB, *BAND	D14
BALL, E. QUID PRO QUO. 3TPT, 3TRB, *BAND	F54
BARNARD. PALS, THE. 2TPT, *BAND	C11
BARNES, C.P. THREE DEBONAIRS. 3TPT(3TRB), *BAND, *PF	G10
BARNES, C.P. THREE GAYBRIELLOS. 3TPT, *BAND, *PF	D52
BENNETT, D. FOUR HORNSMEN. 4HN, *BAND, *EF	C11
BENNETT, D. FRENCH HORN FRAPPE. 4HN, *BAND, *PF	C11
BENNETT, D. TOURNAMENT OF TRUMPETS. 4TPT, *BAND, *PF	C11
BENNETT, D. TROMBONE TROUBADOURS. 4TRB, *BAND	C11
BINGE, R.-MOLENAAR. CORNET CARILLON. 3TPT, *BAND	D92
BINGE, R. CORNET CARRILLON. 3TPT, *BAND	E59
BOUCHEL. DEUX COUSINS POLKA, LES. COR(2CCR), *BAND	D64
BRUYNS-VEENENDAAL. SLEDEPAARDJES, DE. 2TPT, *BAND	D92
BURKE, J.F. MAGIC TRUMPET. 3TPT, *BAND, *PF	C11
BUTTS, C.M. SWINGIN' SLIDES. 3TRB, *BAND, *PF	D52
CANIVEZ. SIMONE-YVONNE POLKA. COR, BUGLE, *BAND	D64
CATELINET, P.B. TRIPOLKA. 3TPT(SOP COR & 2 COR), *BAND	A69
CATIZONE, J.-YODER. VALVETTE. 3TPT, *BAND	G10
CHRISTENSEN, J. BEGUINE FOR TROMBONES. 4TRB, *BAND	D14
CLARK, M. SPANISH HORNS. 2HN, *BAND	A78
CURZON, F. BUSYBODIES. 2COR, *BAND	A78
DARCY, T.F.JR. TRIO FOR TRUMPETS. 3TPT, *BAND	A84

```
DAVIS, A.O.  THREE CARDINALS.  3TPT, *BAND, *PF                        D52
DAYRIES.  POLKA DES YEUX BLEUS, LA.  2COR, *BAND                       D64
DE LAMATER, E.  CRACKER JACKS.  3TPT, *BAND, *PF                       F07
DELBECQ, L.  DEUX TROUBADOURS, LES.  2EU(2TRB), *BAND                  D92
DELBECQ, L.  DOUBLETTE, FANTAISIE-DUO                                  D64
    2TPT(2COR, 2BUGLES), *BAND,*PF
DOBSON, G.  BLACK NOTE FANTASY.  3COR, *BAND                           A78
ELLIOTT-SMITH, H.  ENTRE NOUS.  2COR, *BAND                            A78
FARIGOUL, J.  TOUT EN ROSE POLKA.  2COR, *BAND                         D64
FARRELL, J.  TWO JOLLY BOYS.  2COR, *BAND                              A78
FINLAY, G.  TRUMPETER'S CARNIVAL.  3TPT, *BAND, *PF                    B52
FINLAYSON, W.A.  BRIGHT EYES.  3TPT, *BAND, *PF                        A78
FRANCESCHINI, P.-NAGEL.  SONATA.  2TPT, *BAND                          D63
FRANK, F.L.  MINKA, MINKA, FANTASY ON A FOLK SONG                      F07
    3TPT, *BAND, *PF
FRANZ, O.-SANSONE.  CONCERT PIECE, OP. 4.  2HN, *BAND                  F60
GLOVER, S.  IRAUTE HEIMAT.  2TPT, *BAND                                F10
HARDIN.  HAUNTING HORNS.  4HN, *BAND                                   F72
HARTLEY, W.S.  CONCERTO.  3TRB, *BAND                                  B98
HELYER.  TRICKY TROMBONES.  3TRB, *BAND                                D92
HERBERT, V.-SCHOENFELD.  THREE SOLITAIRES, THE.  3TPT, *BAND           G31
HERFURTH, R.  ALPINE ECHOES.  2COR, *BAND, *PF                         A78
HUME, J.O.  TIT-LARKS, THE.  2 SOP COR(SOP COR, COR), *BAND            A78
KLING-DIEPENBEEK.  TWEE KLEINE VINKEN.  2TPT, *BAND                    D92
KLING.  TWO LITTLE FINCHES.  2COR, *BAND, *PF                          A78
KORNER, B.  ECHO VOM MYTHENSTEIN.  2TPT, *BAND                         F10
LABOLE.  PINSON ET FAUVETTE POLKA.  2COR, *BAND                        D64
LAMY, F.  DEUX HOMMES DE CUIVRE POLKA, LES.  TRB, COR, *BAND           D64
LANGLOIS.  TROIS INSEPARABLES POLKA, LES.  COR, 2BUGLES, *BAND         D64
LAUNAY.  ROSSIGNOL ET FAUVETTE POLKA.  2COR, *BAND                     D64
LEIDZEN, E.W.G.  TRUMPETERS, THE.  4TPT, *BAND                         A84
LEONARD, C.H.  TRIOLET.  3TPT, *BAND, *PF                              E93
LITTLE, L.  THREE MODERNAIRES.  3TPT, *BAND, *PF                       D52
LOZES.  DEUX AMIS POLKA, LES.  2COR, *BAND                             D64
MACKENZIE, G.  SHALLOWS SERENADE, THE.  2TPT, *BAND                    E83
MAINZER, M.  MERRY MUSICIANS.  2TPT, *BAND                             A82
MAYR, S.-MOLENAAR.  BIRDS OF THE FOREST.  2TPT, *BAND, *PF             D92
MC FARLANE, A.  SPOTLIGHT ON TROMBONEERS.  3TRB, *BAND                 A69
MC FARLANE, A.  THREE TROMBONEERS, THE.  3TRB, *BAND                   A69
MENDELSSOHN, F.  I WAITED FOR THE LORD.  2COR, *BAND                   A78
MIDDIMAN, H.  FLORENCE AND JOAN.  2TPT, *BAND                          A78
MOECKEL, H.  SCHNELLE ZUGE.  3TRB, *BAND                               F10
MORAND.  A NOUS DEUX POLKA.  2COR, *BAND                               D64
MORRISSEY, J.J.  BRAVURA FOR TRUMPETS.  3TPT, *BAND                    E67
MORTIMER, H.  MAC AND MORT.  2TPT, *BAND                               E59
NELHYBEL, V.  ORGANUM.  3TPT, 4HN, 3TRB, EU, TU, *BAND                 N18
PARES.  CREPUSCULE.  2INST ?, *BAND                                    D64
PUTZ.  OLYMPIA MAZURKA.  2COR, *BAND                                   D64
ROMSBERG.  TROIS MOUSQUETAIRES FANTAISIE-CAPRICE, LES                  D64
    TPT(BUGLE), 2COR, *BAND
ROSSOW, A.  HERBSTGEDANKEN.  2FLG, *BAND                               F10
SCARMOLIN, A.L.  THREE SWINGSTERS.  3TPT, *BAND, *PF                   D52
SCHULLER, G.  DIPTYCH.  2TPT, HN, TRB, TU, *BAND, *ORCH                A38
SCHUMANN, R.-MC GOVERN.  CONCERTSTUCK.  4HN, *WIND ENS                 P49
SCULL.  OXFORD FLIER.  TPT, POSTHORN, *BAND                            F54
SEEGER, P.  CONCERTO GROSSO.  BAR, 2FLG, AHN, *BAND                    F31
SIEBERT, E.  THREE JOLLY AIRMEN.  3TPT, *BAND                          D92
SIEBERT, E.  THREE JOLLY SAILORMEN.  3TPT, *BAND                       E59
SIEBERT, E.-MOLENAAR.  THREE JOLLY SAILORMEN.  3TPT, *BAND             D92
SIEBERT, E.  WARRIORS THREE.  3TPT, *BAND                              E59
SIMEONE, H.  SLIDE KICKS.  3TRB, *BAND, *PF                            F43
STANLEY, L.  CASCADE.  3COR, *BAND                                     A69
```

STANLEY, L. TROMBONE TRIO. 3TRB(4TRB), *BAND	A78
STANLEY, L. TROMBONES IN TRIPLICATE. 3TRB, *BAND	A69
STANLYE, L. CHASE, THE. POSTHORN, *BAND	A78
SUTTON, E. HUMMING BIRDS, THE. 2COR, *BAND	A78
SUTTON, E. WARBLERS, THE. 2TPT, *BAND	E83
SUTTON, E. YOU AND I. TRB, COR, *BAND	A78
TANNER, P. CONCERT DUET. 2TRB, *BAND	C77
TANNER, P. CONCERT DUET. TRB, BTRB, *BAND, *PF	G21
TANNER, P. CONCERTO. 2TRB, *BAND	C77
TANTERL, H.-MOSHEIMER. ALMZAUBER IDYLLE. 2FLG, *BAND	B99
TORELLI, G.-CIPOLLA. SINFONIA. 4TPT, *BAND	F43
VANCURA, A. HEIMATERINNERUNGEN. 2FLG, *BAND	B99
VINTER, G. DOVER COACH, THE. 3TPT, *BAND	A78
VIVALDI, A.-LANG. CONCERTO IN B-FLAT. 2TPT, *BAND	B32
WAGNER. CONCERTO GROSSO. 3TPT, EU, *BAND	G21
WALTERS, H.L. FANTASY FOR THREE. 3TPT, *BAND	F07
WALTERS, H.L. JIM DANDIES. 3TPT, *BAND	F07
WALTERS, H.L. SLIPPERY GENTLEMEN. 3TRB, *BAND	F07
WALTERS, H.L. THREE JACKS. 3TPT, *BAND	D52
WALTERS, H.L. TROMBONE CONTRASTS. 3TRB, *BAND	F07
WALTERS, H.L. TRUMPETS WILD. 3TPT, *BAND	F07
WEINZWEIG, J.J. DIVERTIMENTO. TPT, TRB, *BAND	E65
WILBER, W. HORNS A'PLENTY. 4HN, *BAND	D55
WILLIAMS, E.S. ORION. 3TPT, *BAND, *PF	B31
WILLIAMS, E.S. THREE BLUEJACKETS. 3TPT, *BAND, *PF	B31
WRIGHT, D.S. MERRY MOUNTAINEERS. 2COR, *BAND	A78
YODER, P. TRUMPET TRIO. 3TPT, *BAND	D18
ZAAL. BRILLIANT LITTLE BRASS. 3TPT, *BAND	D92

BRASS & WW ENSEMBLE-BAND

HAMM, J.V.-HARDING. DIALOG FOR FOUR. HN, FL, OB, CL, *BAND	D18
LONG, N.H. CONCERTINO FOR WW QUINTET & BAND HN, FL, OB, CL, BSN, *BAND	D34
STOUFFER, P.M. CONCERTINO FOR TWO. TPT, CL, *BAND	B91
WARRINGTON, J. ORIGINAL DIXIELAND CONCERTO TPT, TRB, TU(DB), CL, PERC, TSAX, *BAND	D63

BRASS & MISC. ENSEMBLE-BAND

LONG, P.J. TRUMPET AND DRUM. TPT, SDR, *BAND	D84
WARRINGTON, J. ORIGINAL DIXIELAND CONCERTO TPT, TRB, TU(DB), CL, PERC, TSAX, *BAND	D36

BRASS ENSEMBLE-ORCHESTRA

ANDERSON, L. BUGLER'S HOLIDAY. 3TPT, *ORCH	D84
ANDRIESSEN, J. SYMPHONIETTA CONCERTANTE. 4TPT, *ORCH	B74
ARNE, T.A. ANDANTINO & CON SPIRITO (SYMPHONY NO. 4) 2TPT, *ORCH	C33

```
BACH, J.S.  BRANDENBURG CONCERTO NO. 1, F-DUR                    C03
   2HN, 3OB, BSN, VN, *ORCH
BACH, J.S.-DEHN.  BRANDENBURG CONCERTO NO. 2                     E65
   TPT, FL, OB, VN, *ORCH
BACH, J.S.-SCHERING.  BRANDENBURG CONCERTO NO. 2                 C03
   TPT, FL, OB, VN, *ORCH
BARATTO.  LUX AETERNA.  2TPT, *ORCH                              N40
BARSANTI-PRAETORIUS.  CONCERTO GROSSO, OP. 3/4.  2HN, *ORCH      C03
BERGHMANS, J.  CONCERTO GROSSO.  TPT, HN, TRB, *ORCH, *PF        D36
BIBER, H.I.F.  SONATA I.  4TPT, *ORCH                            F97
BIBER, H.I.F.  SONATA II.  8TPT, *ORCH                           F97
BIBER, H.I.F.-SHERMAN.  2 SONATAS.  6TPT, *ORCH                  F97
BLOW-SHAW.  PRELUDE & CANZONA.  2TPT, *ORCH                      C71
CASTEREDE, J.  CONCERTINO.  TPT, TRB, *ORCH                      D36
CORELLI, A.-WERDIN.  CONCERTINO.  2TPT, *ORCH                    F31
D'ORDONEZ-LANDON.  SINFONIA PER TRE CORI.  4TPT, *ORCH           F97
DEFAY, J.M.  CONCERTO.  TPT, TRB, *ORCH, *PF                     D36
DUBENSKY, A.  CONCERTO GROSSO.  3TRB, TU, *ORCH                  E98
DUBOIS, P.M.  QUARTET.  4TRB, *ORCH                              D36
EDER, H.  MUSIK, OP. 23, NO. 2.  2TPT, *ORCH                     E14
ETLER, A.D.  CONCERTO.  2TPT, HN, 2TRB, PERC, *ORCH              P38
FRANCESCHINI, P.-TARR.  SONATA IN D MAJOR.  2TPT, *ORCH, *PF     E14
GUZINGER-KOCH.  CONCERTO IN C MAJOR.  2TPT, *ORCH                N14
HAYDN, J.-LANDON.  CASSATIO IN D.  4HN, *ORCH                    B73
HAYDN, J.-LELOIR.  CONCERTO IN E-FLAT MAJOR.  2HN, *ORCH         D11
HOEFFNER-BLOCK.  SONATA A 8 IN C.  2TPT, BSN, *ORCH              E14
HUBLER, H.  CONCERTO FOR 4 HORNS.  4HN, *ORCH                    D11
HUBLER, H.  CONCERTO.  4HN, *ORCH                                D11
HUSA, K.  CONCERTO.  2TPT, HN, TRB, TU, *ORCH                    D36
KETTING, O.  CONCERTINO.  2TPT, *ORCH                            B74
KLEBE, G.  ESPRESSIONI LIRICHE.  TPT, HN, TRB, *ORCH             F97
KOERING.  DYNASTIES.  2TPT, HN, TRB, TU, *ORCH                   G60
KOETSIER, J.  KONZERT.  TPT, TRB, *ORCH                          F53
KOX, H.  CONCERTANTE MUSIC.  TPT, HN, TRB, *ORCH                 B74
LEGRENZI, G.-BLOCK.  SONATA, OP. 8 "LA BUSCHA"                   E14
   2TPT, BSN(VC), *ORCH
MANFREDINI, F.-TONI.  CONCERTO IN D MAJOR.  2TPT, *ORCH          B07
MIHALOVICI, M.  VARIATIONS.  2TPT, 2TRB, *ORCH                   A16
MONNIKENDAM, J.  CONCERTO.  TPT, HN, *ORCH                       B74
MOZART, L.-LELOIR.  CONCERTO.  2HN, *ORCH                        D11
PURCELL, D.-NAGEL.  SONATA.  2TPT, *ORCH                         F31
ROSETTI, F.A.-WEELINK.  CONCERTO V.  2HN, *ORCH                  D11
SCHMID, H.K.  TURMMUSIK, OP. 105A.  6TPT, *ORCH                  A89
SCHUMANN, R.  CONCERT PIECE, OP. 86, IN F.  4HN, *ORCH           D11
SCHUMANN, R.  KONZERTSTUCK F-DUR, OP. 86.  4HN, *ORCH            A89
STOKOWSKI.  TRADITIONAL SLAVIC CHRISTMAS MUSIC                   P38
   3TPT, 4HN, 3TRB, TU, *ORCH
STOLZEL, G.H.  KONZERT FUR 2 TROMPETENCHORE.  6TPT, *ORCH        A89
STRADELLA, A.-TARR.  SONATA A 4.  2TPT, TRB, *ORCH               B46
SYDEMAN, W.  DOUBLE CONCERTO.  TPT, TRB, *BAND, *ORCH            G66
TELEMANN, G.P.-THILDE.  CONCERT IN C MINOR.  2TPT, *ORCH         A71
TELEMANN, G.P.-LELOIR.  CONCERTO IN D.  3HN, *ORCH               D11
TELEMANN, G.P.-SEIFFERT.  KONZERT IN E-FLAT MAJOR.  2HN, *ORCH   A89
TELEMANN, G.P.-BRAUN.  OVERTURE.  4HN, *ORCH                     C03
TELEMANN, G.P.-BUTTNER.  SUITE.  2HN, *ORCH                      C03
TORELLI, G.-TARR.  SINFONIA A 4 IN C.  4TPT, *ORCH               E14
TORELLI, G.  SINFONIA IN D, G. 21.  2HN, *ORCH                   E14
TORELLI, G.  SINFONIA.  2TPT, *ORCH                              E14
VEJVANOVSKY, P.J.  INTRADA.  2TPT, ORG                           D78
VIVALDI, A.-SCHROEDER.  CONCERTO IN C MAJOR.  2TPT, *ORCH        C03
VIVALDI, A.-SCHROEDER.  CONCERTO IN F MAJOR, OP. 48/6            C03
   2HN, *ORCH
```

WERDIN, E. FESTLICHE MUSIK. 3TPT, TRB, *ORCH   F31
WUORINEN, C. CONCERTONE. 2TPT, HN, TRB, TU, *ORCH   D55

BRASS & WW ENSEMBLE-ORCHESTRA

ARRIEU, C. CONCERT. HN, FL, OB, CL, BSN, *ORCH   E98
BARBER, S. CAPRICORN CONCERTO, OP. 21. TPT, FL, OB, *ORCH   F23
BAUR, J. PENTAGRAMM. HN, FL, OB, CL, BSN, *ORCH   A90
BENTZON, N.V. KONZERT NR.5, OP.171   H30
   HN, FL, OB, CL, BSN, *ORCH
BLACHER, B. KONZERTSTUCK. HN, FL, OB, CL, BSN, *ORCH   A83
BREVAL, J. CONCERTANTE, OP. 38 IN F. HN, CL, BSN, *ORCH   D11
BURKHARD, W. TOCCATA. TRB, FL, CL, BSN, *ORCH   A51
CLARKE, J. SUITE IN D MAJOR. TPT, 2OB, BSN, BC, *ORCH, *PF   F07
COPLAND, A. QUIET CITY. TPT, EH(OB), *ORCH   A78
CRUSELL, B.H.-SEELINK. CONCERTANTE IN B-FLAT   D11
   HN, CL, BSN, *ORCH, *PF
CRUSELL, B.H. CONCERTANTE. HN, CL, BSN, *ORCH   D11
CRUSELL, B.H. CONCERTANTE, OP. 3 IN B-FLAT   D11
   HN, CL, BSN, *ORCH
DANZI, F. SINFONIA CONCERTANTE. HN, FL, CB, BSN, *ORCH   E14
DANZI, F.-ZIRNBAUER. SINFONIA CONCERTANTE   F31
   HN, FL, OB, BSN, *ORCH
DAVID, T.C. KONZERT. HN, FL, OB, CL, BSN, *ORCH   B73
DI DOMENICA, R. CONCERTO. HN, FL, OB, CL, BSN, *ORCH   D63
ECKHARDT¬GRAMATTE, S.C. TRIPEL-KONZERT. TPT, CL, BSN, *ORCH   F97
ETLER, A.D. CONCERTO. HN, FL, OB, CL, BSN, *ORCH   A38
GHEDINI, G.F. CONCERTO GROSSO. HN, FL, OE, CL, BSN, *ORCH   G41
GYROWETZ, A. SINFONIA CONCERTANTE   E14
   HN, OB, CL, BSN, *ORCH, *PF
HENRICH, H. KLEINE SUITE. HN, OB, *ORCH   C60
HINDEMITH, P. DINNER MUSIC (PLONER MUSIKTAG)   E14
   TPT(CL), FL, *ORCH
HINDEMITH, P. KONZERT. TPT, BSN, *ORCH   F31
HUFFMAN, S. SYMPHONY NO. 8. HN, FL, OB, CL, BSN, *ORCH   A15
IVES, C.E. UNANSWERED QUESTION, THE   F59
   TPT(OB, CL, EH), 3FL(3OB), FL(CL), *ORCH
KLEIN, F.R. KAMMERKONZERT. TPT, FL, CL, BSN, *ORCH   C41
KLUSAK, F. CONCERTO GROSSO. HN, FL, OB, CL, BSN, *ORCH   A51
KROL, E. CONCERTO GROSSO, OP. 15. 2TPT, OB, BSN, EH, *ORCH   A83
KUPZ, S. KAMMERKONZERT, OP. 31. HN, FL, CB, CL, BSN, *ORCH   Z89
MARTELLI, H. CONCERTINO, OP. 85. HN, OB, BSN, *ORCH   E98
MARTIN, F. CONCERTO FOR 7 WIND INST   F97
   TPT, HN, TRB, FL, OB, CL, BSN, *ORCH
MIHALY, A. FANTASIE. HN, FL, BSN, *ORCH   G39
MOZART, W.A. SINFONIA CONCERTANTE IN E-FLAT, K. 297B   E14
   HN, OB, CL, BSN, *ORCH
MOZART, W.A. SINFONIA CONCERTANTE IN MI BEM, K. 297B   E98
   HN, OB, CL, BSN, *ORCH
MOZART, W.A. SINFONIA CONCERTANTE, ES-DUR, K. 297B   A89
   HN, OB, CL, BSN, *ORCH
MUSCARO, M. ODE. HN, BSN, *ORCH   B44
PLEYEL, I.J.-OUBRADOUS. FIFTH SYMPHONY CONCERTANTE   F87
   HN, FL, OB(CL), BSN, *ORCH, *PF
PLEYEL, I.J. SINFONIA CONCERTANTE   E14
   HN, FL, OB, BSN, *ORCH, *PF
RAWSTHORNE, A. CONCERTANTE PASTORALE. HN, FL, *ORCH   E51
RIETI, V. CONCERTO. HN, FL, OB, CL, BSN, *ORCH   F97

SCHULLER, G. CONTRASTS. HN, FL, OB, CL, BSN, *ORCH   F31
STARER, R. CONCERTO A TRE. TPT, TRB, CL, *ORCH   D37
SWANN, J. SINFONIE CONCERTANTE. HN, FL, OB, CL, BSN, *ORCH   B35
VOGEL, J.C. SINFONIA CONCERTANTE, C   A38
   2HN, 3OB, 2OB(2CL), BSN, *ORCH
VOORMOLEN, A. SINFONIA CONCERTANTE. HN, CL, *ORCH   B74
WOLF-FERRARI, E. CONCERTINO, OP. 34. 2HN, EH, *ORCH   A38

BRASS & MISC ENSEMBLE-ORCHESTRA

AUSTIN, L. IMPROVISATIONS   D86
   TPT, CL, JDB, JDP, TSAX, BARSAX, *ORCH
BARBER, S. TOCCATA FESTIVA, OP. 36A. TPT, ORG, TIMP, *ORCH   F23
BENTZON, N.V. KONZERT NR.1, OP.167. TPT, HN, FL, *ORCH   H30
BENTZON, N.V. KONZERT NR.4, OP.170. TRB, CL, DB, *ORCH   H30
BLACHER, B. CONCERTO, OP. 36. TPT, HN, CL, BSN, HP, *ORCH   A83
BURY, E. SYMPHONY NO. 2 FOR 6 SOLO INST & ORCH   A31
   TPT, FL, OB, CL, BSN, XYL, *ORCH
COPE, D. MUSIC FOR BRASS AND STRINGS   B35
   2TPT, 4HN, 4TRB, PERC, *ORCH
CORBEEL, R. SUITE NO. 1. 2HN, PF, *ORCH   D67
DELANO, J. OFFRENDA MUSICAL. HN, VA, *ORCH   F59
HAINES, E. CONCERTINO FOR 7 SOLO INST   A15
   TPT, HN, FL, CL, VN, VA, VC, *ORCH
HELM, E. CONCERTO FOR 5 SOLO INST   F31
   TPT, FL, OB, BSN, VN, *ORCH
JARRE, M. POLYPHONIES CONCERTANTES. TPT, PERC, PF, *ORCH   E98
KOUTZEN, B. CONCERTO FOR 5 SOLO INST   A15
   HN, FL, CL, BSN, VC, *ORCH
KUBIK, G. SYMPHONY CONCERTANTE. TPT, PF, VA, *ORCH   B32
LEVY, F. DIALOGUE. TU, TIMP, HP, *STR CRCH   G66
MARTIN, F. CONCERTO   F97
   TPT, HN, TRB, FL, OB, CL, BSN, PERC, TIMP, *ORCH
MILHAUD, D. SYMPHONIE CONCERTANTE. TPT, HN, BSN, DB, *ORCH   C65
MONNIKENDAM, M. CONCERTO. 2TPT, 2TRB, ORG, *ORCH   B74
PFISTER, H. FANTAISIE CONCERTANTE. HN, FL, HP, *ORCH   C71
POSER, H. CONCERTINO, OP. 19. TPT, PF, *ORCH   F50
RESPIGHI, O. CONCERTO A CINQUE. TPT, OB, PF, VN, DB, *ORCH   E98
RYTEL, P. SINFONIA CONCERTANTE. HN, FL, CL, HP, *ORCH   A31
SHOSTAKOVITCH, D.D. CONCERTO, OP. 35. TPT, PF, *ORCH   A98
SHOSTAKOVITCH, D.D. CONCERTO, OP. 35. TPT, PF, *ORCH   F13
SMYTH, E.M. CONCERTO FOR VN, HN, & ORCH. HN, VN, *ORCH   G58
STAMITZ, K. KONZERTANTE SYMPHONIE   F97
   2HN, FL, OB, CL, VN, VC, *ORCH
TELEMANN, G.P.-LELOIR & WEELINK. CONCERTO IN D   D11
   HN, VN, HPCD, *ORCH
VAN DELDEN, I. PICCOLA MUSICA CONCERTATA, OP. 79   B74
   3TRB, TIMP, *ORCH

BRASS-ELECTRONICS

BOTTJE, W.G. TRIANGLES. TPT(COR), TU, RT   A13
BROWN, E. TIMES 5. TRB, FL, VN, VC, HP, RT   F97
BROWN, J. IMPROMPTU. TRB, RT   M80

```
CHILDS, B.  INTERBALANCES VI.  HN, PF, RT                          A13
COPE, D.  BRIGHT ANGEL.  TPT, RT                                   G66
DIEMENTE, E.  HOSANNA II.  BTRB, RT                                G66
DIEMENTE, E.  SOMETHING ELSE.  TPT, RT                             G66
DODGE, C.  EXTENSIONS.  TPT, RT                                    A13
ELLIS.  MUTATIONS (USES FILM & TAPE).  2TPT, HN, TRB, TU, RT       F78
ERICKSON, F.  RICERCARE A 5.  TRB, RT                              G66
ERNST.  EXIT.  TPT, RT                                             F43
FENNER, B.  PRELUDE.  BRASS, TIMP, TAPE                            G66
HELLERMANN, W.  PASSAGES 13.  TPT, RT                              A13
HEUSSENSTAMM, G.  LAMINAE, OP. 50.  TPT/PICTPT, RT                 G66
HUTCHISON, W.  HORNPIECE I.  HN, RT                                G66
LAZAROF, H.  PARTITA.  2TPT, HN, TRB, TU, RT                       A38
MELBY, J.  91 PLUS 5.  2TPT, HN, TRB, TU, COMPUTER                 A13
OTT, J.  BART'S PIECE.  TU, RT                                     A65
OTT, J.  CONCERTO.  TU, RT                                         A65
OTT, J.  3 LITTLE PIECES.  TPT, RT                                 A65
OTT, J.  TIMBRES.  2TPT, HN, TRB, TU, RT                           A65
PINKHAM, D.  OTHER VOICES OF THE TRUMPET, THE.  TPT, ORG, RT       F22
SCHWARTZ, E.S.  MUSIC FOR NAPOLEON & BEETHOVEN.  TPT, PF, RT       P37
SCHWARTZ, E.S.  OPTIONS I.  TRB, PERC, RT                          N29
TANENBAUM, E.  IMPROVISATIONS.  2TPT, HN, TRB, TU, RT              A13
TANENBAUM, E.  PATTERNS.  2TPT, HN, 2TRB, RT                       A13
TROMBLY, P.  TOCCATA/2.  TRB, RT                                   A13
VARESE, E.  DESERTS                                               B32
     3TPT, 1HN, 3TRB, 2TU, 2BL, 2CL, PERC, PF, RECORDED TAPE
```

BRASS-HARP

```
AERVOETS, R.  MUSICA PER 14 STRUMENTI                              E98
     TPT, HN, TRB, FL, OB, CL, BSN, VN, VA, VC, DB, BCL, HP, CEL
BABBITT, M.  COMPOSITION                                           A38
     TPT, HN, FL, OB, CL, BSN, VN, VA, VC, DB, HP, CEL
BIRTWISTLE, H.  WORLD IS DISCOVERED, THE                           F97
     2HN, 2FL, OB, CL, 2BSN, EH, BSTHN(BCL), HP, GUIT
BROWN.  5 PIECES.  4TRB, EU, TU, PERC, HP, ORG                     A43
BROWN, E.  TIMES 5.  TRB, FL, VN, VC, HP, RT                       F97
BROWN, E.  CONCERTINO.  2TPT, HN, TRB, TU, HP                      G21
COSSART, L.A.  SUITE FOR 10 WINDS & HARP                           C60
     2HN, 2FL, 2OB, 2CL, 2BSN, HP
DIMOV, B.  INCANTATIONES.  TPT, FL, VA, S, HP                      D88
DUBOIS, T.  FANTASIE.  TPT, ORG                                    C65
FRANKO, J.  PSALM FOR BRASSES & HARP.  3TPT, HN, TRB, HP           E68
GENZMER, H.  SEPTET.  HN, FL, CL, VN, VA, VC, HP                   F30
GHEDINI, G.F.  ADAGIO E ALLEGRO DA CONCERTO                        E98
     HN, FL, CL, VN, VA, VC, HP
HAYDN, J.  HARFEN-SEPTETT, OP. 7.  HN, CL, BSN, VN, VA, VC, HP     C59
HINDEMITH, P.  KONZERTMUSIK, OP. 49 (SOLO PF)                      F31
     3TPT, 4HN, 2TRB, TU, PF, 2HP
KETTING, O.  2 CANZONI                                             B74
     TPT, 2HN, TRB, FL, OB, 2CL, BSN, PERC, HP, CEL
KLEBE, G.  7 BAGATELLEN, OP. 35.  BSTHN, HF, BELLS                 TRB
KOELLREUTTER, H.J.  CONSTRUCTIO AD SYNESIN                         D88
     TPT, FL/PIC, OB/EH, CL/BCL, PERC, PF, VN, CONTBSN, HP, CEM
LEWIS, P.T.  LAMENT FOR MRS. BRIDGE                                E68
     TPT, 2HN, TRB, FL, OB, 3DB, PIC, CONTBSN, PERC, MND, HP(VIB)
MAMANGAKIS, N.  KASSANDRA.  HN, TRB, FL, 2PERC, S, HP              D88
MIKULICZ, L.  ROMANTISCHES SCHERZO.  2HN, HP                       C30
```

```
MOEVS, R.   MUSICA DA CAMERA                                          D 36
    HN, 2FL, 3CL, 2BSN, PERC, HP,VN, VA, VC
MOULAERT, R.  CONCERT.  HN, FL, OB, CL, BSN, HP                       B 12
PFISTER, H.  FANTAISIE CONCERTANTE.  HN, FL, HP, *ORCH                C 71
RAVEL, M.-RYKER.  PAVANE POUR UNE INFANTE DEFUNTE                     D 94
    2TPT, HN, TRB, TU, HP
RINGGER, R.U.  4 LIEDER AUF JAPANISCHE LYRIK                          D 88
    HN, CL, VN, VA, DB, S, HP
RYTEL, P.  SINFONIA CONCERTANTE.  HN, FL, CL, HP, *ORCH               A 31
SALMHOFER, F.  KAMMERSUITE, OP. 19                                    F 97
    2HN, FL, 2OB, 3CL, 2BSN, 2VN, VA, VC, DB, HP
SCEINKMAN, M.  DIVERTIMENTO.  TPT, TRB, CL, HP                        D 48
SCHMIDT.  MUSIC FOR SCRIMSHAWS.  BRASS QUINTET, HARP                  A 43
SCHMIDT, W.  SHORT'NIN' BREAD VARIATIONS                              A 43
    4TPT, 4HN, 4TRB, EU, 2TU, PERC, HP
SHEINKMAN, M.  DIVERTIMENTO.  TPT, TRB, CL, HP                        E 65
SIBELIUS, J.-STRAVINSKY.  CANZONETTA, OP. 62A                         A 90
    4HN, CL, DB, BCL, HP
SOURILAS, T.  SUITE.  HN, OB, VC, HP(PF)                              D 41
SPOHR, L.  WAS TREIBT DEN WEIDMAN (MED VOICE).  HN, PF(HP), V         D 55
STOCKHAUSEN, K.H.  KONTRA-PUNKTE NR. 1                                F 94
    TPT, TRB, FL, CL, BSN, PF, VN, VC, BCI, HP
TOMMASINI, V.  SCHERZO                                               E 98
    TPT, HN, FL, OB, CL, BSN, 2VN, VA, VC, DB, HP
VAN OTTERLOO, W.  SERENADE (DIVERTIMENTO)                             B 74
    4TPT, 4HN, 3TRB, TU, PERC, HP, CEL
VANDOR, I.  SERENATA.  HN, FL, CL, BSN, VA, VC, HP                    G 41
WIENER, K.  KAMMERSTUCK, OP. 7                                        C 60
    2HN, OB, BSN, PERC, 2VN, VA, VC, DB, BCI, HP
ZELENKA, I.  FRUH-STUCK.  HN, PERC, AFL, BCL, HP, GUIT                D 88
```

TRUMPET-ORGAN

```
BACH, J.S.-BIGGS.  NOW THANK WE ALL OUR GOD.  TPT, *ORG               D 74
FRANCO, J.  BOCK OF JOB, THE.  TPT, *ORG                              B 36
GARLICK, A.  BRIDAL MARCH AND FANFARE.  TPT, ORG                      G 66
HOVHANESS, A.S.  PRAYER OF ST. GREGORY.  TPT, *ORG, *PF               F 59
HOVHANESS, A.S.  SONATA, OP. 200.  TPT, *ORG                          E 65
KAUFFMANN, G.F.  6 CHORALES (HARMONISCHE SEELENLUST)                  B 40
    TPT(OB), *ORG
KENNEDY, J.B.  GLORIA.  TPT, *ORG                                     A 78
KOCH, J.H.E.  5 INTRADAS & CHORALES ON EASTER HYMNS.  TPT, ORG        B 40
KREBS, J.L.  AUSGEWAHLTE ORGELWERKE, 3. FOLGE.  TPT, *ORG             B 40
KREBS, J.L.  8 CHORALE PRELUDES.  TPT, *ORG                           E 10
NAGEL, R.  TRUMPET PROCESSIONAL.  TPT, *ORG                           C 25
PINKHAM, D.  TRUMPET VOLUNTARY.  TPT, *ORG                            E 68
PURCELL, H.  CEREMONIAL MUSIC.  TPT, *ORG                             D 74
PURCELL, H.  SONATA.  TPT, *ORG                                       D 16
ROHLIG, H.  8 INTRADAS & CHORALES.  TPT, *ORG                         B 40
SCHALK, C.  FESTIVAL CHORALE SETTINGS FOR THE SMALL PARISH            B 40
    TPT, *ORG
SOWERBY, L.  FANTASY.  TPT, *ORG                                      C 51
TOMASI, H.  VARIATIONS GREGORIENNES SUR UN SALVE REGINA               D 36
    TPT, *ORG
TORELLI, G.-BERGER.  SINFONIA CON TROMBA.  TPT, *ORG, *ORCH           D 16
VIVIANI, G.B.  2 SONATAS.  TPT, *ORG                                  E 14
```

HORN-ORGAN

```
ALFVEN, H.  NOTTURNO ELEGIACO, OP. 5.  HN, *ORG, *PF        C39
GRANT, P.  ESSAY, OP. 25.  HN(VC), *ORG                     E68
GRANT, P.  POEM, OP. 15.  HN(VC), *ORG                      E68
HUTCHISON, W.  CHORALE FANTASY.  HN, ORG                    G66
MULLER, B.E.  GEBET, OP. 65A.  HN, *ORG, *PF                G43
RAVANELLO, O.  MEDITAZIONE PER ORGANO E CORNO.  HN, *ORG    G38
READ, G.  DE PROFUNDIS.  HN, *ORG                           D16
```

TROMBONE-ORGAN

```
BROWN, C.L.G.  MEDITATION.  TRB, *ORG                       D36
BRUCKNER, A.  AVE MARIA.  TRB, *ORG                         B85
BYRD, W.-ROGERS.  EARLE OF SALISBURY PAVANE, THE            C51
   TPT, HN, TRB, ORG
HUTCHISON, W.  CHORALE FANTASY.  TRB, ORG                   G66
MULLER, B.E.  GEBET.  TRB, *ORG                             G43
STOUT, A.  AUS TIEFER NOTH (J.S. BACH).  TRB, *ORG          E68
STOUT, A.  JESUS CHRISTUS UNSER HEILAND.  TRB, *ORG         E68
STOUT, A.  SOLEMN PRELUDE, OP. 8.  TRB, *ORG                E68
```

BRASS ENSEMBLE-ORGAN

```
AHRENS, J.  KONZERT FUR ORGEL UND BLASER                    E02
   2TPT, 2HN, TRB, ORG, ATRB, BTRB
AICHINGER-KRAUS.  CANZON.  2TPT, *ORG                       A80
ALEXANDER, J.  FESTIVITIES.  2TPT, HN, TRB, TU, ORG(PA)     F59
ANDRIESSEN, H.  PEZZO FESTOSO.  2TPT, 2TRB, ORG             B74
ARNATT.  INTRODUCTION & RONDO.  2TPT, 2TRB, ORG, TIMP       L74
BACH, J.S.  ALLELUIA (CANTATA #142).  2TPT, 2TRB, ORG       D16
BACH, J.S.-CAMPBELL.  ALLELUIA (CANTATA #142).  3TPT, ORG   C51
BACH, J.S.-BITGOOD.  AWAKE, THOU WINTRY EARTH               C51
   2TPT, 2TRB, ORG
BACH, J.S.-CAMPBELL.  CHRIST DOTH END IN TRIUMPH.  3TPT, ORG  C51
BACH, J.S.-BIGGS.  2 CHRISTMAS CHORALES & DOXOLOGY.  2TPT, ORG  A38
BACH, J.S.-CAMPBELL.  CONCERTO (CANTATA #142).  3TPT, ORG   C51
BACH, J.S.-BIGGS.  2 FANFARES & CHORAL.  3TPT, TIMP, ORG    A38
BACH, J.S.  IN DULCI JUBILO.  2TPT, 2TRB(HN), ORG           D16
BACH, J.S.-CAMPBELL.  JESU, JOY OF MAN'S DESIRING.  3TPT, ORG  C51
BACH, J.S.  JESU, NUN SEI GEPREISET (CANTATA #41)           D16
   2TPT, TRB, EU, ORG
BACH, J.S.  MY SPIRIT BE JOYFUL.  2TPT, ORG                 D74
BACH, J.S.-BIGGS.  MY SPIRIT BE JOYFUL.  2TPT, ORG(PA)      D74
BACH, J.S.-BIGGS.  MY SPIRIT BE JOYFUL.  2TPT, *ORG         E77
BACH, J.S.-PARTON.  MY SPIRIT BE JOYFUL.  2TPT, ORG         C51
BACH, J.S.-KING.  NUN DANKET ALLE GOTT (CANTATA #79)        D16
   3TPT, ORG, TIMP(TRB)
BACH, J.S.-BIGGS.  3 WEDDING CHORALES.  2TPT, ORG           B40
```

```
BALES.  FANFARE FOR EASTER.  2TPT, 2HN, PERC, ORG                       P41
BARATTO.  LUX AETERNA.  2TPT, *ORG                                      N40
BAUDACH.  TE DEUM LAUDAMUS.  3TPT, 3TRB, ORG                            A51
BECKLER, S.R.  3 PIECES.  3TPT, 4HN, 3TRB, EU, TU, ORG                  D16
BENDER, J.  COME, HOLY GHOST.  3TPT, 2TRB, ORG                          B40
BERGER, J. (ARR).  SINFONIA CON DUE TROMBE.  2TPT, ORG                  D16
BERTALI, A.-HILL & BLOCK.  6 SONATAS                                    E14
   2TPT, HN(TRE), 2TRB, ORG
BEVERSDORF, T.  CATHEDRAL MUSIC.  2TPT, 2TRB, ORG                       M98
BIBER, H.I.F.-MINTER.  SONATA "SCTI POLYCARPI".  8TPT, *ORG             E14
BIBER, H.I.F.-MINTER.  SONATA A 7.  6TPT, 2TIMP, *ORG                   E14
BIBER, H.I.F.  SONATA.  6TPT, ORG                                       E14
BIBER, H.I.F.  SONATE IN B-DUR.  6TPT, ORG, TIMP                        A51
BINGHAM, S.  CONCERTO, OP. 57.  3TPT, 3TRB, PERC, ORG                   C51
BLISS, A.  CEREMONIAL PRELUDE                                          L69
   3TPT, 4HN, 3TRB, ORG, (OPT CHIMES)
BONELLI, A.  TOCCATA "ATHALANTA".  TPT, TPT(HN), TRB, EU, ORG           D16
BOSWELL (ARR).  ECHO CANZONA.  2TPT, *ORG                               N42
BRAHMS, J.  O WELT, ICH MUSS DICH LASSEN.  2TPT, TRB, EU, ORG           D16
BROWN.  5 PIECES.  4TRB, EU, TU, PERC, HP, ORG                          A43
BROWN, R.  CHORALE PARTITA "HERZLIEBSTER JESU"                          N96
   2TPT, 2TRB, ORG
BUONAMENTE, G.B.-THOMAS.  CANZONA A 5.  2TPT, 3TRB, ORG                 E14
BURNHAM, C.  FESTIVAL CHORALE.  3TPT, 4HN, 2TRB, TU, ORG                D16
BUXTEHUDE, D.-KING.  FANFARE & CHORUS.  3TPT, ORG                       D16
BYRD, W.-ROGERS.  PAVANE.  TPT, HN, TRB, *ORG                           C51
CANTIN.  GRANDE MESSE DE ST. HUBERT.  4HN, *ORG                         D36
CARCASIO-COOPER.  SONATA.  2TPT, *ORG                                   E14
CHAYNES, C.  SEQUENCES POUR L'APOCALYPSE                               D36
   2TPT, HN, TRB, TU, ORG
CLARKE, J.-KINGSBURY.  TRUMPET VOLUNTARY.  3TPT, *ORG                   C51
COWELL, H.  SUPPLICATION.  2TPT, 2TRB, ORG                              E65
CUNNINGHAM, M.  CHURCHES OF UTRILLO.  5HN, ORG                          G66
CUNNINGHAM, M.G.  CHURCHES OF UTRILLO.  4HN, ORG                        B35
DAQUIN, L.C.-KING.  NOEL SUISSE (NOUVEAU LIVRE DE NOELS)                D16
   2TPT, TRB(TPT, HN), ORG
DARASSE.  IN MEMORIAM J.P. GUEZEC.  2TPT, HN, TRB, TU, ORG              F16
DAVID, J.N.  INTROITUS, CHORAL UND FUGUE, CP.25                         A90
   2TPT, 4HN, 3TRB, ORG
DICKINSON.  FANFARES AND ELEGIES.  3TPT, 3TRB, ORG                      E41
DUBOIS, T.-KINGSBURY.  ALLELUIA.  3TPT, TRE, ORG                        C51
DUPRE.  POEM HEROIQUE.  3TPT, 3TRB, ORG, PERC                           G85
EHMANN, W.  VERLEIH UNS FRIEDEN.  2TPT(TRB), 2TRB, ORG                  A51
ELMORE, R.  FANFARE FOR EASTER.  2TPT, 2TRE, PERC, ORG                  H27
ELMORE, R.  FESTIVAL TOCCATA.  2TPT, 2TRB, PERC, ORG                    H27
ELMORE, R.  MEDITATION ON VENI EMMANUEL.  2TPT, 2TRB, ORG               C12
FAUTSCH, L.  CHORALE PRELUDE "IF THOUGH BUT SUFFER...                   D16
   2TPT, TRB(HN), TRB, ORG
FRESCOBALDI, G.  CANZONA #29.  2TPT, 2TRB, ORG                          B40
FRESCOBALDI, G.-DAVID.  CANZONI A DUE.  2TPT, *ORG                      F31
GABRIELI, G.-KING.  CANZON DUODECIMI TONI                               D16
   2TPT, HN(TPT), TRE(HN), TRB, ORG
GABRIELI, G.-BLOCK.  CANZON IN ECHO DUODECIMI TONI A 10                 E14
   4TPT, 2HN(2TPT), 4TRB, 2ORG
GABRIELI, G.  CANZON NONI TONI (SACRAE SYMPHONIAE 1597)                 D16
   2TPT, HN(TRB), EU, ORG
GABRIELI, G.-KING.  CANZON PRIMI TONI (SACRAE SYMPHONIAE 1597)          D16
   TPT, TPT(HN), TRB(HN), TRB, ORG
GABRIELI, G.-BOERINGER.  CANZON SEPTIMI TONI A 8                        B40
   2TPT, 2TRB, ORG
GABRIELI, G.-WOLFF.  O MAGNUM MYSTERIUM.  2TPT, 2TRB, ORG               B40
GABRIELI, G.-KING.  SEPTIMI TONI #1, #2                                 D16
   2TPT(HN), TRB(HN), EU(TRB), ORG
```

GABRIELI, G.-BOSWELL. SONATA CON TRE TROMBE   N42
    3TPT, 3HN, 3TRB, 3EU, *ORG
GABRIELI, G. SONATA PIAN'E FORTE (SACRAE SYMPHONIAE, 1597)   D16
    2TPT, TRB(HN), EU, ORG
GOEB, R.J. 3 PROCESSIONALS. 2TPT, HN, TRB, TU, ORG   E68
GOLLER. CHRIST IST ERSTANDEN. 2TPT, 2HN, TRB, ORG   E49
GOLLER-BEDELL. ITE MISSA EST. 2TPT, 2TRB, ORG   E49
GOLLER-BEDELL. SURSUM CODA. 2TPT, 2TRB, ORG   E49
GRILLO, G.B.-WINTER. SONATA NO. 1. 3TPT, 4TRB, ORG   C41
GRILLO, G.B.-WINTER. SONATA NO. 2. 3TPT, 4TRB, ORG   C41
HAIGH, M. FANTASIA ON A LUTHERAN CHORALE. 6HN, ORG   F78
HARRIS, R. FANTASY. 2TPT, 2TRB, PERC, ORG   A38
HINGESTON. FANTASIA. 2TPT, BTRB, *ORG   F14
HINGESTON-BLOCK. FANTASIA. TPT, TRB, *ORG   E14
INGALLS, M. PRELUDE. 4HN, ORG   P49
IVES, C.E. PROCESSIONAL-LET THERE BE LIGHT. 4TRB, *ORG   E61
JOHNSON. EASTER MUSIC #1. 2TPT, 2TRB, ORG, OPT TIMP   L74
JOHNSON. EASTER MUSIC #2. 2TPT, 2TRB, ORG, OPT TIMP   L74
JOHNSON, D. 6 FANFARES. 2TPT, 2TRB, ORG   B40
KARG-ELERT, S.-KING. NUN DANKET ALLE GOTT (MARCHE TRIOMPHALE)   D16
    3TPT, ORG
KARG-ELERT, S. WUNDERBARER KOENIG. 2TPT, 2TRB, ORG, TIMP   E49
KEE. MUSIC AND SPACE. 3TPT, 2TRB, 2ORG   B74
KING, R.D. PRELUDE & FUGUE. TPT, HN(TPT), TRB, *ORG   D16
KLERK, J.D. CONCERTO. 2TPT, 2HN, 2TRB, ORG   B74
KOCH, F.-EHMANN. TAG, DER IST SO FREUDENREICH, DER   A51
    3TPT, 2TRB, ORG
LASSUS, R.D.-KING. PROVIDEBAM DOMINUM. 3TPT, ORG   D16
LEAHY, M. FESTIVE SUITE. 2TPT, 2TRB, ORG   P48
LIEB. FEATURE SUITE. 2TPT, HN, TRB, TU, ORG   M65
LITAIZE. CORTEGE. 3TPT, 3TRB, ORG   N54
LOCKWOOD, N. CONCERTO. 2TPT, 2TRB, ORG   A38
LOEFFELHOLZ. CHORALBEARBEITUNGEN. 2TPT, 2TRB, ORG   A51
LOVELACE. CONCERTATO ON ADESTE FIDELIS. 2TPT, 2TRB, ORG   L74
MARCELLO, B.-KING. HEAVENS ARE TELLING   D16
    2TPT, TRB(TRB, HN), EU, ORG
MARCELLO, B.-KING. LORD WILL HEAR (PSALM XIX)   D16
    2TPT, TRB(HN), TRB, ORG
MARCELLO, B.-KINGSBURY. PSALM XVIII. 3TPT, TRB, ORG   C51
MEESTER, L.D. POSTLUDIUM. 2TPT, 2TRB, ORG   B12
MENDELSSOHN, F. HOLY IS THE LORD. 2TPT, 2TRB, TIMP, ORG   B40
MONNIKENDAM, M. CONCERTO. 2TPT, 2TRB, ORG   B74
MONNIKENDAM, M. INTRADA & SORTIE. 2TPT, 2TRB, ORG   E14
MULLER. (SEE ALSO "MUELLER")
MULLER, P. CHORALFANTASIE, OP.54/2. 2TPT, 2TRB, ORG   A51
MULLER, P. CHORALTOCCATA "EIN FESTE BURG", OP. 54/1   A51
    2TPT, 2TRB, ORG
NELHYBEL, V. HYMNS. 2TPT, HN(TRB), TRB, ORG   B32
NELHYBEL, V. 3 MOVEMENTS. 2TPT, HN(TRB), TRB, ORG   B32
PACHELBEL, J. CHORALE-PRELUDE "ALLEIN GOTT IN DER HOH...   D16
    2TPT, TRB(TPT, HN), EU, ORG
PEEK. CHACONNE (O FILLI ET FILIAE). 2TPT, 2TRB, PERC, ORG   A94
PEETERS, F. CHORALE-FANTASY "CHRIST THE LORD HAS RISEN"   C51
    2TPT, 2TRB, ORG
PEETERS, F. ENTRATA FESTIVA. 2TPT, 2TRB, ORG   E65
PEZEL, J.C. SONATA #2 (HORA DECIMA, 1670)   D16
    2TPT, TRB(HN), EU, ORG
PEZEL, J.C.-KING. 3 SONATAS (22, 25, 30, HORA DECIMA, 1670)   D16
    2TPT, ORG
PEZEL, J.C.-BLOCK. SONATINAS (61, 62, 65, 66). 2TPT, *ORG   E14
PEZEL, J.C.-BLOCK. SONATINAS (63, 64, 67, 68). 2TPT, *ORG   E14
PEZEL, J.C.-BLOCK. SONATINAS (69, 70, 72, 73). 2TPT, *ORG   E14

```
PEZEL, J.C.-BLOCK. SONATINAS (71, 74). 2TPT, *ORG              E14
PEZEL, J.C. SONATINAS #71 & #74 (BICINIA). 2TPT, TRB, *ORG     F07
PINKHAM, D. ADESTE FIDELES. 2TPT, 2TRB, ORG                    E65
PINKHAM, D. CONCERTANTE. 2TPT, 2TRB, PERC, ORG                 E65
PINKHAM, D. GLORIA (SINFONIA SACRA)                            D16
   2TPT, TRB(HN), EU(TRB), ORG
PINKHAM, D. GOD REST YOU MERRY GENTLEMEN. 2TPT, 2TRB, ORG      E65
PINKHAM, D. SONATA FOR ORGAN & BRASSES. 2TPT, 2TRB, ORG        A13
PIZARRO. TRUMPET TRILOGY. 2TPT, *ORG                           C51
PLOYHAR, J. BRASS FOR FESTIVE HYMNS. 2TPT, 2TRB, ORG           F27
PRAETORIUS, M.-KING. IN DULCI JUBILO                           D16
   2TPT, TRB(TPT, HN), EU, ORG
PURCELL, H.-BIGGS. CEREMONIAL MUSIC. 2TPT, *ORG                E77
READ, G. SINFONIA DA CHIESA. 2TPT, HN, 2TRB, ORG               N09
REICHE, G. SONATA #7 (NEUE QUATRICINIA, 1696)                  D16
   2TPT, TRB, EU, ORG
REICHEL. CHORAL, CANON I & II. 2TRB, *ORG                      A71
ROHLIG, H. GOOD CHRISTIAN MEN REJOICE. 3TPT, *ORG              N62
ROHLIG, H. NOW THANK WE ALL OUR GOD. 3TPT, ORG                 B40
ROHLIG, H. NOW THANK WE ALL OUR GOD. 3TPT, *ORG                N62
ROHLIG, H. O COME ALL YE FAITHFUL. 3TPT, *ORG                  N62
SAINT MARTIN. IN MEMORIAM. 3TPT, 3TRB, ORG                     B81
SCHAFFER, R. PASCHAL TRIPTYCH                                  D16
   3TPT, 4HN, 3TRB, EU, TU, PERC, ORG
SCHEIDT, S.-THOMAS. 4 SYMPHONIES. 2TPT, TRB, *ORG              B40
SCHMIDT. CHAMBER CONCERTO. 2TPT, HN, TRB, TU, ORG              A43
SCHUTZ-MILLER. GIVE EAR, O LORD. 2TRB, ORG                     B98
SCHUTZ, H.-MC CARTY. GIVE EAR, OH LORD. 2TRB, *ORG             B98
SOWERBY, L. FESTIVAL MUSICK. 2TPT, 2TRB, PERC, ORG             C51
SPEER, D.-BROWN. 2 SONATAS. 2TPT, 3TRB, ORG                    C91
STOCKMEIER. VARIATIONEN. 2TPT, 3TRB, ORG                       A51
STRANDBERG, N. MUSIC FOR ORGAN, BRASS & TIMP                   P48
   2TPT, 2TRB, TIMP, ORG
STRAUSS, R.-REGER. FEIERLICHER EINZUG. 2TRB, ORG               D46
SUMERLIN, M. SUITE TRIO. TPT, HN, TRB, ORG                     P48
THILDE, J. SONATE. 2TPT, *ORG                                  A71
TORELLI, G.-CIPOLLA. SINFONIA IN B-FLAT. 4TPT, *ORG            F43
TORELLI, G.-CIPOLLA. SINFONIA IN D. 4TPT, *ORG                 F43
VEJVANOVSKY, P.J. INTRADA. 2TPT, ORG                           D78
VIERNE. MARCHE TRIOMPHALE. 3TPT, 3TRB, PERC, ORG               F16
WATSON, W. MUSIC FOR ORGAN & HORNS. 4HN, *ORG                  F23
WEATHERS. VARIATIONS ON A THEME. TPT, TRB, *ORG                G21
WEEKS. JUBILATE. 3TPT, 3HN, 2TRB, ORG                          C71
WENZEL. MAGNIFICAT IM 9.TON. 2TPT, 3TRB, ORG                   A51
WHITFORD, H. 4 TRUMPET & ORGAN ARRANGEMENTS FROM THE CLASSICS  C12
   2TPT, ORG
WIDOR. SALVUM FAC POPULUM TUUM. 3TPT, 3TRB, PERC, ORG          E49
WIESNER, H. ELEGY TO PASSING MOMENTS. TPT, TRB, PERC, ORG      B35
WOLFF, C. BAROQUE COMPOSERS OF THE CHAPELS ROYAL. 2TPT, *ORG   B40
WOLFF, C. BAROQUE SUITE. 2TPT, *ORG                            B40
WOLFF, C. 3 HYMNS OF PRAISE. 2TPT, 2TRB, ORG                   B40
WOLFF, C. MUSIC FOR THANKSGIVING. 2TPT, 2TRB, ORG              B40
WOLFF, C. SUITE FROM THE FRENCH BAROQUE. 2TPT, *ORG            B40
ZIPP. CHORALKONZERT-SONNE DER GERECHTIGKEIT. 2TPT, 2TRB, ORG   A51
```

BRASS & MISC. INSTRUMENTS-ORGAN

BARBER, S. SONATA FESTIVA. TPT, VN, VA, VC, ORG, TIMP	F23
BLISS, A. SALUTE. 3TPT, 3TRB, PERC, ORG	L69
BOVET, G. FANTASIE POUR FLUTE, COR, ET ORGUE, OP. 17	H03
HN, FL, ORG	
CARCASIO-COOPER. SONATA. 2TPT, 2OB, ORG	E14
DICKINSON, C. JOY OF THE REDEEMED ("O QUANTA QUALIA")	C51
2TPT, 2TRB, PERC, ORG	
ELMORE, R. CONCERTO. 3TPT, 3TRB, PERC, ORG	C51
GORCZYCKI, G.G. COMPLETORIUM. 2 CLARINI, ORG, 2VN, SATB	E72
HORN, P. WIE SOLL ICH DICH EMPHANGEN	E65
2TPT, VC(BSN), ORG, SATB	
VIERNE. MARCH TRIOMPHALE. 3TPT, 3TRB, ORG, TIMP	F16
WRIGHT. FANTASY ON WAREHAM. 3TPT, 3TRB, ORG, TIMP	C51

ONE BRASS INSTRUMENT-VOICE(S)

AMATO, B. TWO TOGETHER. TU, S	G66
BERGER, J. WAKE PSALTERY AND HARP. TPT, S, A, T, B	F43
BREVE REGNUM. TRB, V	E72
BRIGHT, H. HIGH TIDE. HN, TTBB	C33
CAIN, N. BLOW, BUGLE, BLOW (TENNYSON'S THE PRINCESS)	D18
TPT, S, A, T, B	
HUTSON-HAYWARD. TRUMPET SONG, THE. TPT, S, A, T, B	F43
KOUNTZ, R. HUNTER'S HORN, THE (OPT TPT). TPT, V	E11
LENEL. CHRIST IS NOW RISEN AGAIN. TPT, TTBB	B40

BRASS ENSEMBLE-VOICE(S)

BACH, J.S. PSALM 150. 3TPT, 2HN, 2TRB, CHORUS	B40
BENDER, J. CHRIST IS ARISEN. 2TPT, 2TRB, SATB	B40
BERGER, J. LET THE PEOPLE PRAISE THEE, O GOD. 2TPT, STAB	B40
BIESKE, W. VATER UNSER IM HIMMELREICH. 2TPT, 2TRB, SATB	A51
BOUMAN, P. JESUS CHRIST, THE LORD OF JOY. ORG, 4INST ?, STAB	B40
BRUCKNER, A. ABENDZAUBER. 4HN, V	F97
BRUCKNER, A. INVENI DAVID. 4TRB, TTBB	E65
BURNS, J.M. PRAISE TO OUR FATHER IN HEAVEN. 3TPT, SATB	L69
BUXTEHUDE, D. FANFARE AND CHORUS	D16
4TPT, TPT(HN), TRB(HN), 2TRB, SATB	
CASNER, M. ONLY-BEGOTTEN, WORD OF GOD	B40
3TPT, ORG, UNISON VOICES	
COOPER, A. GREAT IS THE LORD. 2TPT, SATB	F43
DE LASSUS. PROVIDEBAM DOMINUM	D16
4TPT, HN(TPT, TRB), TRB(HN), EU, *CHORUS	
DES PREZ. (SEE ALSO DESPREZ)	
DESPREZ, J. ABSALOM, FILI MI	D16
TPT, TRB, TPT(HN), TRB(HN), CHORUS	
DICKINSON, C. ALL HAIL THE VIRGIN'S SON. 2TPT, SATB	C58

```
DIEMENTE, E.  FORMS OF FLIGHT & FANCY.   2TPT, HN, TRB, TU, S    N91
DIRKSEN, R.  NATIVITY, THE.  3TPT, TRB, SATB                     C58
DUFAY, G.-CRAMER.  GLORIA.  TRBS(HNS), SA(TB)                    D63
ERNRYD, B.  LAUDATE DOMINUM.  TPT, HN, TRB, SATB                 B90
FETLER, P.  JUBILATE DEO.  3TPT, 2HN, 3TRB, *CHORUS              L74
FRACKENPOHL, A.R.  GOD BLESS OUR NATIVE LAND                     F43
   3TPT, 3TRB, EU, TU, SATB
FRACKENPOHL, A.R.  MARCHES OF PEACE                              F43
   2TPT, 2HN, 2TRB, EU, TU, SATB
FRACKENPOHL, A.R.  SHEPHERDS, REJOICE                            D16
   3HN, 3TRB, EU, TU, TTBB
GALLUS, J.  THIS IS THE DAY.  4INST ?, SATB                      B40
GILBERT.  STAR, THE.  BRASS, SATB                                C33
HANDEL, G.F.-EHRET.  WE PRAISE THEE, O GOD                       F43
   6TPT, 4TRB, 2TU, SATB
HARRIS (ARR).  BLESSING AND HONOR.  TPTS, SATB                   E80
HARRIS, R.W.  PRELUDE.  2TRB, EU(HN), TU, *CHORUS                B35
HASTINGS-RIEDEL.  OUR LORD IS RISEN.  2TPT, TRB, SAB             L74
HAYDN, J.-ADES.  SPACIOUS FIRMAMENT.  3TPT, 3TRB, SATB           F43
HILLERT, R.  MAY GOD BESTOW ON US HIS GRACE                      B40
   3TPT, 2TRB, CHORUS
HOKANSON.  SING TO GOD.  TPTS, SATB                              B40
HOLDEN-SIMEONE.  ALL HAIL THE POWER OF JESUS' NAME               F43
   3TPT, 3TRB, SATB
IVES, C.E.  3 HARVEST HOME CHORALES.  *CHORUS                    D74
JOHNSON, N.  COME, YE THANKFUL.  3TPT, SATB                      J94
KENNEDY, J.B.  LIFT UP YOUR VOICES NOW!.  2TPT, 2TRB, SATB       A84
KOCH, J.H.E.  CHRIST LAG IN TODESBANDEN                          A51
   2TPT, 2TRB, TU, CHORUS
KOCH, J.H.E.-FORTSETZUNG.  KOMM HEILIGER GEIST, HERRE GOTT       A51
   3TPT, 2TRB, CHORUS
KRAPF, G.  EASTER ANTIPHON.  2TPT, 2TRB, SATB                    B40
KUBIK, G.  LITANY AND PRAYER.  BRASS, MALE VOICES                F59
LEEUW, T.D.  PSALM 118.  2TRB, CHORUS                            B74
LESTER, W.  3 CHORALES.  2COR, TRB, TRB(TU), SATB                E11
LOWRY-FOLLETT.  LOW IN THE GRAVE HE LAY.  3TPT, SATB             E80
LUEDEKE.  WONDERLAND DUETS.  2TU, NAR                            F80
MAKER-WETZLER.  CHRIST IS RISEN! ALLELUIA!.  TPTS, SATB          L74
MARX, K.  MEIN SCHONSTE ZIER UND KLEINOD BIST                    A51
   2TPT, 2TRB, CHORUS
MARX, K.  NUN FREUT EUCH, LIEBEN CHRISTEN GMEIN                  A51
   3TPT, 2TRB, CHORUS
MC COWEN, R.  FANFARE FOR A CHRISTMAS FESTIVAL                   D18
   TPT, TRB, SATB
MC GRAW.  THESE THINGS SHALL BE.  BRASS, SATB                    C33
MENDELSSOHN, F.  FESTGESANG AN DIE KUNSTLER                      D16
   4TPT, 4HN, 3TRB, EU, TU,TTBB
MICHEELSEN, H.F.  ALLEIN ZU DIR, HERR JESU CHRIST                A51
   3TPT, 3TRB, CHORUS
MICHEELSEN, H.F.  CHRIST IST ERSTANDEN.  3TPT, 3TRB, CHORUS      A51
MICHEELSEN, H.F.  O CHRISTENHEIT, SEI HOCHERFREUT                A51
   5TPT, HN, 4TRB, BTRB, CHORUS
MONTEVERDI, C.  SONATA SOPRA SANCTA MARIA                        D16
   4TPT, 2TRB, EU, TU-EU, SATB
NELSON, P.  3 SONGS FOR SOPRANO & 8 HN.  8HN, S                  P49
PESTALOZZI, H.  BAUERNGEBET, OP. 86.  2TPT, 3TRB, TU, CHORUS     F82
PINKHAM, D.  ANGELUS AD PASTORES AIT                             D16
   2TRB, TU-TRB, SSAA,(OPT 4TPT)
PINKHAM, D.  CHRISTMAS CANTATA (SINFONIA SACRA)                  D16
   4TPT, TRB(HN), 3TRB, EU-TU, ORG, SATB
PRAETORIUS, M.  IN DULCI JUBILO                                  D16
   2TPT, TRB(TPT, HN), EU(TPB), SATB
```

```
PURCELL, H.   MUSIC FOR QUEEN MARY II                              D 16
     TPT, HN(TPT), TRB(HN), EU, SATB
REDA.  2 TE DEUM LAUDAMUS.  3TPT, 3TRB, TU, CHORUS                 A51
REIN, W.  DU MEINE SEELE SINGE.  2TPT, 2TRB, CHORUS               A51
REIN, W.  MACHT HOCH DIE TUR.  2TPT, 2TRB, CHORUS                 A51
REIN, W.  ZU BETHLEHEM GEBOREN.  2TPT, 2TRB, CHORUS               A51
REITER, J.  WINZERLIED, OP. 142.  4HN, CHORUS                     F82
RINGWALD.  MIRACULOUS STAR, THE.  BRASS, CHORUS                   F43
RODBY, W.  ALL EARTH BE GLAD.  BRASS, CHORUS                      D 18
SACCO, P.  3 PSALMS.  T(S), 2TPT, HN, TRB, TU                     B 04
SAUGUET.  3 CHANTS DE CONTEMPLATION.  2TPT, HN, TRB, A, B         D36
SCHAEFERS, A.  2 HYMNEN.  2TPT, 3HN, 2TRB, TU, CHORUS             A83
SCHALK, C.  YE SERVANTS OF GOD, YOUR MASTER PROCLAIM              B40
     2TPT, SATB
SCHEIN, J.H.  4 WALDLIEDERLEIN.  2TRB, T                          E00
SCHUTZ, H.-GERBER.  FILI MI, ABSALON.  4TRB, B, BC               A51
SCHUTZ, H.  PSALM 150                                             D 16
     4TPT, TRB, TU(BTRB), TPT(HN, TRB), CHORUS
SELLE.  DOMINE EXAUDI.  4TRB, B                                   E65
SMART-SIMEONE.  O BROTHERS LIFT YOUR VOICES.  3TPT, 3TRB, SATB    F43
SONNENBURG, K.  UND WIEDER STEIGT DER HEILE TAG                   A83
     3TPT, 2TRB, 2TU, CHORUS
STERN, H.  LOBT GOTT, IHR CHRISTEN, ALLE CLEIGH                   A51
     3TPT, 2TRB(FLG & AHN), CHORUS
STOKOWSKI, L.  BENEDICITE, OMNIA OPERA DOMINI                     C51
     2TPT, 2TRB, SATB
VERMULST, J.  PSALM 150 (PRAISE GOD IN HIS HOLY DWELLING)         L69
     2TPT, SATB
WALTON, K.  FANFARE FOR EASTER.  4 BRASS, SATB                    D 18
WARREN, E.  GOD OF OUR FATHERS.  3TPT, CHORUS                     D63
WASHBURN, R.  CHILD THIS DAY IS BORN, A.  BRASS, CHORUS           F43
WASHBURN, R.  GLORIA IN EXCELSIS DEO                              E51
     2TPT, 2HN, 2TRB, TU, CHORUS
WENZEL.  GOTT DES HIMMELS UND DER ERDEN                           A51
     2TPT, 3TRB, TU, CHORUS
WENZEL, E.  WORTE DES PROPHETEN JEREMIAS.  2TPT, 3TRB, SSATB      E65
WIENHORST.  WE ALL BELIEVE IN ONE TRUE GOD.  2TPT, SATB           B40
WIENHORST, R.  TE DEUM LAUDAMUS.  3TPT, 2TRB, TU, CHORUS          B 40
WILLAERT, A.-JAMESON.  MOTETTE: O SALUTARIS HOSTIA                G78
     2TPT, HN, TRB, TU(BTRB), A, T
WILSON, J.  CHRIST THE LORD IS RISEN TODAY.  3TPT, SATB           J94
WOOD, D.  ONLY-BEGOTTEN, WORD OF GOD ETERNAL.  BRASS, SATB        B40
WOOD, D.  WAKE, AWAKE, FOR NIGHT IS FLYING.  2TPT, SATB           C51
WORST, J.  PSALM 117.  TPT, HN, TRB, TU, SATB                     B35
YARBROUGH, L.  CHRISTMAS MEDLEY, A..  3TPT, SATB                  J94
YUNGTON, A.  MY HOPE IS BUILT.  3TPT, SATB                        J94
ZANINELLI, L.  SONG OF HOPE.  2TPT, 2TRB, EU(TU), CHORUS          F43
ZINDARS, E.  SONG OF AMERICA.  2TPT, HN, TRB, TU, CHORUS          B04
ZIPP.  SUCH, WER DA WILL, EIN ANDER ZIEL.  4TPT, 2TRB, CHORUS     A51
```

BRASS & WW ENSEMBLE-VOICE(S)

```
BACH, J.S.  CANTATA NO.118, O JESU CHRIST MEIN'S LEBENS LICHT     D82
     TPT, HN, TRB, TU(BTRB), 2CL, S, A, T, B
CATEL, C.S.  ECCE PANIS.  2HN, 2FL, 2CL, 2BSN, A, T, B            D82
CUNNINGHAM, M.G.  SPRING SONNET                                   B35
     3HN, FL, 2CL, B, BCL, ASAX, TSAX
HAUBIEL, C.  FLIGHT INTO EGYPT.  HN, FL, OB, CL, BSN, S           B38
```

SATEREN. CHRIST IS THE WORLD'S TRUE LIGHT   B40
   2TPT, OB(CL), SATB
SIMON, H. PANS FLUCHT. LYRISCH-HUMORISTISCHE SCENE   D46
   HN, FL, CB, CL, BSN, S
WORST, J. AND YE SHALL BE FILLED   B35
   2TPT, HN, TRB, TU, 3FL, *CHORUS

BRASS & MISC. ENSEMBLE-VOICE(S)

AHLE, J. BE NOT AFRAID. 4TRB, S, BC, *CHORUS   B40
ALDROVANDINI & BASANI-ENDSLEY. 2 ITALIAN SONGS. D TPT, V, PF M80
BACH, J.C. ES ERHUB SICH EIN STREIT   E65
   4TPT, BSN, ORG, 3VN, 3VA, DB, TIMP, SATEB-SATBB
BACH, J.S. AUFERSTEHUNG DES LAZARUS, DIE   E65
   TPT, 3TRB, CB, PERC, ORG, A, T, TIMP, STR, SATB-SATB
BACH, J.S. CANTATA NO. 11: LOBET GOTT IN SEINEN REICHEN   E65
   3TPT, 2FL, 2OB, ORG, TIMP, STR, STAB
BACH, J.S. CANTATA NO. 23: DU WAHRER GOTT UND DAVIDS SOHN   E65
   TPT, 3TRB, 2OB, ORG, S, A, T, STR, CHORUS
BACH, J.S. CANTATA NO. 27: WER WEISS, WIE NAHE MEIN ENDE   E65
   HN, 2OB, ORG, EH, STR, SATB
BACH, J.S. CANTATA NO. 29: WIR DANKEN DIR, GOTT   E65
   3TPT, 2OB, TIMP, SATB
BACH, J.S. CANTATA NO. 34: O EWIGES FEUER   E65
   3TPT, 2FL, 2OB, ORG, A, T, B, TIMP. STR, CHORUS
BACH, J.S. CANTATA NO. 46:SCHAUET DOCH UND SEHET   E65
   TPT, 2FL, ORG, A, T, B, 2EH, STR, CHORUS
BACH, J.S. CANTATA NO. 50: NUN IST DAS HEIL UND DIE KRAFT   E65
   3TPT, 3CB, ORG, TIMP, STR, SATB-SATB
BACH, J.S. CANTATA NO. 51: JAUCHZET GOTT IN ALLEN LANDEN   E65
   TPT, ORG, S, STR
BACH, J.S. CANTATA NO. 62: NUN KOMM, DER HEIDEN HEILAND   E65
   HN, 2OB, ORG, T, B, STR, CHORUS
BACH, J.S. CANTATA NO. 65: SIE WERDEN AUS SABA ALLE KOMMEN   E65
   2HN, 3FL, ORG, T, B, 2EH, STR, CHORUS
BACH, J.S. CANTATA NO. 68: ALSO HAT GOTT DIE WELT GELIEBT   E65
   TPT, HN, 3TRB, 2OB, ORG, S, B, EH, STR, CHORUS
BACH, J.S. CANTATA NO. 79: GOTT DER HERR IST SONN UND SCHILD E65
   2HN, 2FL, 2OB, ORG, S, A, B, TIMP, STR, CHORUS
BACH, J.S. CANTATA NO. 80: EIN FESTE BURG   E65
   3TPT, 2OB, ORG, TIMP, STR, CHORUS
BACH, J.S. CANTATA NO.105: HERR, GEHE NICHT INS   E65
   HN, 2OB, ORG, STR, SATB
BACH, J.S. CANTATA NO.127: HERR JESU CHRIST...   E65
   TPT, 2FL, 2CB, ORG, S, T, B, STR, CHORUS
BACH, J.S. CANTATA NO.137: LOBET DEN HERREN...   E65
   3TPT, 2OB, ORG, TIMP, STR, SATB
BACH, J.S. CANTATA NO.140: WACHET AUF   E65
   HN, 2OB, ORG, S, T, B, EH, STR, SATB
BACH, J.S.-WHITTAKER. JESU, JOY OF MAN'S DESIRING   E51
   TPT, CHORUS, *ORCH
BACH, J.S. JESU, NUN SEI GEPREISET. 3TPT, TRB, ORG, *CHORUS D16
BACH, J.S. PSALM 130. 3TPT, 2HN, 2TRB, ORG, *CHORUS   B40
BACH, J.S. VOM REICHE GOTTES   E65
   3TPT,3TRB,3FL,3OB,BSN,ORG,S,A,B,EH,TIMP,STR,*CHORUS
BARRAUD. TE DEUM. BRASS, WW, DB, CHORUS   B32
BEETHOVEN, L.V.-SIMEONE. JOYFUL JOYFUL WE ADORE THEE   F43
   3TPT, 3TRB, S, A, T, B, TIMP

BENDER, J.   AWAKE, THOU SPIRIT, WHO DIDST FIRE   B40
    2TPT, 2TRB, ORG, SATB
BENDER, J.   CHRIST IS ARISEN.   2TPT, 2TRB, SATB   B40
BENDER, J.   GOD THE FATHER, BE OUR STAY   B40
    2TPT, 2TRB, ORG, SATB
BENDER, J.   NUN BITTEN WIR DEN HEILGEN GEIST   A51
    4TPT, 2TRB, ORG, *CHORUS
BIALOSKY, M.   6 RIDDLES FROM SYMPHOSIUS.   TRB, VC, V   B35
BLACHER, B.   5 NEGRO SPIRITUALS.   TRB, 3CL, PERC, DB, V   A83
BORNEFELD, H.   CHORALKANTATE IV: HERR JESU CHRIST...   A51
    2TPT, 2TRB, ORG, STR, CHORUS
BORNEFELD, H.   CHORALKANTATE VII: DU MEINE SEELE, SINGE   A51
    4TPT, 2TRB, ORG, TIMP, CHORUS
BOWLES, P.F.   THE WIND REMAINS   A15
    TPT, HN, TRB, FL, EHN, CL, BSN, PERC,HP, VN, DB, S, T
BRAHMS, J.   BEGRABNISGESANG, OP. 13   D82
    2HN, 2TRB, TU(TRB), 2OB, 2CL, 2BSN, TIMP, SATB
BRAHMS, J.   4 SONGS, OP. 17 (WOMENS CHORUS).   2HN, HP, SSA   E65
BREHM, A.   CYCLE OF SIX SONGS, A   D63
    HN, FL, OB, CL, BSN, 2VN, VA, VC, S
BRIEGEL, W.C.   ICH WILL SINGEN...GNADE DES HERRN EWIGLICH   E65
    2TPT(2VN), 2TRB(2VA), ORG, VC, DB, S,A,T,B, *CHORUS
BRIGHT, H.   JABBERWOCKY.   2TPT, 2HN, 2TRB, TU, PERC, DB, SATB   F43
BRIGHT, H.   SUNRISE ALLELUIA   F43
    2TPT, 2HN, 2TRB, TU, DB, PERC, SATB
BROTT, A.   WORLD SOPHISTICATE.   2TPT, HN, TRB, TU, PERC, S   D94
BRUNCKHORST, A.M.   CHRISTMAS HISTORY   E65
    2TPT, ORG, S, A, T, B, STR, *CHORUS
BUNJES, P.   ALL GLORY, LAUD, AND HONOR.   TPT, ORG, SATB   B40
BUNJES, P.   ALL PRAISE TO GOD, WHO REIGNS ABOVE   B40
    TPT, ORG, SATB
BUNJES, P.   BUILT ON THE ROCK THE CHURCH DOTH STAND   B40
    2TPT, ORG, CHORUS
BUNJES, P.   GOD OF THE PROPHETS.   TPT, ORG, SATB   B40
BUNJES, P.   HOLY IS GOD THE LORD--ISAIAH, MIGHTY SEER   B40
    TPT, ORG, CHORUS
BUNJES, P.   HOW CAN I THANK THEE, LORD?.   TPT, ORG, SATB   B40
BUNJES, P.   I KNOW THAT MY REDEEMER LIVES.   TPT, ORG, SATB   B40
BUNJES, P.   LORD HATH HELPED ME HITHERTO, THE   B40
    TPT, ORG, CHORUS
BUNJES, P.   MIGHTY FORTRESS IS OUR GOD, A.   3TPT, ORG, CHORUS   B40
BUNJES, P.   PRAISE TO THE LORD, THE ALMIGHTY.   TPT, ORG, SATB   B40
BUXTEHUDE, D.   ALLELUIA, ALLELUIA.   2TPT, ORG, 2VA, SATB   E65
BUXTEHUDE, D.   IHR LIEBEN CHRISTEN, FREUT EUCH   E65
    5TPT, 3TRB, BSN, ORG, 3VN, 2VA, VC-DB, S, B, SSATB
BUXTEHUDE, D.   MAN SINGET MIT FREUDEN VOM SIEG   E65
    2TPT, BSN, ORG, 2VA, 2S, A, T, B, *CHORUS
CASSLER, G.W.(ARR).   ADESTE FIDELES   L74
    2TPT, HN, TRB, EU, TU, ORG, CHORUS
CASSLER, G.W.(ARR).   BUILT ON A ROCK   L74
    2TPT, HN, TRB, TU, ORG, CHORUS
CASSLER, G.W.(ARR).   FESTIVAL SERVICE, A   L74
    ORG, 4INST ?, *CHORUS
CASSLER, G.W.(ARR).   NOW LET THE VAULT OF HEAVEN RESOUND   L74
    TPT, ORG, CCR, SATB
CHOU, W.C.   7 POEMS OF T'ANG DYNASTY   E30
    TPT, HN, TRB, FL, OB, CL, BSN, PERC, PF, T
CONVERSE, F.S.   LAUDATE DOMINUM, MOTET, OP. 22   A87
    2TPT, 4TRB, ORG, TTBB
DANIEL-LESUR.   MESSE DU JUBILE.   3TPT, ORG, TIMP, CHORUS   B32
DAVIS, A.   PSALM OF PRAISE, A.   PERC, *CHORUS   G66
DAVIS, A.   SONG FOR DANIEL, A.   PERC, *CHORUS   G66

```
DAVIS, K.K.  HONOR AND PRAISE.  2TPT, ORG, CHORUS              E11
DIMOV, B.  INCANTATIONES.  TPT, FL, VA, S, HP                  D88
DRISCHNER, M.  MAKE A JOYFUL NOISE                             B40
    TPT(FL, OB, CL, RECORDER, VN), PF(ORG, HPCD), CHORUS
DRUCKMAN.  DARK UPON THE HARP.  2TPT, HN, TRB, TU, PERC, S     F56
ELVEY-PELZ.  CROWN HIM WITH MANY CROWNS.  TPTS, ORG, CHORUS    L74
FARBERMAN, H.  EVOLUTION.  HN, PERC, S                         A98
FOSS, R.A.  ALL GLORY, LAUD, AND HONOR.  COR, ORG, T, BAR      A81
FREED, A.  GLORIA.  3TPT, 4HN, 3TRB, TU, TIMP, SATB            A78
GERIG, F.  ALL HAIL THE POWER.  3TPT, VN, HP, SATB            J94
GORECKI, H.M.  EPITAPH, OP. 12.  TPT, PERC, VA, PIC, CHORUS    E72
HAMMERSCHMIDT, A.  EASTER DIALOGUE (WER WAELZET UNS DEN STEIN) E65
    2TPT, 4TRB, ORG, VC-DB, 2S, B, CHORUS
HAMMERSCHMIDT, A.  FREUE DICH, DU TOCHTER ZION               E65
    2TPT, ORG, CHORUS
HANDEL, G.F.-ODE.  ARIAS FOR TPT & VOICE, VOL 1.  D TPT, V, PF M80
HANDEL, G.F.  CONQUERING HERO COMES, THE (JUDAS MACCABEUS)    E80
    2TPT, TIMP, SATB
HANDEL, G.F.-HEGEDUS.  GREAT SHEPHERD OF A LOYAL FLOCK        J94
    TPT, ORG, CHORUS
HANDEL, G.F.-ENDSLEY.  REVENGE.  D TPT, V, PF                 M80
HANDEL, G.F.  UTRECHT JUVILATE                               E65
    2TPT, 2OB, BSN, ORG, 3VN, A, T, B, *CHORUS
HANNA, J.  SONG OF THE REDWOOD TREE                          D16
    2TPT, 2HN, 2TRB, TIMP, NAR
HARRISON, L.  ALMA REDEMPTORIS.  TRB, TACK PIANO, VN, BAR     F59
HARTIG, H.F.  PERCHE, OP. 28A                                A83
    2TPT, FL/PIC, CL, 3PERC, PF, VA, DB, BCL, HP, CHORUS
HARTIG, H.F.  TRINKER UND DIE SPIEGEL, DER, OP. 16           A83
    TPT, FL/PIC, CL, PERC, PF, VA, DB, BAR
HAYDN, J.-SAAR.  ADORATION TO GOD; THANKSGIVING TO GOD       A81
    2HN, CHORUS
HAZZARD, P.  PRAISE BOOK, A.  2TPT, TU, 3PERC, *CHORUS        G66
HENNIG, W.  PSALM 150.  2TPT, TRB, ORG, 2VN, VC, S, B, *CHORUS E65
HERRMANN, H.-RINGELNATZ.  CHORBURLESKEN IM ZOO (MENS CHORUS)  A83
    TPT, TRB, PERC, PF, VN, DB, ASAX, *CHORUS
HERRMANN, H.-NIERENTZ.  SINFONIE DER ARBEIT                  A83
    3TPT, 3HN, 3TRB, TU, PERC, CHORUS
HERRMANN, H.-OFTERDINGEN.  WACHTERRUF                        A83
    2TPT, 2HN, 2TRB, TU, PERC, *CHORUS (MALE)
HOHVANESS, A.S.  GLORY TO GOD                                F65
    4TPT, 4HN, 4TRB, 2PERC, ORG, ASAX, S, A, *CHORUS
HORN, P.  SOMME DER GERECHTIGKEIT.  ORG, 4 BRASS, SATB        E65
HOVHANESS, A.S.  ANGELIC SONG.  HN, S(T), STR               E65
HOVHANESS, A.S.  AVAK, THE HEALER.  TPT, S, *ORCH           F59
HOVHANESS, A.S.  I HAVE SEEN THE LORD.  TPT, ORG, S, *CHORUS  E65
HOVHANESS, A.S.  LOOK TOWARD THE SEA, OP. 158               E65
    TRB, ORG, BAR, *CHORUS
HOVHANESS, A.S.  LORD IS MY SHEPHERD, THE (PSALM 23)         E65
    2TPT, FL, PERC, SATB
HOVHANESS, A.S.  30TH ODE OF SOLOMON, OP. 76                E65
    TPT, TRB, BAR VOICE, CHORUS
IVES, C.E.  NEW RIVER, THE (HIGH & LOW VOICES)              F59
    3TPT, TRB, 2CL, PF, PIC, TIMP, BARSAX, *ORCH & CHORUS
IVES, C.E.  PROCESSIONAL "LET THERE BE LIGHT"               F59
    4TRB, ORG, *ORCH, *CHORUS
JAMES, P.  GENERAL WILLIAM BOOTH ENTERS INTO HEAVEN         E11
    TPT, TRB, PERC, 2PF, MENS CHORUS
JANSE(ARR).  GETTYSBURG ADDRESS, THE.  TPT, SDR, TTBB       D18
JOHNSON(ARR).  MIGHTY FORTRESS IS OUR GOD, A.  TPT, ORG, SATB L74
JOLLEY-HOGGARD.  GLORIA IN EXCELSIS.  3TPT, 3TRB, PERC, CHORUS F43
JOLLEY-HOGGARD.  HOLY LORD GOD OF HOSTS                      F43
    3TPT. 3TRB. PERC. CHORUS
```

```
KAMINSKI, H.   3 GEDICHTE VON EICHENDORFF                              F 97
   3TPT, 3HN, PERC, CHORUS
KAUDER, H.   2 SONGS.   HN, HP, V                                      G 66
KELDERMANS, R.A.   BEHOLD A GREAT PRIEST.   2TPT, ORG, CHORUS          L 69
KENNEDY, J.E.   ALLELUIA FANFARE                                       A 84
   2TPT, 3TRB, TU, PERC, PF, CHORUS
KIRK, T.   NOW LET ALL SING.   2TPT, 3TRB, TIMP, SATB                  F 43
KOCH, J.H.E.   DARUM WACHET.   2TPT, 2TRB, ORG, CHORUS                 A 51
KOCH, J.H.E.   STEHT AUF, IHR, LIEBEN KINDERLEIN                       A 51
   3TRB, 2TRB, TIMP, CHORUS
LACHNER, F.   WALDWARTS.   HN, PF, V                                   D 55
LANG, E.   EASTER ALLELUIA, AN.   TPT, ORG, SSATTB                     A 81
LEICHTLING, A.   RUBAIYAT FRAGMENTS.   HN, CL, PF, BAR                 G 66
LEWKOVITCH, B.   CANTATA SACRA.   TRB, FL, CL, BSN, VC, T, EH          B 56
LUTHER, M.-WIENHORST.   LORD GOD, THY PRAISE WE SING                   B 40
   3TPT, 2TRB, TU, ORG, CHORUS
MAKER-WETZLER.   CHRIST IS RISEN! ALLELUIA!.   3TPT, ORG, SATB         L 74
MAMANGAKIS, N.   KASSANDRA.   HN, TRB, FL, 2PERC, S, HP                D 88
MESTRES-QUADRENY, J.M.   INVENCIONS MOVILS II.   TPT, S, GTR           G 66
MIKOLAJ OF RADOM.   MAGNIFICAT                                         E 72
   4TRB, 4VC, CONTRALTO, BC, CHORUS
MOZART, W.A.   SZENE MIT RONDO "CH'IO MI SCCRDI DI TE"                 D 55
   2HN, 2CL, 2BSN, PF, 2VN, VA, DB, S
NORGAARD.   SERENADE TO YOUNG MAN WITH HORN                            N 53
   TPT, TRB, CL, DB, VIB, VOICES
NYSTEDT, K.   NOW IS CHRIST RISEN                                      L 74
   TPT(FL), ORG, BELLS(CHIMES), SATB
NYSTEDT, K.(ARR).   O COME, ALL YE FAITHFUL.   TPT, ORG, SATB          L 74
PACHELBEL, J.   NUN DANKET ALLE GOTT                                   D 16
   2TPT, TRB(HN), TRB(EU), ORG, SATB
PELZ(ARR).   CROWN HIM WITH MANY CROWNS.   3TPT, ORG, SATB             L 74
PELZ.   HE'S RISEN, CHRIST JESUS, THE LORD.   TPT, ORG, SATB           L 74
PELZ(ARR).   HOLY GOD, WE PRAISE THY NAME.   3TPT, ORG, SATB           L 74
PELZ(ARR).   JESUS CHRIST IS RISEN TODAY.   2TPT, ORG, CHORUS          L 74
PINKHAM, D.   EASTER CANTATA                                          E 65
   4TPT, 2HN, 3TRB, TU, PERC, CEL, SATB
PINKHAM, D.   TE DEUM.   3TPT, ORG, SA(TB)                             D 16
PROCH, H.   ANTWORT, OP. 99.   HN, PF, S                               D 55
PURCELL, H.-ENDSLEY.   FIFE AND HARMONEY OF WAR                        M 80
   2 D TPT, V, PF
PURCELL, H.-ENDSLEY.   2 SONGS.   C TPT, V, PF                         M 80
PURCELL, H.-ENDSLEY.   THUS THE GLOOMY WORLD.   D TPT, V, PF           M 80
READ, G.   REVEILLE, THE.   PERC, ORG, *CHORUS                         G 66
REGNEY, S.-SIMEONE.   DO YOU HEAR WHAT I HEAR?                         F 43
   3TPT, 3TRB, TIMP, SATB
RINGGER, R.U.   4 LIEDER AUF CHINESISCHE TEXTE                         D 88
   TRB, FL, VN, VC, DB, S, BCL, HP, CEL
RINGGER, R.U.   4 LIEDER AUF JAPANISCHE LYRIK                          D 88
   HN, CL, VN, VA, DB, S, HP
RINGWALD, R.   BATTLE HYMN OF THE REPUBLIC.   3TPT, PERC, SATB         F 43
RINGWALD, R.   MIRACULOUS STAR, THE.   3TPT, 3TRB, TU, ORG, SATB       F 43
ROHLIG, H.   CHORALE CONCERTATA....   2TPT, ORG, SATB                  B 40
ROHLIG, H.   CHRIST IS ARISEN.   3TPT, ORG, T, CHORUS                  B 40
ROHLIG, H.   HODIE CHRISTUS, NATUS EST.   3TPT, ORG, T, SATB           B 40
ROHLIG, H.   MAGNIFICAT.   2TPT, 2FL, ORG, CHORUS                      B 40
ROHLIG, H.   NOW THANK WE ALL OUR GOD.   3TPT, ORG, SATB               B 40
ROHLIG, H.   PRAISE TO THE LORD, THE ALMIGHTY                          B 40
   TPT, FL, ORG, CHORUS
ROHLIG, H.   WAKE, AWAKE, FOR NIGHT IS FLYING                          B 40
   TPT, ORG, CHORUS
ROSENMULLER, J.   ALSO HAT GOTT DIE WELT GELIEBET                      E 65
   3TRB, ORG, 2VA, SSATB
```

```
RUPPEL, P.E.  CRUCIFIXION.  TRB, DB, NAR, V, *CHORUS            E65
RUSCH.  EASTER SYMPHONY, AN                                     E11
     3TPT, 2VN, VA, VC, SATB, CHIMES,3 CHOIRS
SCARLATTI, A.  CANTATA "SU LE SPONDE DEL TEBRO"                 E14
     TPT(OB), 2VN, S, BC
SCHALK, C.  O LOVE, HOW DEEP, HOW BROAD, HOW HIGH               B40
     3TPT, ORG, SATB
SCHEIDT, S.  NUN DANKET ALLE GOTT                               E65
     3TPT, TRB, 2VN, 2VA, VC(BSN), BC, 6 CHORUSES
SCHEIN, J.H.  MACH DICH AUF, WERDE LICHT                        E65
     3TRB(2VA, VC), ORG, 2VN(2COR, 2FL), VC-DB, S, T, SSATB
SCHEIN, J.H.  UNS IST EIN KIND GEBOREN                          E65
     ORG, 2VN, VA(ATRB), VC-DB, T
SCHELLE, J.  ALLELUJA, MAN SINGET MIT FREUDEN VOM SIEG          E65
     2TPT, BSN, ORG, 2VA, SSATB
SCHELLE, J.  EHRE SEI GOTT IN DER HOEHE                         E65
     2TPT, 2TRB, BSN, ORG, 2VN, VC-DB, TIMP, SSATB
SCHOECK, O.  GASELEN, OP. 38                                    A90
     TPT, FL, OB, PERC, PF, BCL, BAR VOICE
SCHOECK, O.  WANDERSPRUCHE, OP. 42.  HN, CL, PERC, PF, S(T)     A90
SCHUBERT, F.P.  AUF DEM STROM.  HN, PF, S                       B44
SCHUBERT, F.P.  AUF DEM STROM, OP. 119.  HN, PF, V              A90
SCHUTZ, H.  ABSALOM, FILI MI.  3TRB, ORG, BTRB, MALE CHORUS     D16
SCHUTZ, H.  ATTENDITE, POPULE MEAS, LEGEM MEAM.  4TRB, B, BC    E14
SCHUTZ, H.  ATTENDITE, POPULE MEUS, LEGEM MEAM.  4TRB, B, BC    A95
SCHUTZ, H.  ATTENDITE, POPULE MEUS, LEGEM MEAM                  F23
     3TRB, B, BTRB, BC
SCHUTZ, H.  FILI MI ABSALOM (SYMPHONIAE SACRAE 1, NO. 13)       E14
     4TRB, B, BC
SCHUTZ, H.  GESANG DER DREI MAENNER IM FEURIGEN OFEN            E65
     2TPT, 3TRB, ORG, SSATB, SSATB,(OPT STR)
SCHUTZ, H.  GOTT ABRAHAMS, DER                                  E65
     3TRB, ORG, 2VN, VC-DB, A, T, B, SATB
SCHUTZ, H.-EHMANN.  PSALM 103 "NUN LOB, MEIN SEEL...            A51
     3TPT, 2TRB, VN, VA, VC, BC, SHORUS
SCHUTZ, H.-EHMANN & KOCH.  PSALM 136.  3TPT, TIMP, BC, CHORUS   A51
SCHUTZ, H.-MARIER.  PSALM 150                                   D16
     4TPT, TPT(HN), TRB), ETRB(TU), ORG, CHORUS
SCHUTZ, H.-HUBER.  PSALM 8 "HERR UNSER HERRSCHER", SWV 27       A51
     3TPT, 2TRB, ORG(BC), CHORUS
SCHUTZ, H.-GERBER.  SYMPHONIAE SACRAE I. 13: FILI ME,...        A51
     4TPB, !, BC
SCHUTZ, H.-GERBER.  SYMPHONIAE SACRAE I, NO. 19/20              B23
     2TPT, BSN, 2COR(2FLG OR COR & TPT), BC, CHORUS
SCHUTZ, H.  VENI SANCTE SPIRITUS                                E65
     3TRB, FL, 2CB(2VN), BSN, ORG, VN, VC-CB, DB, CHORUS
SELLE, T.  ES BEGAB SICH ABER ZU DER ZEIT                      E65
     3TPT(3FL), 4TRB, BSN, ORG, 3VN, 2VC, 2DB, S, T, *CHORUS
SELLE, T.  UND ALS DER SABBATH VERGANGEN WAR                    E65
     3TPT, 2TRB, ORG, 2VN, 2VA, VC-DB, 2S, T, B, *CHORUS
SERIO, J.(ARR).  NOW THANK WE ALL OUR GOD                       L69
     TPT, HN, TRB, ORG, SATB
SHAPERO, H.  HEBREW CANTATA                                     F59
     TPT, FL, ORG, VN, SATB, HP, *CHORUS
SHERMAN, S.-SIMECNE.  SUPERGALIFRACILISTICEXPIALIDOCIOUS        F43
     TU, RHYTHM SECTION, *CHORUS
SMITH, H.  2 LOVE SONGS OF JOHN DONNE                           D63
     HN, FL, OB, CL, BSN, 2VN, VA, VC, S
SMOLANOFF, M.  WORLD TODAY IS WILD, THE                         G66
     2TPT, 2HN, TRB, TU, FL, OB, CL, BSN, 3PERC, BAR
STACHOWICZ, D.  VENI CONSOLATOR.  CLARINO, BC, V               E72
STIER.  ICH HABE NUN DEN GRUND GEFUNDEN                         A51
     2TPT, HN, TRB, VN, TIMP, CHORUS
```

```
STOLL, H.M.   FESTE BURG, EIN.   2TPT(2VN), ORG, TIMP, SAB        E65
STOUT, A.   ENGEL, DIE.   6TPT, 3TRB, TU, PERC, PF, VN, S          G83
STRAVINSKY, I.   IN MEMORIAM DYLAN THOMAS                          A78
    4TRB, 2VN, VA, VC, T
STRAVINSKY, I.   IN MEMORIAM DYLAN THOMAS                          E14
    4TRB, 2VN, VA, VC, T
STROHBACH, S.   HALUNKENSONGS                                      A90
    TPT, PERC, VN, DB, ACCORDIAN, BAR VOICE
SUTER, R.   MUSIKALISCHES TAGEBUCH NR. 2                           D88
    HN, FL, CL, VN, VA, VC, BCL,BAR VOICE
SZALONEK, W.   SUITE FROM KURPIE                                   A31
    HN, FL, OB, CL, BSN, PF, VN, VA, VC, CONTRALTO
SZALONEK, W.   SUITE FROM KURPIE                                   E72
    HN, FL, OB, CL, BSN, PF, VN, VA, VC, CONTRALTO
VERMULST, J. (ARR).   SINGERS SING AND TRUMPETS PLAY               L69
    2TPT, ORG, V
VREE, M.   PRAISE TO THE LIVING GOD.   3TPT, TIMP, SATB            F43
WARNER, R.   COME, THOU LONG-EXPECTED JESUS                        C51
    2TPT, 2TRB, TIMP, SATB
WARREN, E.-GEARHART.   GOD OF OUR FATHERS.   3TPT, PERC, SATB      F43
WERNER, F.   HEILGER GEIST, DU TROESTER MEIN                       E65
    TPT, 2OB, ORG, STR, SATB
WHITMER, T.C.   ANOINTING OF SOLOMON, THE                         A15
    TPT, ORG, TIMP, CHORUS
WIENHORST, R.   LORD GOD, THY PRAISE WE SING                       B40
    3TPT, 2TRB, TU, ORG, CHORUS
WOLFF, S.D.   NOW THANK WE ALL OUR GOD.   TPT, ORG, SATB           B40
WOOD, D.   WATCHMAN, TELL US OF THE NIGHT                          C51
    2TPT, 2TRB, FL, OB, HP, CHORUS, (OPT HAND BELLS)
WORST, J.   3 BIBLICAL CHANTS.   HN, FL, VN, DB, A(BAR)           B35
WROCHEM, K. VON.   ORATORIUM MEUM PLUS PRAEFERTURI                 B35
    TPT, PERC, 2VN, VA, VC, 3V, ASAX, PNEUMATIC DRILL
YARBROUGH, L.   STAND UP FOR JESUS.   3TPT, TIMP, SATB             J94
ZANINELLI, L.   BARBARA FRIETCHIE                                  F43
    3TPT, 3HN, 3TRB, TU, PIC, PERC, CHORUS
ZANINELLI, L.   WORLD HYMN                                        F43
    3TPT, 4HN, 3TRB, EU, TU, TIMP, CHORUS
```

POSAUNENCHOR

```
BACHMANN, F.(ED).   AN HELLEN TAGEN                                D91
BACHMANN, F.(ARR).   AUSGABE FUR DIE EVANGELISCHE KIRCHE...        D91
BACHMANN, F.(ARR).   AUSGABE NORD...                              D91
BACHMANN, F.(ARR).   AUSGABE...NIEDERSACHSENS                      D91
BACHMANN, F.(ARR).   LASS DIR UNSER LOB GEFALLEN                   D91
BACHMANN, F.   POSAUNENCHORALBUCH ZUM EKG                          D78
EHMANN, W.   ALTE SPIELMUSIK I                                     A51
EHMANN, W.   ALTE SPIELMUSIK II                                    A51
EHMANN, W.   BLASER INTRADEN                                       A51
EHMANN, W.   CHORALPARTITEN                                        A51
EHMANN, W.   EVANGELISCHES KANTOREIBUCH                            A51
EHMANN, W.   GEISTLICHES ZWEIERSPIEL                               A51
EHMANN, W.   WIEHNACHTSLIEDER                                      A51
FEYERTAG, A.   NEUE SCHULE FUR POSAUNENCHORE                       E81
GLOWATZKI & LANGE.   SAMMLUNG I                                    D78
GRAD, T.   VOLKSLIEDSATZE FUR BLECHBLASER.   3TPT, 5TRB-           A51
HAMM.   30 VOLKSLIEDER                                             D78
HOFFMANN, E.A.   ALTE BLASERMUSIKEN                                D78
```

```
KUHLO, J.   CHORALBUCH ZUM EINHEITSGESANGBUCH                    D91
KUHLO, J.   NEUES POSAUNENBUCH I                                 D91
KUHLO, J.   POSAUNENBUCH I (JUBILATE)                            D91
KUHLO, J.   RUEHMET DEN HERRN                                    F08
KUHLO, J.   RUHMET DEN HERRN                                     D91
LANGE & GLOWATZKI.  SAMMLUNG I                                   D78
MICHEELSEN, H.F.  EI, DU FEINER REITER                           A51
MONCH, F.  SCHULE FUR BLASE￢                                    D78
PEZEL, J.C.-SCHLEGEL.  FUNFSTIMMIGE BLASENDE MUSIK               D78
SCHLEE, M.-HAMM.  DREISSIG VOLKSLIEDER                           D78
SCHLEMM, H.M.  BLAST AN--SPIELT MIT                              D78
SCHLEMM, H.M.  LASS DIR UNSER LOB GEFALLEN                       D78
SCHLEMM, H.M.  LASS DIR UNSER LOB GEFALLEN, BAND II              D78
```

COMPOSER INDEX

COMPOSER INDEX

KEY TO PUBLISHERS

KEY TO PUBLISHERS

Alphabetization is by publisher code. American agents or distributors for foreign firms are indicated in parentheses.

A02	Accura Music, Box 887, Athens, Ohio
A03	Henry Adler, Inc. (G85-Belwin-Mills)
A08	Ahn & Simrock, Bühnenverlag, Taunusstrasse 66, 6200 Wiesbaden, Germany
A13	American Composers Alliance, 170 W. 74th St., New York, New York
A15	American Music Edition, 263 E. 7th St., New York, New York (C11-C.Fischer)
A16	Amphion Éditions Musicales, 9 Rue d'Artois, Paris 8e, France (G85-Belwin-Mills)
A18	Amsco Music Publishing Co., 33 W. 60th St., New York, New York
A20	Johann André, Postfach: 141, 605 Offenbach am Main, Germany
A31	Ars Polona, Krakowskie Przedmieście 7, 00-068 Warszawa, Poland
A33	Artia, Ve Smeckach 30, Prague I, Czechoslovakia (A78-Boosey)
A35	Ascherberg, Hopwood & Crew, Ltd., 16 Mortimer St., London W.1, England
A38	Associated Music Publishers, Inc., 866 Third Ave., New York, New York
A39	Astoria Verlag, Brandenburgische Strasse 22, Berlin-Wilmersdorf, Germany
A42	Augener, Ltd., (C33-Galaxy)
A43	Avant Music (G21-Western International Music)
A51	Bärenreiter Verlag, Heinrich Schütz Allee 35, 500 Kassel-Wilhelmshöhe, Germany
A53	Bärenreiter, Hortus Musicus (A51-Bärenreiter Verlag)
A54	Barger & Barclay, P.O. Box 633, Great Neck, New York
A55	C.L. Barnhouse Co., 110 B. Ave. East, Oskaloosa, Iowa
A56	Baron Co., Box 149, Oyster Bay, Long Island, New York
A58	M.P. Belaieff (E65-C.F. Peters)
A62	Belwin-Mills Publishing Corp., 25 Deshon Dr., Melville, New York
A65	Claude Benny Press, 1401 State St., Emporia, Kansas
A70	Big 3 Music Corporation, 729 Seventh Ave., New York, New York
A71	Editions Billaudot, 14, rue de l'Echiquier, Paris 10e, France (E77-Presser)
A78	Boosey & Hawkes, Inc., P.O. Box 130, Oceanside, New York
A80	Gustav Bosse Verlag, Postfach 417, 84 Regensburg 2, Germany
A81	Boston Music Co., 116 Boylston St., Boston, Massachusetts (C27-Frank Music Corp.)
A82	Bosworth & Co., Ltd., 14-18 Heddon St., Regent St., London W. 1, England (G85-Belwin-Mills)
A83	Bote & Bock, Hardenbengstrasse 9a, 1 Berlin 12, Germany (A38-AMP)
A84	Bourne Co., 1212 6th Avenue, New York, New York (B20-Chappell)
A87	Editions Braun (A71-Billaudot)
A89	Breitkopf & Härtel Musikverlag, Karlstrasse 10, Leipzig C1, Germany
A90	Breitkopf & Härtel, Walkmuhlstrasse 52, D 6200 Weisbaden 1, Germany (A38-AMP)
A91	George F. Briegel, Inc., 4 Summit Court, Flushing, New York
A93	Broadcast Music, Canada (A38-AMP)
A94	Brodt Music Co., P.O. Box 1207, Charlotte, North Carolina
A95	Broekmans & Van Poppel, Van Baerlestraat 92, Amsterdam, Holland (E65-C.F. Peters)
A96	Editions Musicales Brogneaux, 73 Ave. Paul Janson, Bruxelles 7, Belgium (B91-H. Elkan)
A98	Broude Brothers, 56 West 45th Street, New York, New York
B00	Edizione Aldo Bruzzicheldi (D86-MJK)
B04	Camara Brass Quintet, 23 LaFond Lane, Orinda, California
B05	Campion Press (D16-King)
B07	Carisch S.P.A. 20124, Via General Fara 39, Milan, Italy

B12	Centre Belge de Documentation Musicale (CeBeDeM) rue de l'hopital, 31, B-1000 Bruxelles, Belgium (B91-H.Elkan)
B13	Century Music Publishing Co., 263 Veterans Blvd., Carlstadt, New Jersey
B15	Chamber Music Library (C25-Fox)
B17	Le Chant du Monde (G85-Belwin-Mills)
B20	Chappel & Co., Inc. (E77-T.Presser)
B23	J. & W. Chester, Ltd., Eagle Court, London EC1, England (D58-Magnamusic)
324	Edition Choudens, 38, rue Jean Mermoz, Paris 8e, France (E65-Peters)
B30	M.M. Cole Publishing Co., 251 E. Grand Ave., Chicago, Illinois
B31	Charles Colin Music Publishers, 315 W. 53rd St., New York, New York
B32	Franco Colombo, Inc. (G85-Belwin-Mills)
B34	Published by the composer
B35	Composers' Autograph Publications, Box 671, Hamilton, Ohio
B36	Composers' Facsimile Edition, 170 W. 74th St., New York, New York
B38	The Composers Press, Inc., 177 E. 87th St., New York, New York
B39	Concord Music Publishing Co. (B91-H.Elkan)
B40	Concordia Publication House, 3558 S. Jefferson Ave., St. Louis, Missouri
B41	Consolidated Music Publishers, Inc., 33 W. 60th St., New York, New York
B43	Editorial Cooperativa Interamericana de Compositores (F59-Southern, New York)
B44	Cor Publishing Co., 67 Bell Pl., Massapequa, New York
B46	Editions Costallat, 60, rue de la Chauśee-d'Antin, Paris 9e, France (A71-Billaudot)
B52	Crescendo Music Sales Co., P.O. Box 11208, Dallas, Texas
B53	Cundy-Bettoney Co., Inc. (C11-C.Fischer)
B56	Society for Publishing Danish Music (C17-Dan Fog)
B66	Georges Delrieu et Cie, 45 Ave. de la Victoire, Nice, France (C33-Galaxy)
B69	Deutscher Verlag für Musik, Postfach 147, 701 Leipzig, East Germany
B70	De Wolfe, 80-82 Wardour St., London, W.1, England
B72	Oliver Ditson Co. (E77-Presser)
B73	Ludwig Doblinger, Dorotheergasse 10, Vienna 1, Austria (A38-AMP)
B74	Stichting Donemus, Jacob Obrechtstraat 51, Amsterdam-Z, Holland (E65-Peters)
B80	Drŭstvo Slovenskih Sklada Teljev, Ljubljano, Yugoslavia
B81	Durand et Cie, 4, Place de la Madeleine, Paris 8e, France (B92-Elkan-Vogel)
B84	Editio Musica Budapest, Pf. 322, Budapest 5, Hungary (A78-Boosey)
B85	Edition Musicus, Inc., Box 1341, Stanford, Connecticut
B87	Uniunea Compozitorilor, Calea Victoriei 141, Bucharest, Romania
B90	Ehrling Förlagen, Linnégatan 9-11, Box 5268, Stockholm 5, Sweden
B91	Henri Elkan Music Publisher, 1316 Walnut St., Philadelphia, Pennsylvania
B92	Elkan-Vogel Co., Inc. (E77-Presser)
B93	Elkin & Co., Ltd. (A38-AMP)
B98	Ensemble Publications, Inc., P.O. Box 98, Bidwell Station, Buffalo, New York
B99	Rudolph Erdmann, Postfach 471, Wiesbaden, Germany
C01	Editions Max Eschig, 48, rue de Rome, 75008 Paris, France (A38-AMP)
C03	Edition Eulenburg KG (E65-Peters)
C05	Faber Music Ltd., 38 Russell Square, London WC1B5DA, England (F23-G. Schirmer)
C09	Fillmore Music Co. (C11-C. Fischer)
C11	Carl Fischer, Inc., 62 Cooper Square, New York, New York
C12	J. Fischer & Brothers (G85-Belwin-Mills)

C13	H.T. FitzSimons Co., Inc., 615 N. LaSalle St., Chicago, Illinois
C17	Dan Fox Musikforlag, Graadrødretorv 7, DK-1154 Kobenhavn K, Denmark (E65-Peters)
C18	Charles Foley, Inc. (C11-C. Fischer)
C19	Robert Forberg Musikverlag, Mirbachstrasse 7, 53 Bonn-Bad Godesberg, Germany
C25	Sam Fox, Box 850, Valley Forge, Pennsylvania
C27	Frank Music Corporation, 116 Boylston St., Boston, Massachusetts
C29	Samuel French, Inc., 25 W. 45th St., New York, New York
C30	Friedrich W. Fröhlich, Ansbacher Strasse 52, D-1000 Berlin 30, Germany
C33	Galaxy Music Corporation, 2121 Broadway, New York, New York
C35	Galliard, Ltd., Great Yarmouth, Norfolk, England (C33-Galaxy)
C38	Editions E. Gaudet (F16-Salabert)
C39	Carl Gehrmans Musikförlag, Vasagatan 46, Box 505, 101 26 Stockholm 1, Sweden (A78-Boosey)
C40	General Music Publishing Co., P.O. Box 267, Hastings-On-Hudson, New York, New York
C41	Hans Gerig Musikverlag, Drususgasse 7-11, 5000 Cologne, Germany
C45	Gordon Music Co., 2680 Cherokee Way, Palm Springs, California
C46	David Gornston Music (C25-Fox)
C51	H.W. Gray Co., Inc. (G85-Belwin-Mills)
C54	Philipp Grosch Musikverlag, Lisztstrasse 18, 8000 Munich 8, Germany
C55	J. Hamelle & Cie, 24 Boulevard Malesherbes, Paris 8e, France (B92-Elkan-Vogel)
C56	Charles Hansen Publishing Co., 1842 West Ave., Miami Beach, Florida
C58	T.B. Harms Co., c/o Cimino Publications, 1646 New Highway, Farmingdale, New York
C59	Harth-Pro Musica Verlag, Karl-Liebknecht-Strasse 12, 701 Leipzig, Germany
C60	Heinrichshofen Verlag, Liebigstrasse 4, Wilhelmshaven, Germany (E65-Peters)
C61	Editions Henn-Chapuis, 8, rue de Hasse, Geneva, Switzerland
C65	Heugel et Cie, Bois de Brosses, Ravieres, France (E77-Presser)
C67	Max Hieber Musikverlag, Kaufingerstrasse 23, 8 Munich 2, Germany
C68	Highgate Press (C33-Galaxy)
C71	Hinrichsen Edition, Ltd., 10 Baches Street, London N1 6DN, England (E65-Peters)
C75	Friedrich Hofmeister-Verlag, Ubierstrasse 20, 6238 Hofheim Am Taunus, Germany
C77	Holly-Pix (G21-WIM)
C78	Hornists' Nest, Box 2713, Buffalo, New York
C80	Hug & Co., Musikverlag, Limmatquai 26-28, CH-8022 Zurich, Switzerland
C82	Ichtys Verlag, Postfach 834, 7000 Stuttgart 1, Germany
C85	Independent Music Co., 205 E. 42nd St., New York, New York
C89	Interlochen Press (B52-Crescendo)
C91	International Music Co., 511 Fifth Ave., New York, New York
C93	Israel Music Institute, P.O. Box 11253, Tel Aviv, Israel
C94	Israeli Music Publications (P38-A.Broude)
D05	C.F. Kahnt Musikverlag (E65-Peters)
D08	Edwin F. Kalmus, Inc., Box 1007, Opa Locka, Florida
D11	KaWe, Brederodestraat 90, Amsterdam 13, Holland
D14	Kendor Music, Inc., Delevan, New York

D16	Robert King Music Co., 112A Main St., North Easton, Massachusetts
D17	Kistner & Siegel & Co., Postfach 101, 5 Köln 7, Germany
D18	Neil A. Kjos Music Co., 4382 Jutland Drive, San Diego, California
D20	Johann Kliment Musikverlag, Kolinkasse 15, A-1090 Vienna, Austria
D21	Edition Kneusslin, Amselstrasse 43, Basel 24, Switzerland (E65-Peters)
D26	Ludwig Krenn, Reindorfgasse 42, Vienna 15, Austria
D29	Kultura, P.O. Box 149, Budapest 62, Hungary (A78-Boosey)
D33	Lavell Publishing Co., P.O. Box 717, Omaha, Nebraska
D34	Leblanc Publications, Inc. (F60-Southern, SA)
D36	Alphonse Leduc, 175 rue Saint-Honore, 75001 Paris, France
D37	Leeds Music Corporation (G85-Belwin)
D40	Leipziger Kommissions und Grossbuchhandel, Karlstrasse 10, 701 Leipzig, Germany
D41	Henry Lemoine & Cie, 17 rue Pigalle, Paris 9e, France (B92-Elkan-Vogel)
D42	Alfred Lengnick & Co., Ltd., Purley Oaks Studios, 421a Brighton Rd., South Croydon, Surrey CR2 6YR, England
D44	F.E.C. Leuckart Musikverlag, Nibelungenstr. 48, Munich 19, Germany
D46	Musikverlag Robert Lienau, Lankwitzer Strasse 9, 1 Berlin 45 (Lichterfelde), Germany (E65-Peters)
D48	H. Litolff's Verlag, Forsthausstrasse 101, Frankfurt, Germany (E65-Peters)
D52	Ludwig Music Publishing Co., 559 E. 140th St., Cleveland, Ohio
D54	Harold Lyche & Co. Musikforlag, Kongensgt. 2, Oslo, Norway (E65-Peters)
D55	McGinnis & Marx, 201 W. 86th St., New York, New York
D58	Magnamusic Inc., 10370 Page Industrial Blvd., St. Louis, Missouri
D63	Edward B. Marks Music Corp., 1790 Broadway, New York, New York (G85-Belwin)
D64	Editions Robert Martin, 106, Grande-rue de la Coupée, 71, Charney-les-Macon, France
D67	J. Maurer, Avenue du Verseau 7 Watermanlaan, Brussels 15, Belgium
D71	MCA Music (G85-Belwin)
D73	Mentor Music Inc., Broadview Drive, Brookfield, Connecticut
D74	Mercury Music Corporation (E77-Presser)
D76	Merion Music (E77-Presser)
D78	Karl Merseburger Verlag, Alemannenstrasse 20, 1 Berlin 38 (Nikolassee), Germany
D80	Muziekuitgaven Metropolis, Frankrijklei 24, Antwerpen, Belgium
D81	Mezhdunarodnaya Kniga Editions (F23-G.Schirmer)
D82	M-F Music Company, Box 351, Evanston, Illinois
D84	Belwin-Mills Publishing Corp., 25 Deshon Dr., Melville, New York
D85	Mitteldeutscher Verlag, Robert-Blum-Strasse 37, Halle/Saale, Germany (E65-Peters)
D86	MJQ Music Inc., 17 West 60th St., New York, New York
D88	Edition Modern-Hans Wewerka, Franz-Joseph-Strasse 2, 8 Munich 13, Germany
D90	Hermann Moeck Verlag, Postfach 143, 31 Celle, Germany
D91	Rufer Verlag, Gutersloh, Germany
D92	Molenaar's Musiekcentrale, Zuideinde 18, Wormerveer, Holland (B91-H. Elkan)
D94	Montreal Brass Quintet Series, 145 Graham Blvd., Town of Mount Royal, Montreal 16, Quebec, Canada

D98	Möseler Verlag, Postfach 460, 3340 Wolfenbutel, Germany
E00	MS Publications, 946 S. Wesley, Oak Park, Illinois
E02	Willy Müller-Süddeutscher Musikverlag, Marzgasse 5, Heidelberg, Germany (E65-Peters)
E03	Neuer Münchner Musikverlag, Franz Pollak, Imkerweg 42b, 8 Munich 60 (Aubing), Germany
E08	Music for Percussion, 1841 Broadway, Suite 611, New York, New York
E10	Music Press, Inc. (E77-Presser)
E11	Warner Brothers, Music, 265 Secaucus Rd., Secaucus, New Jersey
E14	Musica Rara, 2 Gt. Marlborough St., London W1, England
E19	Muzika USSR Publishing House (A38-AMP)
E30	New Music Edition (E77-Presser)
E32	New Valley Music Press, Sage Hall, Smith College, Northampton, Massachusetts
E33	New Wind Music Co., 23 Ivor Pl., London NW1, England
E36	Pierre Noel, 24, Boulevard Poissonniere, 75009 Paris, France
E37	Otto Heinrich Noetzel, Liebigstrasse 4, Wilhelmshaven, Germany
E39	A.B. Nordiska MusiskaForlaget AB, P.O. Box 745, Drottninggatan 37, S-101 30 Stockholm, Sweden
E41	Novello & Co., Ltd., Borough Green, Sevenoaks, Kent, England or 145 Palisade St., Dobbs Ferry, New York
E43	Louis Oertel, Eichenweg 11a, 3006 Grossburgwedel/Hanover, Germany
E49	L'Edition le Grand Orgue, Box 48, Syosset, New York
E50	Osterreichischer Bundesverlag, Schwarzenbergstrasse 5, Wien 1, Austria
E51	Oxford University Press, Inc., 16-00 Pollitt Dr., Fair Lawn, New Jersey
E53	Pan American Union Music Publications (F59-Southern, New York)
E58	Paterson's Publications Ltd., 38-40 Wigmore St., London W1H OEX, England (C11-C. Fischer)
E59	W. Paxton & Co., Ltd., 36-38 Dean St., Soho, W1V 6EP, England (E41-Novello)
E61	Peer International Corp., 1740 Broadway, New York, New York
E62	Edizioni Pegasus, Locarno, Switzerland (E65-Peters)
E65	C.F. Peters Corporation, 373 Park Ave. South, New York, New York
E67	Piedmont Music Co., Inc. (D63-Marks)
E68	Composers Facsimile Edition, 170 W. 74th St., New York, New York
E72	Polskie Wydawnictwo Muzyczne, Krakowśkie Przedmieście 7, 00-068 Warsaw, Poland
E77	Theodore Presser, Presser Place, Bryn Mawr, Pennsylvania
E80	Pro Art Publications, Inc., 469 Union Ave., Westbury, New York
E81	Pro Musica Verlag, Karl-Liebknecht-Strasse, 701 Leipzig 1, East Germany
E83	Providence Music Press, Box 2362 East Side Station, Providence, Rhode Island
E84	Keith Prowse Music Publishing Co., Ltd., 21 Denmark St., London WC2, England
E87	Pyraminx Publications, 358 Aldrich Rd., Fairport, New York
E89	D. Rahter (A38-AMP)
E93	Remick Music Corporation (H06-Warner Brothers)
E96	Edouard Richli, Geneva, Switzerland (A56-Baron)

E98	G. Ricordi & Co., Viz Salomone 77, Rome, Italy (F23-G. Schirmer)
E99	Ries & Erler, Charlottenbrunner Strasse 42, 1 Berlin 33 (Grünewald), Germany
F02	Rochester Music Publishers, 358 Aldrich Rd., Fairport, New York
F03	Rongwen Music, Inc., 56 W. 45th St., New York (A98-Broude)
F05	Rouart, Lerolle, et Cie (F16-Salabert)
F07	Rubank, Inc., 16215 N.W. 15th Ave., Miami, Florida
F08	Rufer Verlag, Gutersloh, Germany
F10	Emil Ruh Musikverlag, Zurichstrasse 33, CH-8314 Adliswil, Zurich, Switzerland
F13	Russian State Publishing Co., Music Section (A38-AMP)
F16	Editions Salabert, 22 rue Chauchat, Paris 9e, France or 575 Madison Ave., New York, New York 10022
F21	Scherzando Editions Musicales, 14, rue Augustre Orts, Bruxelles, Belgium
F22	E.C. Schirmer Music Co., 112 South St., Boston, Massachusetts
F23	G. Schirmer, Inc., 866 Third Ave., New York, New York
F24	Schlesingerische Musikhandlung (E65-Peters)
F26	C.F. Schmidt (E65-Peters)
F27	Schmitt Music Center, 110 N. 5th St., Minneapolis, Minnesota
F30	Schott Freres, 30, rue Saint-Jean, Bruxelles 1, Belgium (E65-Peters)
F31	B. Schott's Söhne, Weihergarten 1-9, 6500 Mainz, Germany (G85-Belwin)
F36	Science and Art, Boul. Ruski Nr. 6, Sofia, Bulgaria
F43	Shawnee Press, Inc., Delaware Water Gap, Pennsylvania
F50	Hans Sikorski Musikverlag, Johnsallee 23, I Hamburg 13, Germany (G85-Belwin)
F52	N. Simrock, Werderstrasse 44, Hamburg 13, Germany (A38-AMP)
F53	Sirius-Verlag, Wicletstrasse 67, 1 Berlin 21, Germany
F54	R. Smith & Co., Ltd., P.O. Box 210, Watford, Herts WD2 4YG, England
F56	Society for the Publication of American Music (E77-Presser)
F59	Southern Music Publishing Co., Inc., 1740 Broadway, New York, New York
F60	Southern Music Co., P.O. Box 329, San Antonio, Texas
F62	Spratt Music Co., 17 W. 60th St., New York, New York
F64	Staff Music Publishing Co., Inc., 17 W. 60th St., New York, New York
F65	Stainer & Bell, Ltd., 82 High Rd., London N2 9PW, England (C33-Galaxy)
F67	Státní Nakladetelstvi Krásné Literatury, Ve Smeckach 30, Prague I, Czechoslovakia
F72	Summy-Birchard Co., 1834 Ridge Ave., Evanston, Illinois
F74	Swing Lane Publications, P.O. Box 128, Beverly, New Jersey
F78	Templeton Publishing Co., Inc. (F43-Shawnee)
F79	Tempo Music Publications, Inc., P.O. Box 392, Chicago, Illinois
F80	Tenuto Publications (E77-Presser)
F81	Tierolff-Musiekcentrale, Markt 90/92, Roosendaal, Holland (B91-H. Elkan)
F82	Verlag Tischer & Jagenberg (D44-Leukart)
F87	Editions Musicales Transatlantiques, 14, Avenue Hoche, Paris 8e, France (E77-Presser)
F88	Tritone Press, Box 158, Southern Station, Hattiesburg, Mississippi (E77-Presser)
F94	Union of Bulgarian Composers, Ministry of Education & Culture, 2 ul Ivan Vazov, Sofia, Bulgaria
F97	Universal Editions, Karlsplatz 6, Wien 1, Austria

G01	University Music Press (C25-Fox)
G06	Chr. Friedrich Vieweg Musikverlag, Limonenstrasse 10, 1000 Berlin 45, Germany (F43-Shawnee)
G10	Volkwein Brothers, Inc., 117 Sandusky St., Pittsburgh, Pennsylvania
G13	Waterloo Music Co., Ltd., 3 Regina St. North, Waterloo, Ontario, Canada (A38-AMP)
G16	Joseph Weinberger, 10-16 Rathbone St., London W1P 2BJ, England
G17	Weintraub Music Co., 33 W. 60th St., New York, New York
G21	Western International Music, Inc., 2859 Holt Ave., Los Angeles, California
G26	Joseph Williams, Ltd. (C33-Galaxy)
G27	Willis Music Co., 7380 Industrial Rd., Florence, Kentucky
G28	Wind Music, Inc., 1014 S. Goodman St., Rochester, New York
G31	M. Witmark & Sons (H06-Warner Brothers)
G38	G. Zanibon, Piazza Dei Signori, 24, 35100 Padova, Italy (E65-Peters)
G-39	Zenemükiadó Vállalat, P.O. Box 149, Budapest 62, Hungary (A78-Boosey)
G41	Edizioni Suvini Zerboni, Corso Europa 5/7, Milan, Italy
G43	Wilhelm Zimmermann Musikverlag, Zeppelinallee 21, 6000 Frankfurt 1, Germany (E65-Peters)
G47	Verlag vom Paul Zschocher, Hamburg, Germany
G58	J. Curwen and Sons Ltd., 29 Maiden Lane, London WC2, England
G61	Gate Music Co. (C25-Fox)
G66	Seesaw Music Corporation, 1966 Broadway, New York, New York
G68	European American Music Dist. Corp., 195 Allwood Rd., Clifton, New Jersey
G70	Fema, Box 395, Naperville, Illinois
G78	Consort Trios, Box 424, New York, New York
G81	Editio Supraphon, Palackého 1, Praha 1, Czechoslovakia
G83	Autograph Editions, c/o Atlantic Music Supply, 152 W. 42nd St., New York, New York
G85	Belwin-Mills Publishing Corp., 25 Deshon Dr., Melville, New York
G88	Canadian Music Centre, 33 Edward St., Toronto 2, Ontario, Canada
G90	Concert Music Publishsing Co., 5003 Ridgebury Blvd., Cleveland, Ohio (A84-Bourne)
G96	Byron Douglas Publications, P.O. Box 565, Phoenix, Arizona (G85-Belwin)
H03	Schweizerisches Music-Archiv, Bellariastrasse 82, 8038 Zurich, Switzerland
H06	Warner Brothers Music, 265 Secaucus Rd., Secaucus, New Jersey
H09	Wilder Music Inc. (C25-Fox)
H27	H. Flammer (F43-Shawnee)
H30	Wilhelm Hansen Musik-Forlag, Gothersgade 9-11, 1123 Copenhagen, Denmark (D58-Magnamusic)
J39	Metropolis (B91-H. Elkan)
J94	Zondervan Publishing House, 1415 Lake Drive S.E., Grand Rapids, Michigan
K19	Pelikan Musikverlag, Zurich, Switzerland
L69	World Library of Sacred Music, Inc., 2145 Central Parkway, Cincinnati, Ohio
L74	Augsburg Publishing Co., 426 S. 5th Ave., Minneapolis, Minnesota
M63	Alfred E. Weissman (B31-Colin)
M65	Almitra Enterprises (D14-Kendor)
M66	Amberson Enterprises (F23-G. Schirmer)
M70	AR Publishing Co., 756 7th Ave., New York, New York
M71	Arco Music Publishers (G21-WIM)
M73	Artransa Music (G21-WIM)

M75	Berandol Music Ltd., 11 Saint Joseph St., Toronto, Ontario M4Y 1J8, Canada
M77	Berklee Press Publications, 1140 Boylston St., Boston, Massachusetts
M79	Brightstar Music Publications (G21-WIM)
M80	The Brass Press, 159 Eighth Ave. North, Nashville, Tennessee
M84	Charter Publications, c/o J.W. Pepper & Son, P.O. Box 850, Valley Forge, Pennsylvania
M85	Cimino Publishers, 1646 New Highway, Box 75, Farmingdale, New York
M87	Concert Music Publishing Co. (A84-Bourne)
M91	Conservatory Publications, 18 Van Wyck St., Croton-On-Hudson, New York
M92	Crown Music Press, 4119 N. Pittsburgh, Chicago, Illinois
M93	Date Music, c/o Educulture, Inc., Box 1932, Santa Monica, California
M95	DEG Music Products, Lake Geneva, Wisconsin
M96	Dick Noel Enterprises, c/o Educulture, Inc., Box 1932, Santa Monica, California
M97	Duchess Music Corporation (G85-Belwin)
M98	Easton Music Co. (D16-King)
N01	G & C Music Corporation (E77-Presser)
N03	G. Schott Music Publishing Co. (G21-WIM)
N04	Hänssler Verlag, Bismarckstrasse 4, 7303 Neuhausen-Stuttgart, Germany (E65-Peters)
N07	Harold Branch Publications, 42 Cornell Dr., Plainview, New York
N09	Henmar Press (E65-Peters)
N10	Highland Music Co., 1311 N. Highland Ave., Hollywood, California
N14	Harmonia Vitgave (E65-Peters)
N18	E.C. Kerby (G68-European-American)
N19	Lucien Cailliet Publications (F60-Southern, SA)
N20	Luck's Music Library, 15701 E. Warren, Detroit, Michigan
N22	Maggio Music Press, Box 9717, N. Hollywood, California
N24	Marlen Music Co. (C45-Gordon)
N29	Media Press, Box 895, Champaign, Illinois
N32	Norman Lee Publishing Co., Box 2733, Wichita, Kansas
N37	Okra Music Corporation, 177 E. 87th St., New York, New York
N38	Ostara Press (G21-WIM)
N40	Paolo Baratto, Wiesenstrasse 4, CH 8008 Zurich, Switzerland
N42	Philharmusica Corporation, Box 180, West Nyack, New York
N47	Roger Dean Publishing Co., 324 W. Jackson, Macomb, Illinois
N53	Sam Fundet (E65-Peters)
N58	Studio Music Co., 89 Vicarage Rd., London, England
N59	Standard Music Publishers, Box 1043, Turnersville, New Jersey
N60	Southdale Music Corporation (M85-Cimino)
N61	Studio P/R, 224 S. Lebanon St., Lebanon, Indiana
N62	Richard Stegmann, Wald Kugelweg 5a, 87 Wurzburg, Germany
N66	Tromba Publications, 1859 York St., Denver, Colorado
N69	Walton Music Co., 17 W. 60th St., New York, New York
N78	Dean Blair, Dept. of Music, University of Lethbridge, Lethbridge, Alberta, Canada
N81	Tuba-Euphonium Music Publications, Box 524, Muncie, Indiana
N83	Frederick Music Publications, 120 N. Charles, McPherson, Kansas

N85	Thames Publishing, 14 Barlby Rd., London W10 6AR, England
N86	James Aebersold, 1211 Aebersold Dr., New Albany, Indiana
N88	Lillenas Publishing Co. (G85-Belwin)
N91	Smith Publications, 906 E. Water St., Urbana, Illinois
N82	Tomorrow Brass Series (N81-Tuba)
N93	Tetra Music Corporation, c/o Alexander Broude, 225 W. 57th St., New York, New York
N95	Silvio Coscia (D16-King)
N96	Rayner Brown (G21-WIM)
N98	University of Miami Publications (C25-Fox)
P19	Musical Evergreen, c/o Atlantic Music Supply, Box 180, West Nyack, New York
P23	Eble Music Co., P.O. Box 1171, Iowa City, Iowa
P31	Blixt Publications, 15795 Poppy Lane, Los Gatos, California
P36	Opus Music Publishers, 612 N. Michigan Ave., Chicago, Illinois
P37	Bowdoin College Music Press, Brunswick, Maine
P38	Alexander Broude, 225 W. 57th St., New York, New York
P39	Music Services, Box 643, La Puente, California
P40	Miller Music Co. (A70-Big 3)
P41	BMI Canada, Ltd. (A38-AMP)
P42	Manuscripts for Tuba, Tennessee Technological University, Box 5045, Cookeville, Tennessee
P43	G. Henle, Munich (A94-Brodt)
P44	Roger Rhodes, P.O. Box 855, Radio City Station, New York, New York
P45	Musica Viva, 558 Galleywood Rd., Chelmsford, Essex CM2 8BX, England
P46	Lexicon Music (N10-Highland)
P47	Berandol Music, Ltd., 11 Saint Joseph St., Toronto, Ontario M4Y 1J8, Canada
P48	Manuscript Publications, 120 Maple St., Wrightville, Pennsylvania
P49	A Moll Dur Publishing House, P.O. Box 5393, Virginia Beach, Virginia
P51	KSM Publishing Co., Box 3819, Dallas, Texas
P52	Lopes Edition, Ltd., Northway House, Highroad, London N20 9LP, England
P53	Musikverlag Wilhelm Halter, Karlsrue, Germany
P55	Stansfield Music, 9709 Roosevelt Way N.E., Seattle, Washington

CATEGORY CODES

0200	2 Trumpets
0201	2 Horns
0202	2 Trombones
0203	2 Tubas
0210	2 Mixed Brass (Brass-Perc)
0211	2 Parts: Horn-Woodwind
0212	2 Parts: Brass-Woodwind
0217	2 Parts: Wind(s)-String(s)
0218	2 Parts: Brass-Miscellaneous
0300	3 Trumpets
0301	3 Horns
0302	3 Trombones
0303	3 Tubas
0310	3 Mixed Brass (Brass-Perc)
0311	3 Parts:Horn-Woodwind
0312	3 Parts: Brass-Woodwind
0313	3 Parts: Trumpets-Keyboard
0314	3 Parts: Horns-Keyboard
0315	3 Parts: Trombones-Keyboard
0316	3 Parts: Miscellaneous-Keyboard
0317	3 Parts: Wind(s)-Strings(s)
0318	3 Parts: Brass-Miscellaneous
0400	4 Trumpets
0401	4 Horns
0402	4 Trombones
0403	4 Tubas
0410	4 Mixed Brass (Brass-Perc)
0411	4 Parts: Horn-Woodwind
0412	4 Parts: Brass-Woodwind
0413	4 Parts: Trumpets-Keyboard
0414	4 Parts:Horns-Keyboard
0415	4 Parts:Trombones-Keyboard
0416	4 Parts: Miscellaneous-Keyboard
0417	4 Parts: Wind(s)-String(s)
0418	4 Parts: Brass-Miscellaneous
0500	5 Equal Brass Instruments
0510	5 Mixed Brass (Brass-Perc)
0511	5 Parts: Horn-Woodwind
0512	5 Parts:Brass-Woodwind
0513	5 Parts: Winds-Keyboard
0517	5 Parts: Wind(s)-String(s)
0518	5 Parts: Brass-Miscellaneous
0600	6 Equal Brass Instruments
0610	6 Mixed Brass (Brass-Perc)
0611	6 Parts: Horn-Woodwind
0612	6 Parts: Brass-Woodwind
0613	6 Parts: Winds-Keyboard
0617	6 Parts: Wind(s)-String(s)